W9-ASA-119

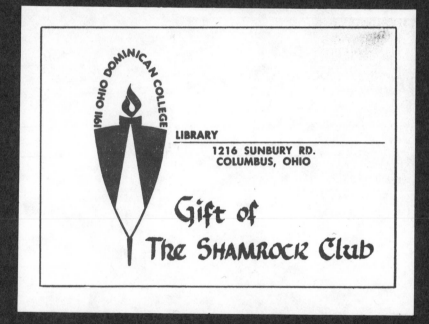

OHIO DOMINICAN COLLEGE 1961

LIBRARY

1216 SUNBURY RD.
COLUMBUS, OHIO

Gift of
The Shamrock Club

FEB 1976

RECEIVED
OHIO DOMINICAN
COLLEGE LIBRARY
COLUMBUS, OHIO
43219

Books by Edwin O'Connor

THE ORACLE (1951)

THE LAST HURRAH (1956)
(Atlantic Prize Novel, 1955)

BENJY: A FEROCIOUS FAIRY TALE (1957)

THE EDGE OF SADNESS (1961)
(Pulitzer Prize for Fiction, 1962)

I WAS DANCING (1964)

ALL IN THE FAMILY (1966)

THE BEST AND THE LAST OF EDWIN O'CONNOR (1970)

The Best and the Last of Edwin O'Connor

The Best and the Last of Edwin O'Connor

EDITED WITH AN INTRODUCTION BY

Arthur Schlesinger, jr.

AND WITH CONTRIBUTIONS BY

Edmund Wilson
and John V. Kelleher

An Atlantic Monthly Press Book

LITTLE, BROWN AND COMPANY · BOSTON · TORONTO

813.54 018S
O'Connor, Edwin
The best and the last of
Edwin O'Connor

813.54
018 S
C,2

COPYRIGHT 1951 © 1956, 1957, 1961, 1962, 1963, 1964, 1966
BY EDWIN O'CONNOR
COPYRIGHT © 1969, 1970 BY LITTLE, BROWN AND COMPANY

ALL RIGHTS RESERVED. NO PART OF THIS BOOK MAY BE REPRO-
DUCED IN ANY FORM OR BY ANY ELECTRONIC OR MECHANICAL
MEANS INCLUDING INFORMATION STORAGE AND RETRIEVAL SYS-
TEMS WITHOUT PERMISSION IN WRITING FROM THE PUBLISHER,
EXCEPT BY A REVIEWER WHO MAY QUOTE BRIEF PASSAGES IN A
REVIEW.

LIBRARY OF CONGRESS CATALOG CARD NO. 74–99902

FIRST EDITION

A shorter version of "The 'Boy' Fragment" appeared originally
in *McCall's*. "For Whom the Novelist Writes" appeared originally
in *The Critic*. Edmund Wilson's contribution, including the text
of "Baldini" appeared originally in the *Atlantic*.

ATLANTIC–LITTLE, BROWN BOOKS
ARE PUBLISHED BY
LITTLE, BROWN AND COMPANY
IN ASSOCIATION WITH
THE ATLANTIC MONTHLY PRESS

Published simultaneously in Canada
by Little, Brown & Company (Canada) Limited

PRINTED IN THE UNITED STATES OF AMERICA

Contents

97492

Introduction

by ARTHUR SCHLESINGER, jr.

Eᴅ O'Conɴor was born in Providence, Rhode Island, on July 29, 1918. He died in Boston on March 23, 1968, four months before his fiftieth birthday. He left at his death portions of two new novels as well as an unfinished collaboration with Edmund Wilson; these texts are printed here for the first time. In addition, this volume includes two essays not previously published in book form and excerpts from four novels and a children's book. I know that reprinting passages from novels is not very satisfactory. But the ones selected here can be read as independent units; and they evoke that marvelous O'Connor fusion of gaiety and melancholy in a way that will, I believe, stimulate readers to turn again to the books themselves.

In addition, two good friends have written accounts of Ed — Edmund Wilson in connection with their collaboration, and John V. Kelleher in connection with the fragment from Ed's unfinished religious novel. I wish also to express gratitude to two more of Ed's close friends, Robert J. Manning and Esther Yntema of the Atlantic Monthly Press. Mrs. Yntema deserves special thanks for working out the excerpts from the novels, writing the introductory paragraphs and providing biographical notes about the author.

i

He was the first son of John V. and Mary Greene O'Connor of Woonsocket, Rhode Island, and was christened Edwin Greene O'Connor. His father, a doctor, had worked his way through medical school to become a general practitioner; then, after half a dozen years, he had returned for further study at Johns Hopkins and Harvard to qualify as a specialist in internal medicine. His mother, a graduate of Rhode Island College, had been a teacher in the Woonsocket public schools. They were both second generation Irish Americans.

In the twenties Woonsocket was a city of about 30,000, notable for its cotton mills and its 122 acres of parkland. The textile industry had begun its long decline, and a gray shabbiness was settling on the lower city. Writing "A Love Letter to Woonsocket" in the *Providence Sunday Journal* in 1951, Ed observed, "Woonsocket is not one of those fortunate communities in which every prospect pleases. To see it is not to love it. No stranger, walking down Main Street, along the hodgepodge stretch from Monument to Market Squares, has ever stood in danger of perishing before beauty."

The French Canadians had by the twenties started to flock into the mills along the Blackstone River, and the Yankees had retreated to the pleasant, shaded streets of the North End. Here, where the residential area trailed into the wooded countryside, the O'Connors lived in a frame house surrounded by trees and a large yard. As a boy Ed played football and baseball at a vacant lot nearby known as Hoyle's Field. Sometimes he wandered north toward the tracks of the New Haven & Hartford Railroad, passing a small pond which he searched for turtles and frogs in summer and on which he skated in winter, to the narrow wooden bridge leading over the railroad tracks into Massachusetts.

Ed, as he later wrote, lived "happily and well" as a boy in Woonsocket — hence the "love letter" — though he did not much like the town when he grew older. His father was a hard-working, respected and somewhat preoccupied professional man. He left Ed alone when it came to choosing a college and a career, and Ed was fond of him, though in time they had political disagreements, especially over Mrs. Roosevelt and Senator Joseph McCarthy. His mother was a remarkable woman with a genuine vocation as a teacher; she must have been like the Miss Hagertys and Miss Trefethens of my own childhood in Cambridge, Massachusetts. When Dr. O'Connor insisted that she stop teaching after marriage, she concentrated her skills on Ed and his younger brother and sister. Ed was a responsive child, who loved to be read to and to read. His literary inclination undoubtedly took root here.

He attended the Woonsocket public schools and then LaSalle Academy, a boys' school in Providence run by the Christian Brothers. In 1935 he went on to Notre Dame University in Indiana. Here, as a freshman, he had a young teacher of English, Frank O'Malley. Ed later recalled O'Malley as "the greatest single help for me in college. There are teachers like him scattered throughout our colleges and universities, and they're worth their weight in uranium." He dedicated *The Edge of Sadness* to O'Malley. When they met, O'Malley himself was new and inexperienced; his encounter with Ed and a group of lively classmates persuaded him he had a future as a teacher. "As a freshman," Professor O'Malley recalls, "Ed was unusual: unusual in his candor, openness to people and existence altogether, and in his humor, that is his consciousness of the foibles of humanity. He was anxious and hopeful and bright."

Ed was a moderately active undergraduate. He became an announcer at the college radio station; he sent back articles to the *Woonsocket Call*; he wrote stories for the college literary magazine. One in November 1938 called "Friends are Made in McCabe's" suggests that Ed was already moving toward a distinctive voice. It begins:

Everybody that hung around Jimmy McCabe's Place knew Ollie Moran and Phil Rotardi. I knew them best of all. I still know them, only now they aren't friends, and the three of us never go out together any more.

But Ed at this time evidently did not see writing as a career. For a moment as an undergraduate he considered entering the priesthood. When he took his degree *cum laude* in English in 1939, he had a notion that he might become a teacher; but a term in graduate school fixed that. He now thought vaguely of becoming a writer and, in the meantime, he decided to exploit his undergraduate experience in radio. In the summer of 1940 Station WPRO in Providence took him on as an announcer, a job for which he was suitably qualified by a deep, resonant voice. In the next couple of years he announced in radio stations in Palm Beach, Buffalo and Hartford. On the side he tried to write. He did not quite know what he was doing, and his non-success as a writer was consistent.

The war came; and in September 1942 he joined the Coast Guard. At first they sent him to Brewster on Cape Cod. Here he patrolled the long (and, in winter, exceedingly cold) beaches to protect the Cape against Nazi submarines, walking twenty miles a day in the shifting sands. After a brief assignment at Chemical Warfare School in Maryland, he was sent to the public relations office of the First Coast Guard District Headquarters in Boston. Here he stayed for two years.

When he returned to civilian life in September 1945, he drifted back into radio as a writer-announcer for the Yankee Network in Boston. In his spare time he wrote satiric skits about radio; Charles W. Morton, associate editor of the *Atlantic Monthly*, bought a couple. Ed decided that "maybe if you want to write, you should do it for yourself, alone." He left the network in October 1946 and began the life of a freelance writer. He also decided that he wanted to write fiction.

Radio, if it no longer dominated his interest, still constituted his main experience. He wrote radio reviews for the *Boston Herald* (under the name of "Roger Swift") as well as further skits for the *Atlantic*. And radio supplied the theme for his first novel. Its original title was *Top of the World*; later it became *The Oracle*. The leading character, a radio news commentator named Christopher Usher, was inspired by Gabriel Heatter and Cedric Foster, broadcasters of the late forties whose orotund pomposities delighted Ed and stimulated him to marvelous mimicry. It also drew on a flatulent Boston newspaper columnist named Bill Cunningham. The story covered two weeks of crisis when Usher attempts to outmaneuver his sponsor and improve his contract; and it dealt lovingly with his microphone manner (nauseating), his politics (reactionary), his sex life (active but unspecific) and his vanity (bottomless).

Ed submitted an outline with sample chapters to the Atlantic Monthly Press early in 1950. Charles W. Morton of the magazine noted to the Director of the Press:

I am impressed by O'Connor's determination to make a full-time independent writing man out of himself in the field of fiction. . . . He worked with Ted [Weeks; the editor of the *Atlantic*] on Ted's radio series and we all got to know him rather well. I should consider him an extremely good risk.

But the Press turned the book down, and it was eventually published by Harpers. The reviews were mixed. J. H. Jackson in the *San Francisco Chronicle* found it "enormously entertaining and first-rate satire"; N. L. Rothman in the *Saturday Review* pronounced it "thin stuff, an approximation of all the popular jokes on commentators." In the bookshops it was a notable flop. Ed later described his own reaction to the disaster.

At that time I knew nothing of publishers or the publishing business. For instance, I was incapable of translating Publisher's Esperanto into a calm and common English. When he said to me, "We all have the highest hopes for your fine book," I did not grasp that what he was really saying was, "Not too bad for a beginning, but if we sell two thousand we'll be lucky."

The publisher was an infinitely kind man, a lavish host, whom I met only over lunch in fairly expensive restaurants. . . . From every lunch I came away with the feeling that I was one week closer to the explosion that was so soon to shatter the field of American Letters.

The explosion, such as it was, came and went. It was unique among explosions in that it was invisible, inaudible, and totally without impact. . . . The publisher, over a final melancholy lunch, was disposed to be philosophical; he told me that these things happened.

"Nobody knows why," he said. *"Nobody knows why."*

Read today, *The Oracle* seems a satirical farce, influenced perhaps by the triumphs of dunderheads in such books as *Scoop*. O'Connor was always a Waugh fan, and one feels here that he was trying for a Waugh tone. But the effects were a little broad. Christopher Usher was almost too smug and swinish; and, in general, the characters tended to dissolve into caricatures. The book provided an outlet for the pent-up exasperation and incredulity engendered by O'Connor's life in radio. But it did not tap his deeper preoccupations. There is not, for example, an Irishman in it; and the two Catholics — a papal count and an old scholarly priest — have walk-on parts. The political commentary is more concerned with issues and less with character and atmosphere than in his later books. There are delicious moments of parody, and occasionally the voice of the Irish storyteller breaks in:

Years before, when, as a sport columnist [Christopher Usher] had been widely read and, indeed, even famous within a more constricted circle, he had occasionally been subjected to these painful batterings at his dignity. It had been the habit of his managing editor — a small, sharp-faced man with the air of a raffish mouse — to address him, in the presence of others, by the simple, inaccurate name of "Charlie." More, along with the false diminutive, he would supply an entirely unnecessary identification, whose very superfluousness would serve to further minimize Christopher:
". . . and now I want you to meet Charlie Usher, one of our staff. I'll tell you what Charlie does: he does sports. Been doing them for years. Nice lively style if you like sports. Take a look at his stuff sometime if you get the chance. Now come over here and meet our copy chief . . ."

But the dialogue in *The Oracle* is mostly held in check. The novel evidently aimed to achieve English urbanity rather than Irish extravagance. Perhaps this is why it did so much better in England (where Noel Coward was reputed to admire it) than in the United States. Ed used to claim that the American sales netted him $720.

ii

In the meantime, he had been living in various Beacon Street and Brimmer Street boarding houses. In 1949 he settled in a rooming house on Marlborough Street. That year he also taught a night course in writing at Boston College. With the arrival of television, he began a column of television criticism, three days a week, for the *Boston Post*. He received $15 a column and had to buy his own set, but the stipend gave him something to live on while he did his own writing. Nearly every weekend he went back to Woonsocket to see his family.

In the late forties he also began to spend his summers in the town of Wellfleet, a dozen miles short of Provincetown on the tip of Cape Cod. This had been part of the area he had so valiantly defended during the war, and he usually took a room in the village, where he worked in the morning and from which he bicycled to the ocean beach in the afternoon. A tall, lithe, robust man, with wavy hair and a pleasant, easy manner, he would stop a moment for a chat and a joke or two, then dive boldly into the surf, take a long swim, dry in the sun and ride back to the village. I was then a newcomer to Wellfleet; and, after one of these amiable but brisk visitations, I asked Mary McCarthy about him. "His name is Ed O'Connor," she said. "He has a television column in the *Boston Post*. He's working on a novel. I hope it will be OK." She sounded dubious but friendly.

Wellfleet at this time was largely given over in the summer to writers and artists. Edmund and Elena Wilson were there, Francis and Katharine Biddle, George and Helene Biddle, Edwin Dickinson, Paul and Nina Chavchavadze, Daniel and Janet Aaron, and, for a time after her divorce from Wilson, Mary McCarthy with her new husband Bowden Broadwater (who used to speak of Wilson as "my father-in-law"). In the neighboring town of Truro were Gilbert Seldes, Peggy Day, Edmund Duffy, E. J. Kahn, Jr., and a horde of psychiatrists. Provincetown itself had older folk who remembered Dos Passos and O'Neill as well as such new arrivals in the fifties as Abe Burrows and Norman Mailer. Later William Gibson, Montgomery Clift, Kevin McCarthy, Arthur Kober, Serge Chermayeff, Robert Manning, Herbert Wechsler, Burke Marshall, Stacy May, Harry Levin, Richard Hofstadter, Heyward Cutting, Frank Freidel, Lee Falk and many others joined the summer throng and increased the chatter on the beaches from Newcomb's Hollow to Ballston. Mary McCarthy's *A Charmed Life* was her arresting, if somewhat personal and acrid, farewell to Wellfleet. It was filled, alas, with recognizable portraits and caused considerable distress and recrimination.

Many of us lived in the area between the Mid-Cape Highway and the outer beach known locally as the "woods." Here, as Thoreau had noted a century ago, "small rustling groves of oaks and locusts and whispering pines, on perfectly level ground, made a little paradise." Scattered through the woods were serene ponds containing clear fresh water of notable softness. Beyond the ponds and the dark leafy forests lay the high dunes and then, in a moment, the great beach itself, one of the magnificent beaches of the world, whether sparkling in the sunlight or swathed in the not infrequent fog. The woods are now part of the Cape Cod National Seashore, established by John F. Kennedy of Hyannis Port on the Upper Cape. Kennedy was greatly admired in the woods, but the Upper Cape was dismissed by partisans of the Lower Cape as "the Irish Riviera."

Ed loved the woods, the great beach and the foaming ocean; and, as soon as he could afford it, he built a house on a hill commanding a noble view of land and water. But this was some time to come. In the early fifties he was still bicycling in from the village, kidding about the failure of *The Oracle* and working quietly away on a new novel. At first he tackled a variation on the Enoch Arden theme called *A Young Man of Promise*. But it did not come off and, after completing a text of more than two hundred pages, he bravely discarded it. Now he turned, apparently with a sudden sense of inner recognition, to a new theme.

iii

"I got interested in the political set-up of an American city," he told Lewis Nichols of the *New York Times* in 1956, "when in the Coast Guard during the war. My station happened to be in Boston. Before that I had been at Notre Dame with the sons of some Chicago politicians, and I suppose that started it."

Certainly Boston had precipitated a new set of concerns. In Woonsocket Ed had lived in a predominantly Yankee neighborhood. As a child, he had probably never heard a good Irish brogue. Boston now confronted him with the Irish-American experience; it brought his latent sense of Irishness to the surface; and it soon established the argument of his new book. "I wanted to do a novel on the whole Irish-American business," as he later said. "What the Irish got in America, they got through politics; so, of course, I had to use a political framework."

In spite of the conventional liberalism implicit in *The Oracle*, Ed was not greatly interested in politics *per se*. He had never worked in an election, had never been a political reporter, and did not now make any systematic effort to interview or hang about with politicians. When John K. Hutchens of the *New York Herald Tribune* asked him about this, he observed, "As Henry James said, you don't have to live in a barracks to know about soldiers. You need a little intelligence and creative imagination. You know a little, and imagine the rest. You concentrate for a short time, absorbing it through the pores. And maybe, because nobody else knows much about it either, they'll say it's OK."

What interested him was politics as a distillate of the Irish-American experience. He was well aware that the life of the Irish in America was entering a new phase. "As I began thinking," he told Lewis Nichols, "it seemed to me that [the older day] was a wonderful time, the time of the eccentric in politics. It was both wonderful and not fully appreciated, mostly misunderstood." This taste for the eccentric found rich sustenance in Boston. Here, like a geologist inspecting a cliff, he could see every stratum of the Irish-American experience. The city of John Boyle O'Reilly and John L. Sullivan, of Martin Lomasney and Honey Fitz and

James Michael Curley, of Knocko McCormack and the Honorable Frankie Kelly, of Maurice Tobin and Joe Casey and Jack Kennedy, was a mine of lore and anecdote. Someone had better get it all down, Ed must have thought, before the antic wild men of the old time gave way entirely to the new generation.

Boston still had its share of characters. In the Coast Guard Ed had served under a jaunty man named Louis Brems, a former vaudevillian who had later become the city's greeter. It is not even clear that Brems was Irish, but he had officiated in the midst of Irish politicos, and he was a great raconteur. As Ed worked on the new novel, Brems was in process of transmutation into a character named Cuke Gillen. Even more notable was a Boston politician Ed came to know in the late forties named Clement A. Norton. Clem Norton had served on the School Committee, been Superintendent of Commonwealth Pier and was a permanent free-lance in the tong warfare of Boston politics, engaged in unrelenting guerrilla activity against the lords of the city. He used to patrol the streets in a sound truck from which he issued ironic and scornful denunciations of the eminent figures of the commonwealth. In private, he was a glorious Irish talker, his long, pungent sentences spiraling out in a sort of self-parody, punctuated by interjections of "my dear man" and other devices designed to hold his listener's (sometimes wandering) attention. He was a splendid eccentric, given to remorseless hypochondria, to suits made of strange synthetic materials, to electric razors plugged into the dashboard of his cluttered car, to small notebooks in which he condensed the results of his reading. "I've got your *Age of Jackson* down to four hundred words," he once told me gleefully, waving a notebook rapidly before my eyes. Ed adored him, cherished his stories, imitated his voice with uncanny precision and rechristened him Charlie Hennessey.

Politics thus became a vehicle through which he could explore the Irish-American personality. And he had another objective. As he had pondered the question of Irish-American fiction, "I began to say to myself, 'Where the hell is the humor?' It was sullen stuff, depressed. Now the Irish writers — O'Casey, Joyce — they have humor, but the Irish-Americans never seemed to capture it." Certainly the old, free humor had been a casualty of the Irish-American search for lace curtains and respectability. Ed's friend John V. Kelleher, professor of Irish literature and history at Harvard, has reminded us of "the public humorlessness that settled down over the American Irish about the turn of the century when the Irish societies drove the Irish comedians off the stage." "Irish-Americans can be very funny people," Ed thought, "but no one seemed to set it down. I thought I'd try." Yet his ambitions were more complex. He hated being taken as a professional Irishman and especially as a professional Irish entertainer. He once said to a friend, "I would like to do for the Irish in America what Faulkner did for the South."

The new book's working title, which no one but Ed liked, was *Not Moisten an Eye*. For four years he plugged away. There were interruptions. In January 1953 he collapsed in his rooming house and was rushed to the Boston City Hospital. A duodenal ulcer was hemorrhaging, and a priest administered last rites. But Ed recovered, though his stomach remained in precarious condition until a large part was removed by an operation in 1961.

Later that same year he invested his royalties from *The Oracle* in his first trip to Ireland, leaving Boston on St. Patrick's Day. In these years Ed also served as literary consultant and semi-collaborator for Fred Allen on *Treadmill to Oblivion*, a volume of annotated scripts from the popular radio program Allen's Alley, and then on Allen's autobiography *Much Ado About Me*. In the first book Allen wrote in a section of acknowledgment: "Ed O'Connor, who has the memory of an elephant, helped me with this tome. Ted Weeks, who has the energy of a beaver, also helped. It proves that with an elephant's memory, a beaver's energy and two friends, a radio actor can write a book." The copy for Dr. O'Connor was inscribed: "If you didn't have a son named Ed, it never would have come to pass." In the fall of 1954 Ed went to Ireland again, this time on a hilarious trip with Allen and Portland Hoffa.

In spite of the rejection of *The Oracle*, his association with the *Atlantic Monthly* had grown. Ted Weeks now published his work with some regularity and was an encouraging editor, always tactful with new writers lacking confidence in themselves. Charles Morton was a loyal friend. The Atlantic Monthly Press was offering an award of $5000 for the best new novel, and Ed raced to meet the deadline. His friends at the Press were hoping for the best when the manuscript arrived in January 1955. Oddly the first readers were critical, doubting whether the book would have an audience. "You may be relieved to know," Esther Yntema of the Press later told me, "that the authors of these reports have since found happiness outside the publishing profession." Mrs. Yntema herself wrote with greater perception, "I think the two main things to be said about the book are: that it is profoundly moving, and that its scope is very great." Ed won the prize, sent the Press a long memorandum on how to "handle" the book ("go easy on this business of the *political* novel") and changed the title to *The Last Hurrah*.

iv

The Last Hurrah portrays the evolution of Irish America through an account of the rise and fall of Frank Skeffington, twice governor of an eastern state, now mayor of its largest city. The book begins with Skeffington's decision on his seventy-second birthday to run for re-election. He summons his cohorts, lays on the style of campaign that had so often carried him to victory, battles his political enemies in the Irish community, feuds with the Cardinal, negotiates with the Italians, in-veighs against the Yankees, gives speeches, attends wakes, goes down to unexpected and disastrous defeat, dies.

Skeffington, a subtle, cynical, generous, vengeful, witty, resourceful, high-spirited man drawn with Dickensian lavishness and exuberance, dominates the book. But the Irish supporting cast is brilliantly perceived and differentiated, and the Yankees and the Italians, though cast in more conventional molds, are serviceable. The characters reveal themselves above all through talk; and the talk is magnificent. As the panorama un-folds, a larger picture emerges. Skeffington, the "tribal chieftain," has lived beyond his time. He has accumulated too many enemies among the Irish. The Italians are escaping from political peonage and becoming claimants for power in their own right. The Yankees have waited a gen-eration for revenge. The outs have found a new Irishman, young, bland and meaningless — "nut-boy McCluskey," as Charlie Hennessey calls him — who sweeps through to triumph. In the end, O'Connor, speaking through the character of Jack Mangan, offered his own explanation for Skeffington's downfall:

What really did the job, sport, wasn't McCluskey, or Garvey, or Cass or Amos Force. . . . You can forget all of us. All you have to remember is one name: Roosevelt. . . . He's the man, sport, who really put the skids under your uncle, and he did it years ago. It's just that it took until now to catch up with him. . . .

He destroyed the old-time boss. He destroyed him by taking away his source of power. He made the kind of politician your uncle was an anachron-ism, sport. All over the country the bosses have been dying for the last twenty years, thanks to Roosevelt. . . . The old boss was strong simply because he held all the cards. If anybody wanted anything — jobs, favors, cash — he could only go to the boss, the local leader. What Roosevelt did was to take the handouts out of the local hands. A few little things like Social Security, Unemployment Insurance, and the like — that's what shifted the gears, sport. No need now to depend on the boss for everything; the Federal Government was getting into the act. Otherwise known as a social revolution.

So you can see what that would do in the long run. The old-timers would still string along with the boss, of course, because that's the way they always did things. But what about the kids coming along? . . . To begin with, they were one step further away from the old country; he didn't have the old emotional appeal for them. You know, the racial-spokesman kind of thing. For another, a lot of them had been educated away from home. . . . It was a new era, sport, and your uncle belonged to the old.

It was not only the end of the old-time political boss; it also, O'Connor suggested, marked the exhaustion of the distinctively Irish impulse in the Irish-American community. Skeffington and his generation had been an embattled group within American society, united by external ethnic and religious hostility, cherishing their own tradition and identity, advancing to the fight under weird native war cries. Theirs had been the generation that battered down the gates of the old establishment. In many respects they won their fight. The new generation proceeded to rush through the opening — and lost its Irishness along the way. Acceptance was turning the sons and grandsons of Erin into Americans quite as commonplace and tepid as any other Americans. Respectability had become a curse. "Where there had been a Skeffington," muses the old Yankee Nathaniel Gardiner (a character suggested by Henry Lee Shattuck), "there was now a McCluskey. The old buccaneer, for all his faults, had at least been a capable, vivid, unforgettable personality; he had been succeeded by the spearhead of a generation of ciphers."

Ed made quite separate judgments about these two themes of *The Last Hurrah*. The downfall of Skeffington and his brand of politics seemed to him inevitable, desirable and in the public interest. But he could not conceal regret over the passing of gaudy and positive Irish personalities or over the disappearance of Irishness in the process of Americanization. Some critics, taking the second as the only judgment, misconstrued the book and denounced it as romantic, immoral and subversive. It was argued that O'Connor had not only perpetuated the ancient tradition of the Irish as maudlin and roistering buffoons but had made the unscrupulous Skeffington a lovable old rogue with a heart of gold and had thereby placed a sentimental gloss on wicked times and transformed vices into virtues.

But this was to convert a human observation into a political judgment. It is, for better or worse, a fact — as Lincoln Steffens and many others have testified — that the old-time bosses often had a warmth of feeling, a vividness of style and a confidence and charm of personality not invariably encountered among the reformers. To portray bosses in this light is not necessarily to honor their deeds. Indeed, the pervading undercurrent of *The Last Hurrah* is O'Connor's sense of the wanton waste of Skeffington's exceptional personal gifts. Skeffington's sins, after all, brought about his doom; and the author, as John Kelleher discerningly wrote, "has no doubts about what Skeffington cost the city or the Irish.

. . . The tragedy is collective, the failure of the Irish as a whole to have the courage of their own qualities and to make better use of them."

The critical notes, such as they were, were drowned out in a general crescendo of applause. The Book-of-the-Month Club took the book; it became a quick best-seller and by 1969 had sold over a million copies in the United States alone. The name of Skeffington has passed into the speech, and *The Last Hurrah* is properly regarded as the best American novel about urban politics. Nor is its appeal confined to Americans. In 1961 Prime Minister Nehru, going away for a brief vacation, asked J. K. Galbraith, then American Ambassador to India, for some books to take with him. Galbraith gave him, among others, *The Last Hurrah*. "He called me on his return," Galbraith later wrote, "to express his intense delight and to say it was the best political novel he had ever read. Some in this country have suggested that Ed O'Connor's special talent was Boston and its ethnic groups. There could be no better demonstration that his was a universal sense of the problems of political organization and leadership than this reaction of an experienced politician like Nehru."

v

The question whether Skeffington was based on James M. Curley is entirely trivial. Obviously in some early sense Curley suggested the idea of Skeffington, as Maurice Tobin, who beat Curley in 1937 and 1941 and later became Truman's Secretary of Labor, suggested the idea of Kevin McCluskey; but the characters in the novel, as re-created in the author's imagination, departed extensively from the original. Curley, for example, was a mean-spirited and bitter man, with few of Skeffington's private charms (as Ed himself put it, "I know very little about Mayor Curley. My man is far different. He has more extensive capacities") just as Tobin was a far less vapid and more independent man than McCluskey.

However, the story of Curley's reaction to *The Last Hurrah* is worth telling, since it might almost have been an episode from the book itself. The *Boston Globe* had asked Curley to review *The Last Hurrah*. After taking a fast look, Curley bounced the book back with a crisp note saying that the matter was in the hands of his attorneys. For the next few weeks, as Ed later described it, "threats of lawsuit were coming regularly from the house on the Jamaicaway, all filtered through a succession of middlemen whose appearance, to put it mildly, did not inspire trust." One day a month or so after the book was published, Ed strolled out of the Parker House and saw Curley getting into a taxi. The opportunity was too good to miss. Ed put his head in the cab window and, as Curley looked up, slightly startled, introduced himself.

There was a long pause; then suddenly Curley laughed. "Well, well," he said, putting out his hand. "Nice to see you. You've written quite a book. I like that book." Ed said he was glad to hear this; rumors to the contrary had been reaching him with some persistence. "No, no," Curley said, waving all such rumors to the side. "That's a fine book. I enjoyed it. Do you know the part I enjoyed most?" "No," Ed said. "I don't." Curley said, "The part where I die." Ed thought he had better nail this down quickly and said, "Isn't it strange, Governor, how so many people confuse fact with fiction? Skeffington with yourself, for instance? I know, and you know, the difference between the two, that the one isn't like the other —"

But Curley was not to be stopped. "Yes," he said, nodding gravely. "Yes, there I am in my bedroom, dying. Breathing my last. I'm lying flat on my back with my eyes closed when suddenly into the room comes . . ." and he went on to repeat most of the scene. (Telling this story, Ed would reproduce Curley's sonorous, fruity voice with perfection.) When Curley finished, he congratulated Ed once more, shook his hand, wished him well, and they parted on the most cordial terms. "I should add," Ed later said, "that this pleasant encounter in no way diminished the threats of lawsuit. They continued: out of the shadows came the by now familiar voices of the middlemen, muttering darkly of financial ruin for me and all those associated with me."

The more Curley discoursed on the book, the more he merged Skeffington and himself. The cherished deathbed scene reaches its climax in the novel when a detested acquaintance of Skeffington's, an Irish merchant, piously remarks, "I think we can say this: that knowing what he knows now, if he had it all to do over again, there's not the slightest doubt but that he'd do it all very, very differently." Skeffington, outraged, bestirs himself for a final blast: *"The hell I would."* Lecturing at the University of New Hampshire, Curley rewrote the scene to introduce his own villain:

I feel that the last paragraph [*sic*] of that book contains everything that is worthwhile reading in the book. I am supposed to have received the last rites of the Catholic Church and I'd been in a state of coma for about 12 hours when the owner of the *Boston Herald* [a notorious enemy of Curley's] comes in and looks at me in that sad state, and he said, "I suppose, Skeffington, if you had to do it all over again, you'd do different." And I replied to him . . . "The hell I would."

When Curley came to write his own autobiography, he called it *I'd Do It Again.*

vi

The Last Hurrah was not only highly successful as a novel but was soon sold to the movies. Ed, beyond expressing a wish that Claude Rains should play Skeffington, declined to have anything to do with the enterprise. The film, released in 1958, should have been excellent. It was directed by John Ford and written by Frank Nugent. Spencer Tracy played Skeffington, and reliable Irish character actors like James Gleason, Edward Brophy, Frank McHugh, Edmund Lowe and Pat O'Brien adorned the cast. However, it was a curiously tired and stereotyped production. Ed hated it. When someone asked him about it, he said grimly, "The back of the seats at Loew's Orpheum ought to have the same kind of equipment they have on airplanes."

For the first time, Ed now had a sufficiency of money. He moved out of his room in Marlborough Street into the top floor of a tall apartment house on Beacon Hill where his living room commanded a sweeping view of the Charles River. He bought an automobile, took his meals at the Ritz (those he did not cook himself) and abandoned the rooming houses in Wellfleet village for cottages he could rent in the woods. Affluence amused him (one day he dropped by the *Atlantic Monthly*, announced "Money means nothing to me any more" and, with elaborate ceremony, took a penny from his pocket and threw it out the window). But, except for an addiction to foreign cars, he spent very little on himself. His Beacon Hill apartment had an almost monastic air, especially in the cell-like bedroom where a simple crucifix hung above what can only be described as a pallet. He wore the same terrycloth jacket to the beach for years despite the protest and derision of friends, and his hat, when he put one on, was disreputable in the extreme.

After *The Last Hurrah*, *Life* and other magazines deluged him with offers, but he turned nearly all down. He knew, though, that the *Boston Post*, the paper that had employed him when he needed help, was in deep trouble; and, while he had no use for the *Post*'s new owner, he had great concern for the men on the staff who would be on the streets if the paper folded. He thereupon went to his good friend Elliot Norton, the *Post*'s drama critic, and said that, "if it would be of any help," he would be glad to write a regular Sunday article. Refusing all payment, he wrote the column every Thursday for some months, taking it over to the paper by hand, chatting with his friends and then going on about his business.

1956 also brought saddening changes to his life. His father, who had been sick for some years, died in September, and Ed took his mother to Atlantic City for recuperation. There the sight of an odious little boy in the hotel stimulated him into beginning a cautionary story for children.

This grew into the *jeu d'esprit* entitled *Benjy: A Ferocious Fairy Tale*. This ambiguous little volume, couched in the wide-eyed prose of a children's book and illustrated by his friend Ati Forberg, described a typical American family: a doting mother, a sadistically virtuous son and a father who spends his evenings playing solitaire and eating sandwiches inside a television set. Benjy's insatiable goodness soon wins him a visit from a foul-mouthed Good Fairy commissioned in the traditional manner to dispense wishes. Benjy makes his wish and considerately includes his mother in it. A horrific climax finally disposes of the pair.

The reaction to this black comedy was exceedingly mixed. Tender-hearted adults were repelled by what they considered the violence of the underlying fantasy; tougher readers were delighted by the satire. Children, less given to weighing psychological implications, seem to have relished it. But it sold hardly more than five thousand copies.

In the meantime, Ed was pursuing more serious matters. If the Irish-American consciousness found part of its outlet in politics, it also found an even more vital outlet in religion; and religion was closer than politics to the heart of Ed's concern. He attended Mass faithfully, often daily as well as Sunday, received Holy Communion regularly, was well read in Roman Catholic theology (he particularly liked Newman and also was rather struck by Teilhard de Chardin) and was a tremendous admirer of John XXIII. I am not a religious man; so I write of these matters with diffidence. But Ed's faith was plainly one of such strength and purity that it could withstand all doubt and permit all irreverence.

Because his faith was so great, he made it the measure of performance; and this enabled him to see the human problems of Church and clerisy with cheerful and sometimes anxious lucidity. He worried a good deal about the Church — both about the rigidity and bigotry of the old Irish Church in America and the slackness and ingratiations of the new. "A Meeting on Sunday," the talk he gave at the Paulist Center in 1963, expressed some of this worry. John Kelleher, who heard the talk, said, "It rocked, and delighted, the faithful." Ed welcomed the modernization of the Church in theory but found himself dubious over certain practical results. He had been all for liturgical reform, he would say, but had not expected that reading the Mass in English would require the communicant to have a tin ear. He thought that changes were being imposed too quickly and at the expense of the older people, priests and laymen alike, who might, he believed, have been permitted to live out their days in their familiar devotions. The new breed of priests, overflowing with plans for lawn parties, barbecues, smokers, bridges, beanos and monster outdoor rallies, irritated him.

The new Church also amused him, and the vicissitudes accompanying modernization provided him with an endless fund of stories. As early as 1945 he invented a Brother Agnew Bresnahan in whose name he wrote solicitous letters to friends:

Say "YES!" to God

Crescent View House
Apothegm Heights
March 22, 1945

My dear Miss ——:

It is with sincere pleasure that I am able to inform you that, on the afternoon of Thursday next, the Reverend Brother Benedict Croteau, F.S.C., will call upon you in your office. He is to be in Boston for approximately two weeks, gathering the necessary material for his new book: *You Can Fool Neither God Nor Benedict Croteau.*

Because Brother Benedict is the youngest religious in the country (he is only thirteen years old, by the way), the Christian Brothers may be excused, I think, for betraying a justifiable pride in his work. You may recall that it was Brother Benedict who was the first to advocate the abolition of all religious orders within the Catholic Church, a statement which, both because of its profundity and unorthodoxy, set many of our best minds to thinking. I believe that I can safely say that Brother Benedict's most recent proposal, made after a prolonged fast of seven months, during which time Brother Benedict subsisted entirely on gingerbread and Seven-Up, will be even more startling. He advocates the elimination of the priest during the celebration of the Mass. We in the Order consider this rather revolutionary, and certainly thought-provoking. Much of Brother Benedict's thinking, I believe, springs from a deep personal animus towards the present Pope, whom he regards as something of a usurper.

Might I suggest, incidentally, that Brother Benedict should be protected from the sun at all times during his visit to your city? Due to rather unusual pigmentation, his skin turns bottle-green when exposed to the direct rays of the sun, and Brother Benedict himself begins to twitch. If this *should* occur — and let's hope that it does not —, the condition may be alleviated by applying a slight pressure on Brother Benedict's windpipe, and murmuring "Benziger Brothers" into his right ear.

Since our Order is, by foundation, a French one, I think I can most appropriately close by saying "Au revoir."

Sincerely,

Brother Agnew Bresnahan, F.S.C.

Nor were such letters confined to Catholic friends. Here is one I received some twenty years later:

> Diocesan Headquarters
> Boston
> Feb. 24, 1967

Dear Monsignor:

Hope everything is working out well: the English are a terrible people, according to a number of my ancestors. They're always trying to intermarry with us, but a few people like myself are making it tough for them. . . .

Ecumenical note: at Sunday Mass in these days of the new church, a layman, instead of the priest, reads the epistle out loud to the congregation. Last Sunday the appointed layman read the wrong epistle. The minor confusion that resulted at the time was compounded when the visiting preacher — a huge priest, bald, red-faced, and an old-fashioned orator to whom twenty solid minutes are merely openers — got into the pulpit, obviously shaking with rage. It turned out that his entire sermon had been based on the epistle proper to that Sunday — which, of course, none of us had heard, and because of which his sermon was literally incomprehensible. I will not go into what happened at length; I will only inform you that the priest was a sore loser.

The letter was signed "Fulton Sheen."

It should be evident both that his faith was serene and impregnable, and that, as John Kelleher has written, "he was finding the Church increasingly discomforting." The discomfort was a source both of comedy and of anguish. Moreover, the Church offered another way of getting at the exhaustion of the Irish-American impulse — the transformation he had seen from the viewpoint of politics in *The Last Hurrah*. These motives — the religious quest and the sociological change — now mingled in his new novel.

vii

The Edge of Sadness came out in 1961. In telling the story of Father Hugh Kennedy and his old friends the Carmodys, O'Connor fused his two themes — the search for grace and the end of Irish America — into a single text. It is technically an impressive work, more complex in its construction and precise in its writing than *The Last Hurrah*. In achieving tighter control of his narrative, O'Connor was serving the needs of his new subject. For, if the discursive extravagance of *The Last Hurrah* communicated a sense of the explosiveness of Irish-American politics, the careful orchestration of *The Edge of Sadness* was exactly right to convey the inward-looking, almost claustrophobic, absorptions of Irish-American religion. Politics, after all, was the means by which the Irish expanded into the American world outside, religion the means by which they withdrew to themselves. Where *The Last Hurrah* takes place in the midst of a mixed and bustling community, hardly a non-Catholic appears in *The Edge of Sadness*.

The essential story is the redemption of Father Hugh Kennedy, who, falling into spiritual aridity, had become an alcoholic and then had restored himself sufficiently to receive a new parish but not enough to recover a full sense of vocation. The parish is Old Saint Paul's in the city in which he had grown up. Once a thriving Irish church, now it is "a derelict, full of dust and flaking paint and muttering, homeless, vague-eyed men . . . hardly a parish at all any more, but a kind of spiritual waterhole: a halting place for transients in despair." The permanent families are Syrians, Greeks, some Italians, a few Chinese, the advance guard of the Puerto Ricans. Pervading the parish "is this spreading, endless despair, hanging low like a blanket, the fatal slow smog of the spirit . . . faces from which hope and joy and dignity and light have been draining so steadily and for so long that now there is nothing left but this assortment of indifferent, damaged masks."

One morning a telephone call summons Father Hugh back to his earlier days. The call comes from Charlie Carmody, one of O'Connor's terrible old men ("as fine a man as ever robbed the helpless," Hugh remembers his father saying); and abruptly the priest finds himself caught up in a life he thought he had abandoned. Charlie Carmody's son, John, another priest and once Hugh's great friend, is a brilliant, desperate man who hates his father and has come to hate his flock. The old buccaneer's grandson Ted O'Donnell is the new breed: clean-cut, Brooks Brothers, A.D.A., now running for Congress. Watching old Charlie Carmody play malignantly on his family, watching Father John Carmody despond and then die, Father Hugh recognizes "the sin of despair . . . the greatest sin of all, because it means that in the end you've given up, that you no longer trust in the love and the mercy of God." Entering into the agony of the Carmodys, he attains a new strength for himself, "an awareness, an *assurance* that while something was over forever, something else had just begun," a conviction that "I might, through the parish and its people, find my way not again to the simple engagement of the heart and affections, but to the Richness, the Mercy, the immeasurable Love of God."

So bald a summary suggests a conventional Catholic novel; but this is the last phrase to be applied to *The Edge of Sadness*. O'Connor's observations of the Church and the priesthood are notably detached and unsentimental. Like the political boss, the Irish-American priest had also once been a tribal leader, commanding an ignorant and devoted flock. Now Americanization — education, affluence, respectability — had undermined the position of priest as well as politician and altered both types. So the modern priest could talk more easily to a parish committee than to God and "had become little more than a recreation director: a cheerleader in a Roman collar."

The account of the evolution, or devolution, of an Irish-American family is equally unsentimental: the tyrannous and mean if gamy old man; then his unhappy children whom he had done his best to destroy; then the third generation forgetting the old tradition, exploiting the old faith and losing the old flavor. When Father Hugh asks young Ted whether his grandfather shows any interest in his congressional ambitions, Ted replies, "He's interested all right. I get the political history of the city every time we get together. . . . It's made up mostly of people with names like Big Thumb Connerty and Jumbo Riley and Snake Devlin. Was there *really* a Snake Devlin, I wonder?" Then Ted casually betrays his own attitude toward the Church when he proposes that he be permitted to pass the collection basket at Saint Paul's on a Sunday before the primaries. Father Hugh has two conclusions: "that this boy was separated, not only from Charlie and his world but from me and mine, by a distance incalculably vast" and, more enigmatically, "that this was, at least in part, our fault."

It was no more true of *The Edge of Sadness* than of *The Last Hurrah* that, because O'Connor chronicled the passing of the older day with evident regret for the loss of vigor and individuality, he was therefore voting for the past against the future. He was not developing an argument; he was delineating a process. As Father Hugh remarks, "If the new might not seem the equal of the old, that might be because the two were not to be compared." The end of Irish America produced dilemmas for Irish Americans. Father Hugh showed how some could be resolved through the insight and compassion gained from suffering. Could it not be that the new might in time seem the equal of the old? For all its melancholy, *The Edge of Sadness* is perhaps the most affirmative of O'Connor's novels.

It was an instant success. *The Last Hurrah* had been improbably passed over for the Pulitzer Prize in 1957; no award at all had been made that year. Now, to general applause, *The Edge of Sadness* won the prize in 1962. It remained his own favorite among his novels.

viii

An event of greater importance than the Pulitzer Prize took place the same year: his marriage. Ed's friends had come to suppose him an incorrigible Irish bachelor. He took out girls and had many agreeable friendships; but his way of life was now well set, and we thought it unlikely that he would endanger his cherished pattern by marriage. But in 1961 he encountered Veniette Caswell Weil in Wellfleet. She was a willowy and striking blonde of great loveliness of face and spirit; she also found Ed irresistible and dissolved into helpless laughter whenever he made a joke or told a story; and she immediately fell in love with him. There were problems from Ed's viewpoint: Veniette was a divorcee and had a small boy. But the problems rapidly dwindled in importance.

They were married quietly by Monsignor Francis J. Lally at the Holy Cross Cathedral in Boston on September 2, 1962; young Steve Weil became an indispensable part of the family; and Ed left his celibate apartment, first establishing his new household in an ornate quasi-Renaissance house on Chestnut Street and then buying an even more opulent mansion on Marlborough Street, across the way from the boarding-house in which he had lived in a single room a decade before. (It was in the Chestnut Street house one day when the Charles River was in spring flood and water was surging into the O'Connor basement that Ed and Veniette changed into bathing suits and spent a long, exasperated time bailing out the water and pouring it down the drain. After several hours Ed suddenly disappeared. Veniette, wet, exhausted and not a little irritated, began to wonder where in the world her craven husband had gone when he strode down the basement stairs, elegantly dressed in a dinner jacket and a top hat, and said, "OK, let's get back to work.")

About this time, relaxing after *The Edge of Sadness,* he began to write for the theater. But when the play, *I Was Dancing,* was delayed in stage production, he turned the script into a novel, and it was published in 1964. The novel showed its theatrical origin in the strict unity of its scene, time and theme. Its central problem was once again the conflict of generations in the Irish-American community — the terrible old men, crafty, profane and selfish, vs. the smooth, washed-out young men who in the process of assimilation into WASP society had lost in identity what they gained in miscibility. Waltzing Daniel Considine, the old vaudevillian, is an astute study in the duplicities of age, scheming with his cronies to live forever with his son, whom he had abandoned twenty years earlier, and his daughter-in-law, whom he had never seen before. The talk is abundant and funny; and the light thrown on character — whether of the egomaniac old or of the other-directed young — is sometimes frightening. As before, O'Connor's young women are perfunctory. But his men (and his old crones), his sense of family, his sense of confrontation, and the wit and zest of the dialogue are, as always, limpid and uproarious.

The flow of talk, indeed, almost swamped *I Was Dancing* when David Merrick produced it on Broadway later in 1964. Burgess Meredith played Waltzing Daniel; and his free, sometimes forgetful, way with the lines drove Ed to distraction. The critics complained that the copious exuberance of the dialogue slowed down the plot. Elliot Norton was among those who found the play static; but Ed, showing a forbearance unusual among authors, did not allow this candor to affect their friendship. After a mild success out of town, the play finally ran only seventeen performances in New York.

The novel had mixed notices. Julian Moynahan wrote in the *New York Review of Books* that O'Connor "transcends his limitations by a process of purification and concentration" and that *I Was Dancing* was "probably his best book and one of the subtlest and most suggestive novels to come out of the Hub since *The Bostonians*." On the other hand, a critic in the *Saturday Review* denounced the book, and O'Connor's work as a whole, for ignoring the "fact that even in Irish Boston, even in the city hall and in parish rectories, women as women — not as docile child-brides, idealized sisterly old friends, or cackling crones — play a far greater part in the emotional, social and professional lives of most men than he shows any sign of recognizing."

In retrospect, I think, *I Was Dancing* bears the same relation to O'Connor's more serious work as, say, Graham Greene's "entertainments" do to his novels. Like *Benjy*, it represented a lighter interlude in between major efforts. And such a major effort was already evolving in his mind. Once more, he wanted to use politics as a perspective on the evolution of Irish-Americanism; only this time he would carry his exploration into a new generation, the generation beyond *The Last Hurrah*.

ix

The result, published in 1966, was *All in the Family*. The new novel's narrator, Jack Kinsella, had as a young man, almost twenty years earlier, worked for Frank Skeffington; "I had been the last of his secretaries to be employed by this extraordinary old man before his death." (Kinsella is not named in *The Last Hurrah* where Tom Lacy is described as Skeffington's "chief secretary"; he must have been one of the "two young men from his secretarial corps" mentioned early in the book.) This had been Kinsella's single fling in politics. Thereafter he had turned to writing and, after some unsuccessful novels, had become a proficient author of suspense thrillers.

Politics was a secondary theme in Kinsella's life and, in spite of surface appearances, it is a secondary theme in *All in the Family*. The first section of the novel is perhaps O'Connor's best sustained sequence of writing. Except for the character of Jack's Uncle Jimmy, it is almost completely devoid of the outrageous old Irishmen and the tumbling Irish talk which were supposedly his trademarks. It returns to Jack Kinsella's childhood — a sunlit time, suddenly interrupted when his mother, momentarily crazed, drowns his younger brother and herself. Then, for recuperation, Jack's father takes him to Ireland where he stays with his Uncle Jimmy, an American tycoon who has dabbled in politics and is known as "the Irish Baruch." Uncle Jimmy has bought an Irish castle, and here Jack gets to know his three cousins — James, Philip and Charles. These pages have a subtle, lyric, poignant beauty quite unlike anything else in O'Connor's work and conceivably the consequence of the release of emotion brought about by his own marriage.

But Jack Kinsella, psychologically disabled by the childhood tragedy, was withdrawn and self-protective as an adult, incapable of love. His wife Jean, frozen out by his absorption in himself and his work, had left him for another man; now she wishes to return, and he wants her back. At the same time, the other Kinsellas have re-entered his life, drawing him into a more complex social existence, as Charlie Carmody had drawn Father Hugh Kennedy in *The Edge of Sadness.*

Some time earlier, Jimmy Kinsella had summoned his sons to a family conference and announced that one — he didn't care which one — ought to enter politics; the city and the state were going to hell in a handbasket, and it was high time that the family stepped in and began to straighten out the mess. James, the oldest, had become a new-style, highly ecumenical Catholic cleric and was out of the question; Philip, the second son, a tough but idealistic lawyer, was not interested in elective office; and the choice fell on Charles, the youngest. With his father financing him and Philip managing his campaigns, Charles becomes mayor and, as the story resumes, governor.

Charles represents the Ivy League Irish in politics. The days of Skeffington, whom Jimmy Kinsella dismisses as "that old chromo" ("all these mushmouthed Micks around here thought he was God with that fake voice and the big hello!") are gone. The time has arrived for the new politics of television, ethnic coalitions, academic advice and low-keyed urbanity. O'Connor may not have been greatly interested in politics *per se*; but he was extraordinarily acute about it, and he understood that the secret of the new politics lay less in technology or in money than, as Phil tells Jack, in knowledge: "That's our secret, Jack . . . all sorts of information that the others never bothered with because it was too small or too unimportant or too hard to get at." Charles succeeds as the new type of Irish Catholic. ". . . all the peculiar snobberies of the whole family situation," he frankly says: "all those little Irish secretaries daydreaming away. A kind of glamor, I suppose. I got the Catholic vote because everybody knows I am one. I got the non-Catholic vote because the others don't think I'm a very good one. Or, as they'd put it, I'm not 'typical.' "

Always behind Charles Kinsella's success lay the family, held together by the irascible will of Jimmy Kinsella. "Among themselves they argued as much as anybody, but this was all in the family; whenever anything outside the family came up they were all very loyal to each other and always stuck together." The family cohesiveness had grown with the years, and they made few decisions without a family council. "All for one, one for all," Jimmy Kinsella used to say; then, citing his own father, "If he ever caught you going outside saying anything about the rest of us, he gave it to you good. He wouldn't say a word; he'd just shoot you one of those looks and reach for the razor strap. I had a sore tail for ten years, but I wound up knowing what you could do if you all stuck together!"

But could they all stick together now? James, the worldly churchman, had long since drifted away from the family. Then Charles, as governor, feels he must compromise with the old politics, operate within the old structure. "We have an enormous number of people in this state who seem to have changed in a great many ways," he tells Jack, "but the more you know them, and the closer you think and get to bedrock, the more you find that they still think and feel — and vote — precisely as their fathers and grandfathers did. . . . You have to watch them every minute, and whether you believe it or not, you have to work within the limitations they place upon you." For Philip, the radical reformer, this becomes intolerable. The two brothers break up. Philip threatens to expose Charles; and Charles takes a quite horrible revenge on Philip.

But the novel is less concerned with the dilemmas of politics than with the fate of the family; and the family is the casualty less of ideological disagreement than of the Americanization process. "As a family, we're done, Jack," Philip tells his cousin; and old Jimmy's concluding bellow sums up the story: "What the hell has happened? *What the hell has happened to my family?*" "I don't know, Pa," Philip replies. "I guess we all grew up."

This expresses, I think, O'Connor's verdict. Americanization had sloughed off the outrageous old eccentrics; it had replaced the fierce clan by the often faceless chaps in Brooks Brothers suits; it had turned out smooth young opportunists, whether insipid like Kevin McCluskey or ruthless like Charles Kinsella. Yet Americanization was inevitable; it was also a process of a growing up, of the acceptance of reality, and in due course it could perhaps produce a new strength and individuality, even perhaps a new sense of family. The harsh idealism of Philip Kinsella showed a possible recrystallization of the Irish-American character in the new time; as Jack Kinsella's own reconciliation with his wife, his renewed love for her, her pregnancy, demonstrated the reconstitution of family. The book closes: "And so, the next morning, I left Ireland again, to go back to the city I had always loved, to the house which had always been my home, but now, for the first time, with my dear Jean, to a family of my own."

x

The reception of *All in the Family* was complicated by the insistence of reviewers on reading the novel as a *roman à clef* about the Kennedys. This prospect worried Ed a good deal as he worked on the book. But he could not see any way around it without discarding the idea entirely, and he was unwilling to let the fear of transitory journalistic scandal stop him from using a scheme he cared deeply about.

Actually any resemblance between the Kinsellas and the Kennedys is entirely superficial. Ed himself was a friend and admirer of both John and Robert Kennedy, and, in the weeks before his own death, had enthusiastically welcomed Robert Kennedy's entrance into the 1968 presidential contest. Certain characters in *All in the Family* were, indeed, suggested by Massachusetts politics — Margaret Lucille Elderberry, for example (by Louise Day Hicks) and Frank Dooley (by Eddie McCormack) — but the Kinsellas were authentic products of the author's imagination. (Edward Kennedy reading the jacket description of Jimmy Kinsella — "a tough, irascible little tycoon whose pride in his sons is matched only by his determination to get them what he wants: high political office"— said to Ed with Kennedy irony, "I never knew anyone like that.")

Removed from the Kennedy connection and assessed in its own right, *All in the Family* must be considered, I think, his most accomplished work. It has satirical portraits and set pieces in the familiar O'Connor manner, like James Kinsella, the perambulant prelate, or the celebration of Charles's election as governor; and these are marvelous. But he was also breaking new ground. As we have noted, he deepened his interpretation of the Irish-American experience. The technical control with which he told an intricate and highly articulated story, weaving back and forth from the past to the present and from Jack Kinsella's private agony to his public concerns, showed an impressive mastery of the art. His success in depicting and differentiating the young Kinsellas and their wives showed that his gifts of characterization were not dependent on the use of types left over from the Abbey Theatre. And he displayed in *All in the Family* for the first time an ability to create convincing young women.

One feels that marriage had accelerated his process of self-exploration and self-knowledge. His growing ability to portray young women showed itself again in the play he wrote after *All in the Family*. This was called *The Traveler from Brazil*, and it was about the third generation of an Irish-American family now gone to seed and illusion. The leading figure, a grandson of Big Charlie Doyle, the politician and saloon-keeper, and the victim of his termagant mother, Big Charlie's daughter, has come to suppose the world crazy ("Today madness is everywhere: it's part of the air we breathe, like oxygen. . . . *We've got used to it*. We're addicts; we can't live without it"). The author, using ingenious technical devices to show the craziness of the world as reported on the mass media, seems to come close to endorsing this view himself. From time to time, Gerald, the grandson, has disappeared on trips, allegedly to Brazil; but his "Brazil" turns out to be only a sanitarium. Eventually one of O'Connor's best female characters appears to draw Gerald back to life. She persuades him to accept reality, and they go off to the real Brazil. The play, with streaks of satire and sadness, is both funny and desperate. Unfortunately it does not lend itself to excerpts.

At the time of his death he was working on two novels; the unfinished texts are published in this volume. His intention in the novel about the Cardinal was to portray the changing Church through the consciousness of an old man, stricken with cancer and pondering the problem of his successor. The old Cardinal would have received a variety of pressures and considered a variety of candidates; and this would have afforded the novelist a chance to survey the evolving complexities of the Catholic community. Then it would turn out that the diagnosis was wrong, that the Cardinal did not have cancer after all. Yet this would not make much difference, for, a man of eighty, he would soon die anyway.

John Kelleher in his note on "The Cardinal" speculates persuasively on the reasons which may have led Ed to lay this draft aside and take up the novel about the boy. As for this second fragment, Mrs. Yntema, with whom he discussed the book before his death, writes:

The scheme was slight. Ed never did stick with his schemes anyway. The boy's father's mysterious absences, the boy's separation from his father, were the interesting part, to Ed. He thought of various ways of accounting for them: the latest was to make the father be a crook, a professional gambler, maybe card-shark. The climax would be the boy's discovery of this. Then the book would end with the father being shot down by the big criminals in whose power he had been, and whom he had decided to defy.

She felt that this might have been his best book. "In it, all sorts of inhibitions and adhesions had come unstuck. He was writing very fast and happily in the two weeks before his death; and he had a fresh consciousness of his powers."

Ed also planned to write a novel about the first stage of the Irish migration — Boston in the eighteen forties and fifties. Dealing with the generations before Skeffington, this would have completed his panorama of the Irish experience in America. And he sometimes talked of doing a novel about a publisher. This would have been based on his friend Arthur Thornhill, Sr., of Little, Brown (who was definitely not the publisher somewhat acidly portrayed in *All in the Family*).

Early in 1968 he sold the huge Marlborough Street house and moved with his wife and stepson into a light and spacious apartment on Commonwealth Avenue overlooking the Charles River. There, as he was working on the novel about the boy, he was suddenly stricken by a massive cerebral hemorrhage. He never regained consciousness and died almost immediately.

He would have rejoiced at the diversity of the mourners who flocked to his wake.

xi

"It would seem," Lionel Trilling has written, "that Americans have a kind of resistance to looking closely at society. They appear to believe that to touch accurately on the matter of class, to take full note of snobbery, is somehow to demean themselves. . . . Consider that Henry James is, among a large part of our reading public, still held to be at fault for noticing society as much as he did." Explaining the American resistance to the novel of manners by an obsession with a generalized conception of "reality," Trilling insisted that the power to create character derived from intense and specific concern with manners.

It is inescapably true that in the novel manners make men. It does not matter in what sense the word manners is taken — it is equally true of the sense which so much interested Proust, or of the sense which interested Dickens or, indeed, of the sense which interested Homer. The Duchesse de Guermantes . . . Mr. Pickwick and Sam Weller, Priam and Achilles — they exist by reason of their observed manners. So true is this, indeed, so creative is the novelist's awareness of manners, that we may say that it is a function of his love.

As a consequence of the American commitment to generalized reality, "our social sympathies have indeed broadened, but in proportion as they have done so we have lost something of our power of love, for our novels can never create characters who truly exist."

O'Connor was in this sense a novelist of manners, and he manifested his "power of love" in the surging abundance and vitality of his creations. The people in his novels are rich and unforgettable; they stride out of the pages in exuberant life; they inhabit one's memory long after the incidents in which they were involved fade away. They disclose themselves in their cascade of talk — their fears, vanities, pretensions, evasions. O'Connor loved Irish talk — and recognized its perils. Thus Father John Carmody in *The Edge of Sadness* on the conversation at his father's table:

They all have that special, dreadful kind of talk that doesn't exist anywhere but here. It's not conversation. It's not anything. Just a suffocating cloud of words that keeps on growing and growing and coming and coming. Like a fog. . . . I simply like talk to have some point. And this had none. It never does. In the first place because no one is talking *to* anyone. They're just *talking*. And secondly, because in all rational talk, no matter how much you digress, you usually come back to the main road once in a while. But in my father's house no one comes back to the main road for the simple reason that there *is* no main road. Everybody there deals exclusively in detours. . . .

Just as you think that maybe this time there just might be a possibility of some sort of logical progression you suddenly find yourself trapped in the middle of some lunatic story about a man named Danny McGee who always slept in a maple tree or Little Philsy Kerrigan who once saved up a trunkful of doughnuts. And there you are. God knows how you got there, but there you are and there you stay.

Sometimes O'Connor had to struggle to bring his gift of mimicry under control. He did so with increasing success as his work ripened.

It was sometimes observed, and I think justly, that he was an heir of James and Howells, or that he was doing for the Massachusetts Irish what Marquand had done for the Massachusetts Yankees. (But he distinguished himself from Marquand, observing once, "The trouble with Marquand is that he got to like the people he wrote about.") He caught and transfixed the Irish-American community in its ordeal of acculturation, chronicling the modes by which Micks turned into WASPs and suggesting the losses and gains in the process. Committed neither to the past nor the future, he accepted change as the law of life. He left behind an ironic chronicle of a vital part of American society — a chronicle that, along with the more somber and desperate early work of James T. Farrell (and Chicago was a more somber and desperate city than Boston), future historians must consult to understand a way of living that will have ceased to exist. The fact that Ed's work came to fruition in the brief but brilliant age of the Kennedys validated, for the time being at least, his equability as against Jim Farrell's despair. And in the end, as his friend Daniel Aaron has acutely commented, he was no more an "ethnic" writer than Saul Bellow or Ralph Ellison. He had no minority hang-ups, and the lucidity with which he perceived the world about which he wrote made that world a universal human experience.

The sort of thing he did and the way he did it were somewhat out of fashion in the America of the sixties — out of fashion, at least, among the younger and more modish critics, fascinated by the extremities of technique required to deal with the extremities of experience. When Edmund Wilson noted in a self-interview that O'Connor, James Baldwin and J. D. Salinger were the living American novelists whose works he regularly read, this caused some astonishment in rarefied literary circles. Those who found the excitement of life in the margins rather than the centralities did not hold in high esteem the older virtues of characterization, dialogue and narrative power. Ed recognized the prevailing mood and did not much care.

He was a careful and unhurried writer, working away on a portable typewriter, shaping his work according to unconscious predispositions rather than by a set plan. He once described his method of composition to the *Providence Evening Bulletin*: "I never have outlined. When I start I have no idea how to carry through. I write — I form the story, as I go along. The first draft of the book is final, although I correct as I go along. I rewrite a great deal as I go. I may rewrite a page a dozen times, but then it is final; I don't go back. I don't write easily: the work is painstaking; but I write consecutively." He generally began writing early in the morning, breaking off around noon. In Boston he would then stroll over to the *Atlantic Monthly*, stick his head in various doors, joke for a moment about the events of the day and pass on to the Ritz-Carlton, a hotel he adored, for luncheon. In Wellfleet after a morning's writing in his handsome modern house in the woods, he would go to the beach. Here he read and lay in the summer sand, occasionally bestirring himself to serve as games manager for the children, literary and social raconteur for the adults and (to his increasing irritation) lifeguard for swimmers who ventured too far out into the ocean. (Marian Cannon Schlesinger has well described this: "On three different occasions he saved people from drowning in that treacherous surf, and I remember being a witness to his last act of heroism. It seemed to me a perfect example of the conflict between his instinctive desire not to get involved in other people's business and his great sense of responsibility and duty.

He was furious at the drowning people because they had acted foolishly and their predicament was of their own making. But he was the only able-bodied, sensible man around, so, swearing and mad, he jumped into the rip tide and succeeded in bringing the victims to safety, almost losing his life in the process. 'That's the last time I'll ever do *that*,' he said, coming up to the beach more dead than alive. Well, perhaps, but one would not lay a bet on it.")

Weather on the Cape was unpredictable; and my visits seemed too often to come during overcast weeks. This delighted Ed; here is a letter of August 4, 1958:

Dear Arthur:

You have no idea how astute you were in getting away when you did! Almost since the moment you left this area has been drenched in a relentless rain of sunshine which I, for one, find repellent. One wants to work, but this is impossible, for great surf breaks constantly on the shore, and endless, windless, baking afternoons on the sand have completely broken up my productive routine which I so enjoyed during the cold and rainy last few days of July.

You'd hate it. No sooner does the sun go down than a terrible cool breeze sweeps over the Cape, cleaning all humidity out of the air, and all clouds out of the sky, thereby promising to all of us that tomorrow will be just one more damned fair day.

He had an extraordinary gift for friendship. After I left Cambridge in 1961, we chatted over the phone every week or so; and his letters, signed with a variety of names, were enchanting. For example:

48 Beacon Street
Boston
March 2, 1961

My dear Mr. Schlesinger,

My employer, Mr. Edwin O'Connor, has been somewhat disturbed of late by President Kennedy's recent challenge: What will YOU do for your country? It seemed to him, after some weeks of experimentation, that perhaps dining four times a week at Locke-Ober's instead of five was not quite what the President had in mind. That is, it was a sacrifice, yes, but it was at best no more than an indirect approach to the new frontier.

Therefore he has determined upon a more positive course of action. Well aware of the fact that there are members of our academic community who, in their transfer to governmental activity, have incurred some financial loss, he had quietly resolved to ease their lot. A modest man, he wants no thanks for this. It is entirely in keeping with his lifelong habit of unrestricted generosity; moreover, a recent decision of the Book-of-the-Month Club promises to add appreciably to his already substantial holdings.

You will be pleased, I know, to learn that you are the first beneficiary of Mr. O'Connor's extraordinary kindness. He has decided to make over to you IN THEIR ENTIRETY all domestic royalties, for the calendar year 1961, accruing from his novel *The Oracle*. It should be explained at once, perhaps, that foreign royalties are not included in this bounty. At the present time, they amount to somewhat more than the domestic: last year, from England alone, *The Oracle* returned $.27. While domestic royalties for some years past have not approximated this level, Mr. O'Connor believes that with a new, young administration a fresh wind blows through the land and that this royalty gap will soon be closed. If so, you will, of course, profit beyond all expectation.

Mr. O'Connor expressly requests that no publicity attend this benefice. Reserved rather than shy, he prefers to perform good works in silence and receives his reward from the knowledge that, thanks to what I may call his "controlled lavishness," there are hearts that are lighter in the world today.

May I close on a personal note? I don't know if you will remember me, but some time ago we had some slight acquaintance with each other. Indeed, it could be said that we both labored in the same vineyard. Unfortunately, due to severe and wholesale personnel changes around me, my function was sharply reduced, and I was forced to seek other employment. It was here that Mr. O'Connor stepped in, most generously, and I became his social secretary. It is not quite like the old days, but it is, at least, something.

Most Cordially,

[signed] Nathan Pusey

Here are excerpts from a few others:

I'm grateful for the kind words about me [in a sketch for a book club bulletin] but . . . when you write about me in the future I wonder if you'd mind throwing in a few casual references to my home — Yasnaya Polyana — or to the fact that, although a born aristocrat, I have done much for the serfs.

Count Leo

[*enclosing a royalty check for a few cents*] You fellows who fool around with non-fiction never get to see the really big money, so I'm forwarding the enclosed check to you, just to let you peer into the kind of world which, I fear, will be forever closed to you. Will you return the check, please? Not that I need the money — a man in my position can count on several checks just like this during the course of the year — but I think it would be harmful for you to keep it around. You'd start dreaming wild dreams of rewards similar to those we successful novelists enjoy, and pretty soon the odds are that you'd abandon history or biography or whatever it is that you won that prize for and try your hand at the big leagues. If that temptation should occur in any case, my advice is to resist it. Very few of us ever reach the point where we can command, with any degree of regularity, sums of this amount.

Is it in fact true that you and your wife received a communiqué from Mary McCarthy which contained the chilling sentence: "I have been thinking of you"? This is the equivalent of the guillotine operator experimentally rubbing across the back of your neck.

The novel I Was Dancing, written by a prominent novelist of your acquaintance — I'm sorry that I can't accede to your request and give a party so that you, as you put it, can "get to know him better" — has picked up one book club (Reader'$ Dige$t) so far, and rumor has it that it is on its way to a $econd. Oh well. The Broadway production of that thrilling beautiful play of the same name moves on "apace."

[*a postcard with a picture of a South Bend motel*] This is the Fairmont of the middle west, just inside the famous Quemoy-Matsu line and therefore indefensible.

[*another Notre Dame despatch*] Everybody out here wild about the Brownson book. Best thing you've ever done. One comment sure to please: "Schlesinger combines the gaiety of a Kissinger with the sharp penetration of a [here he named a Wellfleet acquaintance]." Regards
                                                    Clement A. Norton

[*a postcard from Rome*] Ignazio Silone wants a bid to one of the Cambridge dinner dances. Can this be arranged?

John Kelleher, who was spending his scholarly hours in research on Irish history, used to receive letters signed by a certain Bucko Donahue, the only ex-slave of Bernard Baruch educated by the Christian Brothers solely in Latin and also the greatest living expert on Irish annals. Here is a letter from Harbor Island:

My dear Kelleher,
It's all cod, you know, this work you're doing on the Annals. Mother of God, I've been through it all a dozen times — the first time I went through the whole business it took me nearly a week. A week lost, is what I say. . . . I reject the Annals *in toto* for two reasons. First, it was all swiped from the Jews. Second, it's all crap anyway. . . .

I've met O'Connor: A HELL OF AN IMPRESSIVE MAN, IF WE HAD MORE LIKE HIM A SENSIBLE MAN COULD LIVE IN THE WORLD TODAY.

Erin go ha ha

Then came "Bucko Donahue," in a wavering scrawl. A more serious letter, this time written from Boston to Kelleher who was then in Dublin, illuminates Ed's attitude toward Ireland.

Joyous greetings from the little bit of Ireland we have over here to all of yez over there where, as I love to say, "we all of us come from!" Your letter almost makes me weep with longing to be over there with you, over there playing with the laughing lads on Stephen's Green, swimming up the clear blue waters of the Liffey with a good strong pair of water wings, standing outside the Abbey with the cheering throng as one after another the nation's idols come out of the stage door after another thrilling performance of another play by Louis Dalton or Councillor McCann. By God, you can't beat none of that for pleasure! And on a nice soft Sunday, to stop on the way to Phoenix Park to play a game of squat tag in the rain with a few of the Augustinian Fathers! . . .

But a backwater is a backwater and Dublin is one and will be one forever and ever, amen. I like it; but then I stay a couple of weeks and go. . . . I have no hopes for it as a *place*, and have no deep feelings about it, one way or the other; to me it's seen in terms of a few people of whom I'm very fond. . . . Write and let me know how you're doing. As Clem Norton once said to me, "My dear man, remember this: NOTHIN' LASTS!"

xii

He was an exceptionally considerate and affectionate man. No one had a more various range of loving friends; there was no one whose success aroused less envy or resentment. Philip Toynbee, after a literary tour of the United States, told me how he had come back to New York and was debriefed by Mary McCarthy. She asked him whom he had seen and then dismissed each name with a devastating comment. Finally, thinking to stop her, Toynbee said how much he had liked Ed O'Connor — "what an extremely nice man!" Mary, hard put for dissent, could only say after a moment, "Almost *too* nice?"

Ed was an unusually nice man; but his amiability covered an idiosyncratic and almost taut personality. He was formidable in his independence, his reserve, his observant and often caustic wit, his self-possession and his self-discipline, his sense of his own identity. Some people bored him, especially the pretentious and the portentous, and he developed great skill in turning them aside. He could not abide Irish chauvinists, Yankee snobs, specialists in civic brotherhood and other forms of self-righteousness, freeloaders, bigots, or Secretaries of State. He absolutely refused to go through the rituals expected of authors on the publication of books — television interviews, autographing sessions, Book and Authors luncheons and the like. He never signed statements or took public positions or accepted honorary degrees or tailored his books so they could be sold to the movies. He guarded his privacy fiercely.

His tendency to ulcers was no doubt a sign of the tension underneath the surface. Though he was a very funny writer, the undercurrent of his work was melancholy; his humor was always on the edge of sadness. But he was, as Mrs. Yntema has suggested, working through his "inhibitions and adhesions." As his life and work moved on, more things were rising to the surface; he was showing a new readiness to deal with the blackness of life — as in the drowning at the start of *All in the Family,* for example, or the terrifying device by which Charles Kinsella silenced his brother at the end. "Ed would never say, at least to me," Mrs. Yntema writes, "whether the mother had drowned her smaller son on purpose. The boy's book [on which he was working at his death] was to have a, not exactly scary, but *baffling* dark place in it, like the bottom of that cold lake." Because of his clear plan for dramatizing the "dark place" in the new book, it seemed as if he were getting through to a new sort of candor.

Father Hugh Kennedy in *The Edge of Sadness* well expressed, I think, Ed's view of human nature:

We all share in a shattering duality — and by this I don't mean that soggy, superficial split that one so often sees: the kind of thing, for example, where the gangster sobs uncontrollably at an old Shirley Temple movie. I mean the fundamental schism that Newman referred to when he spoke of man being forever involved in the consequences of some "terrible, aboriginal calamity"; every day in every man there is this warfare of the parts. And while all this results in meanness and bitterness and savagery enough, God knows, and while only a fool can look around him and smile serenely in unwatered optimism, nevertheless the wonder of it all to me is the frequency with which kindness, the essential *goodness* of man does break through, and as one who has received his full measure of that goodness, I can say that for me, at least, it is in the long succession of these small, redemptive instants, just as much as in the magnificence of heroes, that the meaning and the glory of man is revealed.

He saw life steadily, without sentimentality or illusion and with an invincible gaiety, joyousness and grace of spirit. He penetrated to the edge of sadness and beyond, but he always returned with a new and exhilarating sense of the absurdity and possibility of life.

The Oracle

Christopher Usher, hero of THE ORACLE, is an unctuous radio commentator, rather like Gabriel Heatter; for the author he was a means of ridiculing much of the popular cant of the late 1940's. Christopher is entangled in difficulties with his wife and his pneumatic mistress Lura; his house is invaded by General "Beak" Blackburn, a garrulous old simpleton; and his job is menaced by a slick network executive and by the sponsor, Mr. Bernie Udolpho, "ruler of an intricate empire of vegetable lotions." However, all these difficulties are solved or surmounted by the end of the book.

The following selections appear, closely spaced, at the opening of the book, and exhibit Christopher in his professional capacity.

I<small>T</small> was late September, and the summer had not yet gone. All day, the normally temperate city had sweltered, and now, as darkness approached, the heat remained: a sullen, humid blanket of air, so unfairly blown north from subtropic muck. . . .

In the broadcasting studio, the temperature was scarcely endurable; the air conditioning had failed unaccountably more than two hours before, and had not been repaired. Christopher Usher, attempting to beat the heat, had removed his clothing; for the first time in his career he was naked as he broadcast to the nation. Squares of cardboard had been hastily placed across the studio windows, shielding him from the gaze of the curious or the prurient. White and pink and intermittently hairy, he sat poised before the microphone, and as he read from the pages of his script, little globes of sweat bubbled, burst, and raced down the meaty concourse of his trunk. He was uncomfortable, but he was not unhappy, for he was *talking*: it was the scheduled hour of his nightly communication with his public. As he read from the script before him, he addressed the microphone with an air of personal persuasion, as if it were an agreeably unenlightened companion, as if, under the ripe sigh of his baritone, it had become magically endowed with the property of conscious audition.

". . . higher taxes for everyone? Uncle Sam to say to you and to me: 'Now just hold still while I cut myself another slice of that family dollar; don't move, this won't hurt a bit!' Well, a lot of big men in Washington are saying that it's got to come. They're saying that when more money goes out, more has to come in. They're saying: 'That's just good old-fashioned arithmetic, and we ought to know, we're economists!' Well, ladies and gentlemen, I'm no economist, but like millions of other Americans, I *do* drive an automobile. And I know that when that automobile starts going too fast, starts getting out of control, the good old-fashioned remedy is *not* to give it more gas, but to start thinking about putting on the brakes. . . ."

He read on, moving and bobbing with the words, lending each phrase gymnastic emphasis. Christopher was a big man, a solid man, and at the age of forty-five, he was in excellent physical condition. A slight tendency to fat he controlled by exercising vigorously each morning, clad in a curious all-rubber garment which was styled like a child's pajamas. From time to time he fasted, following a diet of his own devising. He was not a particularly good-looking man: his face was large and rather granitic, the type of face often seen in group photographs of professional football teams. It was redeemed from any suggestion of brutality, however, by the eyes: they were large, pale-blue, and rather pious. As of the past few months, they were also mildly presbyopic, and as a result Christopher was forced to hold his script at a distance which was not altogether comfortable. There was the alternative of wearing glasses, but although Christopher prided himself upon being without personal vanity, he found in this suggestion something singularly distasteful.

Leaving national affairs for the moment, he turned to Europe. He had little time for Europe tonight; he contented himself with recommending a plan for the furtherance of Western European unity. . . .

". . . adoption of English as a common language by France, Italy, the Benelux countries. The language of Chaucer, the language of just plain John Smith, so admirably suited to the breaking-down of ancient barriers of mistrust and fear! Think it over, you gentlemen who have the fate of a continent in your hands. This is not the time for false national pride. . . ."

Whenever possible, he preferred the simple solution; here was the common sense out for the inheritors of Dante and Racine.

He left Europe and moved far to the East, to China, and here he paused to expand. He liked China; he knew China; he had even been there. He had seen this land under conditions of peril when, as a correspondent during World War II, he had journeyed there barely a year after the cessation of hostilities. He had remained there for four, almost five weeks; he had seen Chungking, the Bund, the Great Wall, and Chiang Kai-shek (twice). He had been deeply moved by the little yellow men, scurrying so docilely through filthy streets; in their enigmatic faces he had discerned a peasant contentment, of a kind unknown to people who ate regularly. He had been impressed, even flattered, by the elaborate courtesies extended the distinguished visitor; not here, in this subtle cocoon of hospitality, was to be found the Occidental brush-off. He had grown thoughtful; he had seen that there was something here worth preserving; he had left China a friend. It was a friendship which did not wither under the adversities of battle. . . .

". . . China hopelessly lost? Beaten into the dust by the boots of Mao

Tse-tung and his Muscovite masters? Well, not according to this observer. I say we can't sell the Chinese short. I say that the sob-sisters who cry 'Give up! No more money down the rat hole!' don't know China, don't *understand* China. I say they're badly underestimating the Chinese little man, the *coolie;* underestimating his loyalty, his pride, his willingness to fight for the things he loves. This afternoon I talked for two hours with a man whom the late, beloved Vinegar Joe Stilwell called one of the most remarkable military minds in Asia. He had hope, courage, *assurance.* 'Give us the guns, the planes, the money,' he said, 'and leave the rest to us. . . .' "

Perspiration gushed; broad bare buttocks twitched in rebellion on the unpleasant perch of wet leather. Christopher talked on, unheeding; in the happy moment of autohypnosis, he was immune to physical misery. Because China was so important, he gave it forty-five seconds more; then, wrapping it up, he came back home for a driving finish with the heartening domestic items from which his broadcasts derived their special flavor. He talked of a Day for Grandparents, of a newly discovered miracle analgesic. He talked of schooldays, with a nostalgic footnote on the early days of his own educational experience. He talked of a happy Hollywood marriage; of a new method of sucking cheap heat from the earth; he talked of a hero cat. . . .

". . . what inscrutable Providence watches over children and the pets they love. Tonight we know that little Rosemary Chaplin, of Decatur, Illinois, is reunited with her kitten, Amber . . . that same kitten whose love and alertness saved the life of its little mistress . . . fire broke out in child's room . . . kitten's frantic mewings roused dormant household . . . fire extinguished, but Amber overcome . . . death feared imminent . . . Rosemary's prayers . . . stroke of fortune . . . famous veterinarian visiting in city . . . rushed to scene . . . skilled fingers on furry body . . . touch and go . . . at last . . . heart-warming conclusion to a story of loyalty, fidelity, *faith.* . . ."

He continued, his pace accelerated by emotion, the rich pump of his voice flooding the living rooms of the land with knowledge, hope, inspiration. Like all members of his authoritative profession, Christopher dealt harshly with the world and its people when they failed, as they so often did, to meet the standards that he had established for them. However, he differed from many of his colleagues in his refusal to become discouraged. He was an optimist. His primary task, as he saw it, was the communication of this optimism, as a kind of tonic, to his fellow citizens. To this end, he forever probed the dark clouds of human endeavor for the barely discernible ray of sunshine. When he talked daily to the great and the near-great of ruin and disaster, he never failed to pluck from these conversations some wisp of cheer. Above all else, he was the apostle of the pneumatic sidelight. In a world where budgets soared and taxes swelled, where nations muttered in mutual infelicity, where the footfalls of the dispossessed echoed hollowly through the night, Christopher uncovered the deeds of possible redemption: a dictator dancing with his aged mother at a state ball; a United States senator manfully hurling his sagging frame through a Kiwanis romp; a Boy Scout bandaging a puppy's paw. These were the human, the homely cores, the silver linings around which Christopher could expand in moving, often memorable fashion. He was not an unsentimental man, and sometimes, as he read the words which he had written, he was touched; occasionally he wept.

He had been broadcasting in this manner for close to nine years. He was popular with his listeners; he was extremely well paid. . . .

After the broadcast, in the little bathroom off his office, he took a shower: it was a slow, voluptuous procedure, suds as thick as whipped cream melting in the warm, nozzled rain. Outside it had grown cooler; a sudden shift of wind had brought the smell of the sea across the city, possibly signaling the end of the heat. He smiled and hummed in satisfaction; as he dried himself, he thought of a new derisive nickname for the President.

As for the broadcast, he reflected that it had been one of his best. He was pleased by this, but unexcited; excitement was for the beginner. For Christopher, long accustomed to the production of the distinctive, there was merely a pastoral euphoria, an awareness of public responsibility, expertly discharged.

He dressed quickly, for he was to join his wife at a dinner party across the city. Friends were giving it: companionable people, eager to learn. He reached for his hat, and prepared to leave, then paused to jot down a memorandum. On the following evening he planned to devote a portion of his broadcast to an analysis of Soviet public opinion; for the sake of certainty, he would contact authority.

Phone Louis Budenz, he wrote. Then he went off to the party.

———————

Christopher's broadcasts did not evolve with the easeful magic of clouds in the summer sky. Before they were spoken, they had to be written, and although the writing itself presented no problem (on the sports page Christopher had acquired facility of expression; now, writing in the graver idiom of humanity, he had achieved the peak of his productive powers, and as one after another the plump, heartening phrases spilled from him, he realized that he was writing better than he had ever writ-

ten before: with dignity, wisdom, beauty, *speed*), behind the writing lay
a daily program of research and reflection almost Carthusian in its inflex-
ibility. It began in his office each afternoon at two o'clock.

First of all, he read his mail. He did not, could not, read all of it: out
of the huge, ever-renewing flood his secretary, a polite, efficient young
man, sieved a score or so of the more representative letters. These were
brought in to Christopher, and he read them with pleasure. In the main,
they were highly approving, but Christopher considered even the sour
notes: a turbulent blast of Old Testament epithet from a prominent
labor official; several challenges to public debate from Unitarian clergy-
men; a letter from Norman Thomas. He read these, smiled, and threw
them in the wastebasket. Then he passed on to more congenial reading:

Dear Sir:

Your stirring broadcast of Friday last, in which you so ably scored the taxa-
tion policies of the current "administration" merits the appreciation of every
right-thinking citizen. It is high time that a man of courage called attention to the criminal waste and negligence which are fast driving this once
great country into the role of a second-class power. Your views coincide
exactly with my own; I wish to God there were ten thousand more like you!

If you should be in Seattle in the near future, please feel free to call upon
me. I should deem it a pleasure and a privilege to see that every facility of
our splendid city is made available to you. . . .

Appreciation from civic authority came often; it was always welcome.
Christopher placed it aside for filing, and moved on:

Dear Mr. Usher:

It gives me great pleasure to inform you that at the last semi-monthly meeting of the Improved Order of Red Men, Oak Park Chapter, you were selected as the outstanding radio commentator of the year by *unanimous* vote.

We wonder if by any chance we might present this award to you in person?
Each year our chapter holds its annual dinner-dance on the third Friday in
December, at which time it is our policy to present some figure of national
importance to address us. In view of the above mentioned vote, we would
be delighted if this year you could be that speaker.

Would you kindly write us and let us know whether you would be able to
attend? And also, if a fee would be expected? While we have a *small* budget
set aside for such purposes, we are not a large chapter. . . .

During the year, Christopher went off on several lecture tours; in addition to providing revenue, they enabled him, as he said, to "keep in

touch." On the margin of the letter he penciled brief notations to his secretary: *Thank for honor; check mid-December schedule; if can do, Gandhi & Christ, $200, EXPENSES.* He was his own lecture bureau, and he had discovered, long ago, that a modest fee, plus expenses, could prove far more lucrative than a flat, all-inclusive fee of a much larger size. He went on to the next letter:

My dear Sir:

For reasons too obvious to mention, I sign this preliminary letter to you with a pseudonym. My real name? It would mean nothing to you, therefore. . . .

I will come right down to things. During the last year of the war and also until recently I was in the government employ working for the development of atomic power. A big cog? No, but always in the position to see what did go on.

For more than a year and a half, side by side, I worked with a man who today is a *power* in the atom program. I distrusted him always, why I do not know. I observed him on all occasions, and because of my learning in those days it is by no means astonishing to me that a certain land across the sea has now the secret of the bomb.

Everything I say to you I can prove. Many, many national magazines suspect I have this story and press me about it. But because I listen to you on the radio with great admiration I would prefer you to be the one to bring my story to the American people. If as a sincere patriot your interest is aroused you may contact me by . . .

Unimpressed, he pushed it away. In general, he was content to leave the fertile field of the exposé to a more aggressive colleague, a man whose envenomed bite had been felt by most of the responsible public servants of his time. As for Christopher, it was not normally his cup of tea. It was, at best, uncertain work, demanding long hours, untiring investigation, and the final untidy contact with the Un-American Activities Committee. Still, he was not a prude: there were times when he enjoyed a good, lively, confidential betrayal, and in a way he rather regretted that this was not one. Unquestionably, it was spurious; worse, it was not exclusive. It was a carbon copy, and he wondered idly how many of his colleagues had received identical offers that day. He passed along to the next letter:

Dear Mister Usher,

Thank you thank you and God bless you for all the good things which you say on the radio every night to which I and my dear husband Becker listen.

There is not a night goes by I do not get down on my knees and Becker does too to pray for you and ask The Good God to let you keep on with your good work for many many years. . . .

Of all the letters he received each day, it was response of this kind which pleased him most. It constituted by far the greater part of his mail, arriving in plain, smudged envelopes, upon which had been super-imposed improbable postmarks. This one came from a small community in Arkansas; he noted this without surprise, for he was exceptionally strong in the Bible Belt. Vox *populi*, he thought comfortably; in the homely, semiliterate outpourings, it was possible to detect the heartbeat of a nation. This, he knew, was his *real* public: this lovable, untutored, but infinitely educable core. Toward it he felt a sense of dedication verging upon the mystical. It was not, fortunately, a unilateral affection; reciprocity came in the form of letters of faith and appreciation, as well as in the vast purchases of the nasal unguent which had sponsored Christopher's broadcasts from the beginning. He thought with fondness of this immense and loyal band, and as he thought his lips automatically formed usable little phrases: *a living natural resource of this our ample land; diamonds in the rough whose rich gleam warms a nation.* . . .

Christopher had finished the reading of his mail, and now began the actual preparation of his broadcast. The world had bubbled while he had slept; his desk was piled high with records of the overnight doings of the human race. There were neat piles of teletyped dispatches from the wire services: AP, UP, INS, Reuters. There were the daily newspapers; each day he read the *Times,* the *Herald Tribune,* the *Journal-American,* and the *Christian Science Monitor;* it was thus he attained balance, proportion. There were the country weeklies which had arrived; although less timely than the dailies (with the exception of the *Monitor*), they served to provide a sturdy, indispensable, rustic pulse. There was his private news letter, a lengthy and somewhat ponderous roundup of fact and hypothesis mailed to him nightly from the national capital by a venerable ex-senator turned tipster.

In addition, there were the magazines: *Life, The National Geographic, Quick, Time, Newsweek, Asia, Popular Science, The Infantry Journal.* These were the periodicals he had selected as being more or less essential to his professional survival; disparate in character, each contributed its special essence to the rich stock from which Christopher drew so freely. They were supplemented by a number of lesser-known journals which, although valuable, were, because of their sectarian nature, restricted in scope: *Red Cross Facts, Hygeia, The American Indian,* and *Pal.* The last-named was an antivivisectionist quarterly; it was sumptuously produced, and edited with appeal and imagination. On the front cover was a photograph of a partially dismembered collie; under the picture ran the legend: "vivisection is an UNMANLY crime!"

Beyond the newspapers and magazines, there were also books — a permanent reservoir of analysis and conclusion which Christopher seldom consulted. Years ago, in that transient moment of uncertainty (and even some self-doubt) which had followed his departure from the sports page, he had hastily acquired several volumes which, he hoped, might support him in the preliminary hours of his new calling. For almost a month he had plowed through the heterogeneous classics: Clausewitz, de Tocqueville, Marx, Spengler, Major George Fielding Eliot. It had been arduous going, and not too rewarding. Then, suddenly and beautifully, he had realized that it was all nonsense, that the problem was not one of growth, but of simple adaptation, that the Old Christopher with the Old Equipment — faith, compassion, understanding, style — was more than adequate to this larger arena. The uncorrupted Usher Point of View, transferred to the macrocosm — *that* was the answer. He had stopped all reading, immediately, and from that moment he had done well. His library remained on the office shelves, a dusty, humbling memento of shameful days of self-mistrust.

He began to examine the newspapers, his practiced eye roving quickly up and down the columns in search of truth, corroboration; the two, in his experience, were seldom mutually exclusive. He marked with a red pencil those items which would be first assimilated, then converted into the ripe undulance of broadcast diction. In addition to the routine items, he concentrated on the food and clothing advertisements, for he had decided that it was high time for another body blow at the high cost of living. He delivered these frequently and effectively, employing the simple economics of nostalgia: a pork chop, a quart of milk, the two-trouser suit; how cheap at the turn of the century, how dear today! To reinforce his position, he told the vivid story of offal: animal innards, rejected as dog food or mulch in the abundant days of our ancestors, now gracing American tables at a dollar a pound. He scribbled rough notes: he condemned the human consumption of entrails; he recommended a buyers' strike, a temporary shift to vegetarianism; he drew the happy picture of frightened meatmen, their freezers bursting with unsold roasts, falling to their knees in supplication. He turned from sweetbreads to Italian land reforms; then to a border dispute in Pakistan; and then his work was interrupted by the entrance of Mr. Churchill Chan.

The two men talked, generally, of China; particularly, of China in relation to Christopher.

". . . express gratification on behalf of my unhappy land," said Mr. Chan, with a fluid little bow. He was an ageless, graceful Cantonese, a vigilant sentinel of the Kuomintang. "You are striking mighty blows," he said. "One could not ask for more."

Christopher shifted in his chair, his forehead wrinkling in deep thought. "I wonder about that," he said. "As a matter of fact, I've been wondering for some time whether we haven't been on the wrong track altogether."

"Ah?"

"What I mean is that we've been neglecting something. Something serious, something important. As I see it, we've been overlooking entirely the spiritual aspect of the struggle!"

Mr. Churchill Chan, in the course of an industrious lifetime spent along the highest levels of international diplomacy, had had intimate contact with every known form of greed, duplicity and madness; it was his soft boast, made only to his wife, that no word or deed of the human animal could astonish him. Nevertheless, his old eyes now popped slightly at the use of the unusual word. . . .

"Spiritual?" he echoed. "Ah yes, *spiritual*." He wondered: another betrayal?

"America," said Christopher, "at the present time is a profoundly spiritual nation. All our best-selling books are about religion: *Peace of Soul*, *Peace of Mind*, and a good many others. As a matter of fact, I'm told that the country's number-one writer from the point of view of sales is a monk. And in my own case, one of my most popular lectures had to do with two great spiritual leaders: Gandhi and Christ."

"Men of greatness, without doubt." Puzzled, attempting to anticipate these queer, oblique, typically Occidental turns of mind, Mr. Churchill Chan said tentatively, "The Republic of China, although not a Christian nation, has ever been most friendly to Christianity. I myself have a relation, a very fine young man, who is a Methodist. A Methodist-*Episcopal*, I believe. . . ."

"Well, I wasn't thinking in terms of Christianity, precisely; I want to put the whole thing on a broader basis than that. I'll tell you my idea, Mr. Chan. I want," he said, his voice rising, his head ducking and feinting slightly with the words, as though the old Oriental head confronting him had suddenly dissolved into a microphone, "to put it on the basis of a humble people, a religious people, fighting for their traditional beliefs against an atheistic enemy! In other words, I want to interest the people of the United States in a spiritual crusade for China!"

Light dawned, alarmingly. "Prayers," said Mr. Churchill Chan, with a perceptible dullness of tone. "The Republic of China, one does not need to say, would be profoundly grateful for the prayers of the American people. Still, this detestable age in which we live is one of materialism; perhaps assistance of a more material nature would —"

"What I had in mind," Christopher said, "was not so much prayers as the arousing of public indignation to the point where the government would be forced to send planes —"

"AHA!"

"— for the purpose of dropping leaflets, reminding the Chinese people of what they're fighting for, and letting them know that we're with them with all our heart and soul. You know, I think that might provide just the spark that's needed to light the flame!"

"Yes. Well, it is excellent, most excellent. Still," said Mr. Churchill Chan, "one must husband one's resources; it is the law of existence. How good it would be, then, if these aircraft could perform a dual function. How good it would be if they could be supplied with both leaflets and *bombs.* . . ."

"No," said Christopher thoughtfully. "No, I hardly think that would be necessary. I think that the propaganda alone would be more effective, in this case. As I see it," he said, "it's fundamentally a problem of awakening a dormant people to what's happening to everything they hold most dear."

"Yes, yes, that is most astute. Still, there is of course the factor of literacy to consider; so few of these people are able to read, therefore the effects of the leaflets would be minimized . . ."

"Picture books," Christopher said, snapping his fingers. "It's a simple matter to dramatize the spiritual struggle in clear, easy to grasp, cartoon form. It's a method we use in this country for instructing our backward children."

"Yes, all excellent. Yet one cannot help but feel that this splendid plan would find even greater success if implemented by a few mere *tokens* of physical authority: bombs, tanks, guns. . . ."

Mr. Churchill Chan fought on with all the doggedness permitted to one in his essentially conciliatory position. It was all to no avail, for Christopher was talking, already drawing up the blueprint for the all-out, airborne crusade (the great planes sweeping in from the sea, buzzing rice paddies, hills, vast and dusty plains; he saw an oppressed peasantry raising hopeful eyes as high above downy-faced American bombardiers prepared to loose precious cargoes of Confucius Comic Books), and while he talked the bland and desperate words of his companion came to him as an indistinct and rather purposeless buzz, of which he was barely aware, and to which he did not attend. When, finally, he showed Mr. Churchill Chan, shrouded in weary smiles, out of the office, he felt that it had been a most productive talk, that once again, out of the free and friendly interchange of opinion and idea, had come clarity of resolution.

Christopher traveled to Chicago by plane. Turning toward the South, he would take the rest of the tour by rail, for, although he was acutely conscious of the value of time, the communities in which he was most in demand were rarely served by the commercial airlines. On this tour he would visit briefly the states of Illinois, Indiana, Kentucky and Tennessee; his specific points of call were six cities of the type in which he enjoyed speaking most. They were small and entirely inconspicuous; having provided the country with no famous men, and possessing no crafts or industries of more than local importance, they were normally identified by their proximity to the nearest large city. The constant need for such identification had bred in the inhabitants of these small centers a curious sense of isolation, as well as a certain civic truculence; it was this fact which Christopher had grasped some years ago, and which he had turned to considerable advantage.

His first stop was New Paris, Indiana. He had not been there before, but he was not a stranger. As he pulled into the hideous stucco railroad station, he felt already the touch of the familiar; as he drove down the main street, past the pigeon-soiled statue of William Henry Harrison, he felt that he had come home. He had been fortunate enough to arrive on an afternoon of festival; the city, now a center for the production of inexpensive dentures, was deep in the remembrance of its agricultural past. On the old fairgrounds there was a fete: Christopher, whisked there by proud hosts, saw corn shuckers in their competitive fury; saw a cow being manually milked by a dedicated 4-H Club boy; saw a nimble old man, wild of eye, playing "Old Zip Coon" and "The Devil's Dream" on a battered fiddle. It was all real, heart-warming, *good*; it was only after he had been there for some time that he began to feel slightly impatient: remarkable as the performance was, there was no denying that it permitted little instructive conversation. On the whole, he was pleased rather than otherwise when he was taken to the welcoming tea, where gradually the proper balances were restored. Here there was good talk, for the municipal dignitaries who had assembled to meet Christopher were — apart from a certain aggressive insistence on the advanced state of their own community — attentive listeners. Christopher met the mayor: a tall, gaunt man with a Masonic key and a quick, spurting smile which revealed some debt to local industry. He presented Christopher with a huge metal zinnia; it was, he explained, an enduring replica of the official flower of the Hoosier state.

"From one of the country's most up-and-coming *cities*," he said, smiling swiftly, "to one of the country's most up-and-coming *citizens*. And now, Mr. Usher, may I ask: just what is your considered opinion of General George Catlett Marshall?"

From that point on, it was a splendid afternoon. . . .

At night, after the broadcast, there was the public lecture. For this had been reserved the auditorium of the Homer Capehart Memorial High School; long before the appointed hour, cars had begun to arrive from outlying hamlets and farms, for, no matter how up-and-coming the city, Christopher's audiences were seldom dominantly urban. In the auditorium, sections had been set apart for those prominent in politics, in fraternal work, in educational endeavor — even Dr. Mason Calcutt, venerable president of the Calcutt College of Chiropractic had promised to make one of his rare, nonacademic appearances. Fifteen minutes before lecture time, Christopher was backstage, checking his notes in final and careful survey.

He was furious; there had been a blunder. Before he set out on his lecture tours, it was his secretary's duty to fill in a mimeographed information blank for each city to be visited:

1) Name of city; nickname
2) Name of mayor; nickname
3) Leading citizens; occupations of
4) Imp. histor. events
5) Shrines, monuments, natur. phenomena
6) Princ. industries
7) Princ. lodges, societies
8) Princ. relig. groups
9) Items local humor

He shook his head in irritation; there had been a serious error on the sheet for New Paris. Opposite "Princ. industries" his secretary had written: "CORN, HOGS." The reference was hopelessly outmoded; Christopher had seen enough of this sensitive community to realize that the agricultural must necessarily be assigned to the quaint, indulgently remembered past. Still, exactly how to amend the mistake? He could not bring himself to write in "DENTURES" or "FALSE TEETH"; the blunt words lacked style, dignity. Unquestionably there was some local euphemism with which he was unfamiliar. . . . Sighing, he decided to take the quick way out. He scratched out "CORN, HOGS" and substituted "IDEAS." It was unspecific but reliable; he had found that the communities in which he spoke were rarely distressed at the imputation to them of ceaseless mental activity. Sighing again, and jotting down a memorandum to take his secretary to task, he gathered his material together and prepared to go onstage.

He walked on with the mayor; applause broke out from all sides. Christopher saw at a glance that the setting was up to the anticipated standard; every seat occupied, every face eager, a multitude thirsting for knowledge. His feeling of annoyance vanished before this best of all medicines; now, at the center of the stage, he stood at attention, for he knew the unvarying routine to come. The houselights were extinguished; all applause died. Out of the darkness came the beam of a spotlight, focusing full upon a large American flag at the right corner of the stage; an electric fan, concealed behind the flag, started to whir, causing the flag to ripple fervently in the synthetic breeze. Coincidentally, a recording of the national anthem was played over the public-address system; Christopher and the mayor led the audience in strong song. This over, there was a momentary hush; Christopher felt a powerful surge of emotional strength, of pride. As often as he had been through this ceremony, the knowledge that it was all for God, for country, and for him never failed to leave him slightly breathless.

At the rostrum, the mayor had begun the speech of presentation. Judged even by the liberal standards of this part of the world, the introduction was a long one; it was, however, most generous, for the mayor spoke of Christopher with very nearly the same intensity of feeling with which he spoke of New Paris. At last came climactic words, Christopher rose and bowed slightly, there was a torrent of acclaim, and he began to talk.

A seasoned campaigner, he opened slowly, informally. His words — ". . . long admired the administrative abilities of my good friend, Mayor Ev Mosper . . . delightful meeting with the renowned educator and goodly healer, Dr. Mason Calcutt . . . revelation to stand quietly beneath the magnificent bronze statue of the Hero of Tippecanoe, the Ninth President of these United States . . . greatest of pleasures to visit a city so vitally concerned with the production of Ideas . . . community from which springs so much of the strength of our YMCA . . . legionnaires everywhere look with envy upon your Casper Stanwell Post . . . source of deep regret that time does not permit a thorough exploration of the wonders of the world-famed Wabash Scenic Caverns . . ." — were received with the expected mixture of astonishment and joy; they were delivered in tones appropriate to friendly discourse between equals. It was not until he reached the body of his lecture that he assumed the broadcast manner. From somewhere in the audience came a gasp of recognition; then silence. The lecture was under way.

In cities such as New Paris, Christopher gave, whenever possible, his talk titled "One World and Your World"; it was this which he delivered tonight. A rousing philippic, proof against the most apathetic listener, it was by all odds the most successful of his many lectures. If it lacked something of the spiritual ginger to be found in "Gandhi and Christ," it more than made up for this in its greater plasticity. Infinitely adaptable, it could be and was molded to any set of local circumstances. Briefly, it revealed the world in its simplest terms, as nothing more than a vast, imperfect analogue of the community in which Christopher happened to be speaking. Tonight, two social organisms — the world and New Paris — were placed side by side; in the comparison, the world came off rather badly. On the one hand there was disorder, poverty, impiety, a polyglot chaos; on the other, there was neatness, abundance, faith, a resolved monolingual blend. On the one hand was the way of Ev Mosper, the Casper Stanwell Post, the Hero of Tippecanoe; on the other, the way of Stalin, Mao, the State Department, the crafty British, the venal French. Where the world had failed, New Paris had come through. . . .

". . . and the reason is simple. The reason is there, *here*, for everyone to see. No mystery cloaks it; nothing is concealed from view. It's simply the story of a people who *pull together*, people of every race, color and creed, their heads held high, determined from the bottom of their stout hearts to make their city *work*, to make their city *live*. Yes, it's a lesson, a great lesson, one of the greatest in all history. Yet try to give that lesson to the world! Try to give that lesson to the so-called civilized nations of Europe! Try to give that lesson to those cynical statesmen, those leaders to whom double-talk and deceit come as natural as breathing, those same men to whose almighty wisdom the unhappy land of China can today bear mute testimony. . . ."

He went on, caught in the exhilarating rhythm of his own delivery, building step by step to the sanguine, the inspirational, the inevitable close. Could there, *would* there, one day be One World? YES — but only when those in high places were willing to abandon greed, pride, and self-interest, and come to the problems of the world with the one, simple, eminently workable approach: the approach that had been found, long years ago, in the city of New Paris!

There was deafening applause; there were whistles, cheers, the stamping of feet; the Homer Capehart Memorial High School quivered with approval. Christopher stood silent, smiling; he glanced covertly at his watch. The over-all delivery time of this talk was fifty-three minutes; tonight, thanks to the unprecedented frequency of the applause, it ran to a bit better than one hour and eight minutes. Never before had "One World and Your World" been so flatteringly protracted; Christopher waved happily at the crowd and the applause grew louder. It was undoubtedly one of the most successful talks of a not unsuccessful career, and as he stood on the stage, bending graciously to meet the glorious gales of acclaim, he could not help but regard it as an omen. It all tied in, he thought: the victory over Udolpho, the new life to come, a long string of nights just such as this, stretching away in infinite procession into the golden future. He had never before, he decided, been so completely, so unreservedly, happy. . . .

This performance was repeated, with minor variations, in each of the remaining cities of the tour. He gave "One World and Your World" everywhere save in St. Paul, Tennessee; there he had given it only the year before. St. Paul, therefore, got "Gandhi"; the results were perhaps a shade less spectacular, but quite good enough.

Yet important and satisfying as was his work on the lecture platform, Christopher did not forget the primacy of his nightly broadcasts to the nation; before he had left on tour, he had arranged to originate these broadcasts each night from the station of the radio network most convenient to the city in which he visited. As the radio network was a large one, with a great many stations, this posed no problem; on two occasions, indeed, Christopher was able to broadcast directly from the hall where he was to lecture, thus providing his lecture audience a double joy. The preparation of the broadcasts on the road was not perceptibly more difficult than at home; while he was necessarily denied such ready access to his usual news sources, he had the immense advantage of knowing his own mind, of knowing precisely what he wished to tell the world, regardless of any sudden turn in the news. Thus, the deprivation was of small consequence. A quick look at the latest developments on the nearest press association wire, the rapid ingestion of those items which seemed of some importance, a brief session at the typewriter, and then, alchemically produced, another broadcast was ready for immediate delivery to a waiting public. . . .

The Last Hurrah

THE LAST HURRAH *tells of the passing of an era personified by Frank Skeffington, Irish-American mayor of a big, old city on the eastern American seaboard. Skeffington's last campaign, and his death after losing the election, are observed by his nephew Adam Caulfield, a newspaper cartoonist, whom Skeffington comes to treat almost as a son — his own son, Francis, being something of a disappointment.*

Expert politician though he is, Skeffington loses to a more modern campaigner, Kevin McCluskey, the puppet of a cabal which includes a newspaper publisher (enraged by Skeffington's nonchalant spending); the Cardinal (affronted by Skeffington's exploitation of the Church); the WASPs who control most of the city's wealth; various disgruntled Irish and Italian politicians, his lifelong opponents; and the reformers of a younger generation, who are sick of the old-fashioned, ward-heeling, person-to-person style of administration which Skeffington has always embodied.

The first selection is taken from the opening of the book.

The second selection is set in City Hall, on the morning following Skeffington's announcement of his candidacy for re-election.

The third selection is from the first third of the book. Skeffington is still organizing his forces, in the period before he starts to campaign intensively in public.

The fourth selection is from the second third of the book, when Skeffington's campaign is in full swing. (The last and longest part of the book describes the final week of the campaign, Election Night, Skeffington's stroke, his dying reverie, his farewell to his henchmen, and his funeral. It is the most moving section, but it depends on cumulative effect and is too long to quote entire.)

I$_T$ was early in August when Frank Skeffington decided — or rather, announced his decision, which actually had been arrived at some months before — to run for re-election as mayor of the city. This was a matter about which there had been public speculation for a good while: for, in fact, four years, ever since he had been inaugurated for what his opponents had fondly hoped was the last time. Since the beginning of the current year, however, the speculation had increased, not alone because the deadline was drawing nearer, but also because there were no other elections of importance coming up — the municipal elections took place in off years politically and so did not have to share the spotlight with national or state contests. Thus interest had mounted, and as it had, so had the hopes of Skeffington's opponents. For while he was admittedly among the most durable of politicians, he was just as admittedly getting older, and in recent speeches and press conferences he had expressed little interest in continuing his long political career. On one memorable occasion he had gone so far as to speak with a certain dreaminess of the joys of retirement, of the quiet time of withdrawal which would follow a lifetime spent in the service of the public.

"Far from the madding crowd," he had said, gazing at the reporters expressionlessly. "The declining years spent in solitude and contemplation. Possibly in some rustic retreat."

This hint had not been received without a measure of cynicism; one reporter from the chief opposition paper had led the questioning which followed.

"Tell us, Governor," he had said (for, as Skeffington had twice been governor of the state, the courtesy title lingered long after the office itself had been lost), "just how would you propose to adjust yourself to this rustic life? Wouldn't it be pretty quiet? What would you do?"

"Read," Skeffington had replied promptly. "And reflect." At this his pale blue eyes had closed, and an expression of extraordinary benignity crossed the full, faintly veined and rather handsome face; the long, heavy head inclined perceptibly forward, and the reporters found themselves looking at the silver crown of his hair. It was almost as if, in anticipation, he were paying pious tribute to the time of ultimate retreat.

The reporter had coughed. "We know you've always been a great reader, Governor," he had said, a trifle sardonically. "Any idea of the kind of books you'd take with you?"

Skeffington's reply, made with eyes still closed, had been characteristically elusive. "The great books," he had said.

The reporter had been persistent. "Which great books, Governor?"

Skeffington's eyes had opened, the silver head had lifted, and once more the reporters met the deadpan look. "I don't know whether you'd know them or not," he had said thoughtfully. "The Bible, which is a book composed of two parts, commonly called the Old and the New Testaments. The poems and plays of Shakespeare, an Englishman. And during the winter months I would also take the paper which you represent."

The reporter had said warily, "Thanks for the compliment, Governor. I suppose there's some special reason?"

Skeffington had nodded. "During the long winter months a glowing fire might be welcome," he had said, "and I have found from long experience that your paper burns very well. Makes grand kindling. I don't imagine, by the way, that most people are aware of that. If they were, your paper's very small circulation might be substantially increased. Any more questions, gentlemen?"

It had been a typical enough interview, save for the suggestion of retirement. None of Skeffington's opponents quite believed in this, but on the other hand, neither could they afford to discount it. On the whole, any hint of this kind was felt to be encouraging rather than otherwise especially when related to certain other signs. For example, there were the heartening rumors of Skeffington's ill health: among the true optimists it was confidently whispered that a mysterious disease was devouring his brain bit by bit, so that now there occurred intervals in every day during which he reverted to the habits of his childhood and expressed a desire to play marbles or hide-and-seek. The newspaper for which his nephew, Adam Caulfield, worked — the same newspaper whose combustibility Skeffington had praised — offered support of a more oblique kind. It began to run editorials reminding the voters that while the life span of man undoubtedly had been prolonged, the problem of senectitude had by no means been conquered, and that aged men in positions of public trust could constitute a definite hazard (Skeffington, at this time, was approaching his seventy-second birthday). As the year wore on, obituary notices of well-known septuagenarians had been given increasingly prominent display. The paper conducted this campaign with some circumspection, as Skeffington was notoriously quick to strike in all matters of suspected libel, and in the past had actually secured two judgments against this very paper. But as the months went by he paid absolutely no attention to the partially concealed attack; this, taken with his own statement and the persisting rumors, was thought to be all to the good — and hopes which at first had been merely wistful now ripened and grew strong.

But Skeffington smashed them all in a matter of minutes.

On his seventy-second birthday Frank Skeffington had lunch with his nephew, and over the meal told him of his plan to run again. He then swore him to secrecy, and, following this — and almost as an afterthought — revealed the reason which, more than any other, had determined his decision to stay in public life.

"I want to," he said.

That night, at a birthday dinner given him by the party leaders, he made the announcement public. It was substantially the same announcement that he had delivered in private that noon; only the reason behind it had been suitably modified.

"My decision represents a submission to the will of the populace," he said, "and is against my every personal desire. I had hoped, at the end of my current term, to retire to a well-earned rest, but unfortunately one look at the names of those who have declared themselves as candidates for this office forced me to change my decision. Why, the mind positively boggles at the presumption of these men! As one looks down this bold list one would think that the only qualification necessary to run for mayor of this great city was to be without any qualification whatsoever. This is a time for experience, for leadership; I cannot abandon this fine city to the care of such fumbling hands. And so, dutifully if reluctantly, I submit my name to you once again, realizing full well that while my own health and rest are important, it is far more important that this city of ours should not be allowed to revert to Government by Pygmies!"

This announcement had been carefully timed so that it would appear in the city edition of all morning papers; in this way — Skeffington had explained to his nephew that noon — the maximum desirable effect would be achieved; the majority of his opponents would learn the bad news over their morning coffee. It was a thought which appeared to afford him a virtually limitless satisfaction.

"I hesitate to appear vindictive," he said, chuckling softly, "but what a pretty picture it makes: all those red and angry faces sputtering over the coffee cups! The day ruined before it begins . . . I don't mind telling you that that's the kind of thing that warms the cockles of an old man's heart on his birthday. . . . Have some more lobster."

City Hall was a lunatic pile of a building: a great, grim, resolutely ugly dust-catcher which had been designed eighty years before by the then mayor, one Clement "Nutsy" McGrath. An ebullient man of antic behavior, he was the only mayor of the city ever to be kicked to death by a camel. This had happened in Egypt; he had paused there while on an ill-advised world tour. Wandering about Cairo, he had encountered his first camel — hitherto, like the roc, a creature of fable to him. This high-spirited and slightly demented man could hardly resist teasing such an odd beast; the response of the camel had been savagely disproportionate, and that had been the end of Nutsy.

It was from this man's unskilled and laboriously drawn plans that the present City Hall had arisen, and for generations it had been decried as the prime eyesore of the community. Despite this, the building had its defenders, and intermittent suggestions that it be razed had met with howls of protest from those who had worked long within it and who, with a certain rude poetic vision, saw in this inefficient, tangled warren the perfect symbol for municipal administration.

It was a noisy and an active place. In its old, high-ceilinged chambers the elected and appointed officials of government slumbered, mused, or conducted the affairs of the city; in this they were guided by the opportunities afforded them and, to a somewhat lesser degree, by the strictures of conscience. Along the endless, outmoded corridors, hard by elevator shafts and water coolers, ranged little bands of political guerillas; having no perceptible tie with the management of the city, they were nevertheless perpetually busy with concerns of their own. Red of face, shrewd of eye, agile of tongue, they continually nodded, winked, and flashed the cabalistic signs of confederacy, all the while regarding one another with a surreptitious if unremitting attention.

Skeffington's offices were on the third floor. Normally well-filled, this morning they were jammed to the doors, for with the announcement of last night the band wagon officially had begun to roll, and the crowd was rushing to get on board. It was a sight familiar to Skeffington; he had seen it often before, this quick parade of the professionals to the post; and as often as he had seen it, he had felt the same undimmed flush of joyous anticipation. Much as he loved to win, he loved the fight to win even more, and in his appraisal of his own strengths he put in first place that of the born campaigner.

This morning, once within the Hall, progress had been slow: there were more well-wishers lining his path from the outer door. He had greeted them all, addressing the majority by name. At length he reached his reception room, where the process was repeated; in addition to the individual greetings, he made a short speech, thanking all those assembled for their anticipated support in the campaign to come. Under cover of the cheers that followed this, he bowed, waved, and disappeared into his office.

Here three men waited for him: his chief secretary, Tom Lacy, and his two principal advisers, Sam Weinberg and old John Gorman.

"Gentlemen," Skeffington said. "A grand day to start the ball rolling. As well as heads. What's on the schedule, Tom?"

"Everything's fairly routine this morning, Governor," Lacy said, planting a small pile of papers upon the great mahogany desk. "These are all for your signature: the notices to all heads of departments about the collection for Tom McCabe's widow, the Easter Proclamation, thank-you letters to the K. of C. and the Polish-American War Veterans. Then there's the press conference, after which you're giving the keys to the city to Fats Citronella. Then lunch with the members of the Highway Safety Committee."

Skeffington held up a hand. "One moment," he said. "A little amplification is required: who in hell is Fats Citronella? And why am I giving him the keys to the city?"

"He's a piano player, Governor. He's coming here this week for an engagement at the Poli, and the theater people were anxious to have him officially welcomed. Cuke Gillen set it up."

"And I agreed?"

"Yes, one day last week; Cuke caught you on the run. Actually," Lacy said, " it may not be bad from the standpoint of publicity. Citronella's apparently quite well known."

"I imagine he is. It's been my experience that most of our great musicians are called Fats."

Lacy smiled. "No, but this one seems to be the latest fad among the teen-agers. He's what they call a bop-musician."

"Better and better," Skeffington said. "A bop-musician. Sam, you're a knowledgeable man. What do you know about bop-musicians?"

"It's nut stuff," Weinberg said, in a hoarse, uninflected voice. He was a small, lumpy man in his fifties, with a gray, slumping, unmistakably Jewish face, and great dull brown eyes, over which heavy lids blinked with a slow regularity, as if responding to some inaudible metronome. Crumpled in the huge leather chair at the far side of the office, he looked as if in the most desperate physical circumstances; in point of fact, he had never known a day's ill-health. Nominally a lawyer, his talents had for years been displayed in neither courtroom nor law office; his place was close by Skeffington, lingering in the background, an alert, tough, unobtrusive wraith, ready to slide out of the shadows and into action upon an instant's notice. Most of Weinberg's associates in the Skeffington camp regarded him with a mixture of deference and active dislike; they found not much in the make-up of this ruthless little cynic to inspire camaraderie. Skeffington, for his part, liked him and considered him an aide of singular value. He respected his knowledge of the minutiae of ward politics, his shrewdness at assessing trends, his ability as a tactician; he was one of the few people to whom Skeffington listened with attention and to whom, indeed, he almost gave his trust.

"Nut stuff," Weinberg repeated. "You know what it is, this bop? A bunch of hopped-up coons in purple suits blowing horns at a mob of high-school nitwits. The kids wear tight pants and run around screaming 'Crazy! Crazy!' "

"Oh, to be a boy again!" Skeffington sighed. "Sam, you're my bridge to the wonderful world of youth. Where does this go on?"

"A couple of joints up by the ball park."

"What kind of joints? Liquor?"

"Yeh, but no dough. The only ones who buy the booze are the musicians and a few clowns who come in to get warm. The kids are all under age. They buy Cokes and hamburgers and yell at each other. I give it six months."

"And I'm to greet the idol of these splendid young people," Skeffington said dryly. "Charming. Still, it's logical enough. A bop-musician: the Lord knows I've given the keys to everyone else. Acrobats, aviators, professional wrestlers; I remember that on one occasion I even gave them to a dog."

"A water spaniel," Weinberg said, gloomily reaching into memory, "from Hollywood. An acting dog."

Skeffington nodded. "Trixie the Spaniel. In my opinion one of the most intelligent actresses then residing on the West Coast. She was the property of an avaricious Mexican, whom she subsequently bit; I think the man died. All right, Tom, we'll give the keys to Mr. Citronella. Have the photographers stay around. What time do the reporters get here?"

Lacy looked at his watch. "In about twenty minutes."

"Fine. Then we have time to get down to business." He pushed back his chair and looked steadily at Weinberg and Gorman. "All right," he said. "What do you think?"

Weinberg shrugged slightly. "I think just the way I thought a month, six months ago. It'll be a tough one."

"John?"

Gorman spoke for the first time since Skeffington had entered the office. "I don't know, Frank," he said. "I don't know will it be so tough or not. They've no one good man to beat." He spoke softly, his voice still holding the accents of the Galway of his nativity. He was a tall, superlatively erect old man, seven years older than Skeffington; he had come to his new country as a boy, he had made politics his life, and so conspicuous had been his talents and so assiduous his application that for nearly fifty years he had been a ward boss of unchallenged authority. In all these years this withdrawn, celibate, soft-spoken man had never once held public office, and he had rarely so much as appeared on a public platform; but from a single dusty room in an old waterfront building he had ruled his ward firmly, efficiently, and with an inflexible adherence to the rules of party discipline. It was he who found jobs and homes for the recently arrived, who supplied funds in time of distress, who arranged for hospitalization and the payment of medical bills, who gave the son of the family his start in life and the subsequent necessary pushes up the ladder, who built the playgrounds for the children of this populous district, and who, in these days when the aged, the helpless, and the indigent had come to depend increasingly upon government beneficence, saw to it that the baffling complexity of preliminary paper work was solved and that funds were ultimately secured. He had won for his efforts the devotion and obedience of most who lived within the ward, and this in turn, as it was the largest ward in the city, had given him an extraordinary political significance. Although it was possible for a candidate to be elected to municipal office against Gorman's wishes—it had, indeed, happened, on a few widely separated occasions—it was not easy; all aspiring politicians recognized his immense power, and all, at one time or another, had sued for his favor.

Skeffington had paid tribute to this power when, many years before, he had declared war on the ward bosses.

"They must go, every last one of them!" he had rumbled. "Little men who hold the destinies of thousands within their corrupt hands, minor barons who stand between the citizen and his elected representatives, greedy filters through which everything must pass and be soiled in the process: I intend to get rid of them all!"

No one had doubted that he intended to do just that, for his opposition to the ward bosses was well known. This opposition, despite his frequent pronouncements, was not a moral one, for he did not object to such bossism in principle; it was rather that he considered it to be super-fluous, a quite unnecessary intermediary between the voters and himself. He was against the purposeless fragmentation of power, and his aim, like that of Peter the Great when contemplating the position of the boyars, had been essentially a simple one: that of eliminating the middle man. In this, with but a single exception, he had succeeded; the exception had been John Gorman. He had not eliminated Gorman; he had not even tried. Skeffington was a confident man, but confidence alone had not brought him survival; he was also a practical man who could calculate the odds. Because he was himself of the paternalistic type of political leader, he knew well the fierce loyalties which Gorman commanded, and while he knew that Gorman, unlike himself, was a man of severe limita-tions, concerned only with his ward and the problems that affected that ward, he knew that in this very narrowness of concern there lay a highly concentrated strength. Skeffington was reasonably certain that in any city-wide struggle for power he could have defeated Gorman easily; a ward campaign, however, conducted in the very homeland of this formi-dable warrior, was something else again. To have waged it would have amounted to political insanity.

And so, because he was faced with the hard fact of Gorman's position, because he knew that Gorman's ambitions were in no way rival to his own, and because, too, he entertained a warm feeling for the older man (this was an important reason, only slightly less so than the other two), he had not fought him, but had joined him. The two had been allies now for almost four decades; it was an arrangement that had brought profit to them both.

Skeffington said now: "It's true they're in a bad way for candidates. Who *is* their man this time? Here they have all that shining armor left over from the last campaign and no knight to put in it. Charlie Mc-Glinchy's a dying man; he can't run, and I doubt that he would if he could. Frank Collins is their only other bet and he's going to sit this one out."

"He could still come in," Weinberg said. "A tricky guy, that Collins."

"He's out," Skeffington said with finality. "We've reached an under-standing, our Attorney General and myself. He wants to be the next Senator and I've promised him our support. Between ourselves, I gained the impression that he'd just as soon be our next mayor, but apparently there's a nigger in the woodpile in the form of the gracious Mrs. Collins. That good lady is tired of being gracious on a local scale: she wants to be gracious in Washington. And so Frank will run for the Senate next year."

"The man's a lunatic," Gorman said. "He can have all the help we'll give him and it'll still do him no good. Even should he get by the primaries they'll murder him upstate."

"Yes," Skeffington said comfortably. "They will indeed. He hasn't a chance; he'll lose and lose badly. He'd be far better off running against me for mayor, the circumstances being what they are. But Mrs. Collins wants to go to Washington, It's a vivid demonstration of what the love of a good woman can do for a man. In the meantime, however, he's out of our race, which leaves us with our present group of opponents. Seven good men and true." He gazed at the typed list he held in his hand. "Not a man among them ever won an election in his life, and Sam is worried about a hard campaign. I wonder why?"

"O.K.," Weinberg said. "So they're all dogs. Who's arguing? All I say is, even a dog can be tough if everybody gets in back of the same dog."

"A consolidation of the ungodly, born of weakness," Skeffington murmured. The possibility seemed to give him pleasure. "Is that what you think will happen, Sam?"

"It figures. What else can they do? You take guys like old man Force, that little ginzo Camaratta, Mother Garvey, even the Better Government League: they're no dopes. They don't want to run these dogs. They know they're dogs; they're only running them because they got nobody else to run. So what happens? One morning somebody gets real smart and says, 'O.K., let's face it: nobody's got nothing. Maybe we got to get together.' So then if they got any brains they get together, they make up their minds which dog is the best dog, and they start to kick him home. And they got plenty of stuff to kick him home with. Namely, the cabbage."

"Ah well," said Gorman, mildly objecting, "there's the possibility, yes, but I don't know as it's much more than that." He sat regarding his colleagues with calm blue eyes; a snowy veteran of every conceivable combination of political circumstance, he did not think highly of this last suggestion.

"It's all very well," he continued, "all this talk about I have nothing, you have nothing, he has nothing, so let's be pals together and maybe we'll grab it all. But I wonder does it work that way? I wonder does a man like Amos Force jump into the same bed with Mother Garvey? And would Mother have him? You don't get a man to go up to another man who's been kicking him in the behind for forty years and say, 'Put your arms around me, I'm your chum today.' Many's the time in the ward and in the city too I've seen the boys all split up and all without a chance to win, and still you couldn't get them to join hands. And that's because no man is willing to give up his enemies unless he's a saint or unless he's sure of the payoff." His pale old lips twitched slightly and he said, "I don't know but what we can eliminate the saints from our discussion here today. As for the payoff, there'd be no payoff unless they won. And together or apart, the man they'd be running against would still be Frank. Would they care to bet too much on that, d'ye think?"

"Nevertheless," Skeffington said, "there remains the possibility." He leaned forward and placed both hands on the desk; the heavy handsome face changed slightly and the deep voice became less casual. Swiftly and unmistakably, Skeffington took charge. The maneuver was accomplished without abruptness; both Weinberg and Gorman saw it as the natural consequence of deliberation, and it occurred to neither to question or resent it.

"I've been thinking about this for some weeks now," Skeffington said, "and it seems to me that Sam is on the right track. Our trouble is that we're operating in an economy of scarcity: we're faced with an acute shortage of opponents. It's always been a truism that there was nothing like having at least two strong opponents with substantial followings. It splits the vote, they knock each other out, and we come in free. This year things seem to be a bit different. To divide the house of the foe you have to have a couple of good dividers: that's what's lacking at the moment."

"A great ad to put in the papers," Weinberg said. "W ANTED: *two red-hot candidates to run for mayor.*"

"It's a pity Roosevelt isn't still alive," Skeffington said. "If he were, I might request emergency aid from Washington in the shape of a pair of distinguished rivals. He'd be only too happy to supply them. More than that, he'd supply a few hundred thousand cash just to make sure I was defeated. Franklin was like that to his old friends. But as it is, it looks as though we face a vacuum, and I'm inclined to agree with you, Sam, that our vacuum might just possibly be filled by a single candidate, backed by everybody. That could be dangerous. I don't know that it would be as dangerous as you seem to think, but dangerous enough to warrant our taking a few precautions."

"Ah," said Gorman softly. With one thumb he delicately massaged the polished, almost transparent skin above one cheekbone. "You're sold on this, then, Frank?" he said inquiringly.

"No. I'm sold on nothing yet. Not this early in the campaign. I agree with you, John, when you say that they've never been able to work out a successful coalition in the past. You may even be right in thinking they can't do it now; I must admit I don't quite see Festus passing his days in perfect harmony with the elderly maidens of the Better Government

League. Nevertheless it's their best chance whether they take it or not, and I think it might be sensible to assume they'll take it."

Gorman nodded. "They may make the try. I don't think so, but they may. And if they do I don't think it'll amount to damn-all. Still, as you say, there's the possibility, and it's always a good idea to plug up all the holes."

"We might begin by having another look at the field," Skeffington said, examining once more the list of names he held in his hand: CHARLES F. HENNESSEY, ENRICO NUCATOLLA, JAMES NUGENT, FRANCIS X. RYAN, J. J. FARINACCI, KEVIN McCLUSKEY, WILLARD CHASE. At the last name he chuckled.

"Hope springs eternal in the thin bosom of Willard Chase," he said. "That's the best definition of an optimist I know: the head of the Planned Parenthood Committee running for mayor of this city. An Arab would have a better chance in Tel Aviv. And Charlie Hennessey!"

"He's soft as a grape," Weinberg said, "and getting softer every year. You know what he wears around now? A cap!"

Gorman said: "He's up there in the house by the reservoir, all alone with a couple of dirty old elkhounds and a ton of horse meat in the Deep-Freeze. I know damn well they all eat the same meals. Still, the man's a great talker, you can't take that away from him. Mother of God, what a gas-bag! D'ye mind his speech, Frank, at the dinner for Al Smith back in '27?"

"I do," Skeffington said. "One hour and a quarter without stopping, and all of it mush. I never saw the Happy Warrior unhappier." His eyes lit with reminiscent satisfaction, for while he had worked with and for Smith for a number of years, there had always been a conspicuous lack of warmth between the two men, and when, in the presidential election of 1928, Smith had been defeated, Skeffington, although he had campaigned dutifully in his behalf, had shed no tears.

"Charlie Hennessey," he said again, fondly. The memory of Smith's discomfort bred affection; then too, Charlie was a rival with no hope of success. "Now then," he said — "what about the Italian delegation; Nucatolla and Farinacci? Nucatolla's Camaratta's man: what's he got for support?"

"Only Camaratta's longshoremen," Weinberg said. "The other unions won't touch him with a ten-foot pole. On account of they hate Camaratta."

"Nucatolla's a great lad for playing the Church," Gorman said. "The little lickspittle is always pussyfooting around the ward after Monsignor Tancredi, whispering that what the Church needs is a few more Italians in tall hats marching at the head of the Holy Name parade. The Monsignor agrees with him but can't stand the sight of him, so it does the poor man no good."

"We can count him out, then, if all he's got is Camaratta," Skeffington said. "And while we're at it, let's count Camaratta out, too. For good. I'm tired of him. He's a double-crosser we've put up with for years just because he controlled that longshoreman vote. I've never liked him personally, but more important, I don't think he's as strong as he used to be. He's a nuisance: I say it's high time we froze him out permanently; I think we can do it with very little trouble. Any objections?"

The two men looked at each other, then shook their heads; Skeffington said, "All right then: we're agreed. Now let's take a look at Farinacci. I must say he's a new one on me. Apparently he's a new one on everybody: is it true that he's really a barber?"

"A barber for dames," Weinberg said. "He fixes their hair in a couple of beauty shops he owns."

"J. J. Farinacci," Skeffington said. "He has the courage of youth. I understand he's only a boy."

"Strictly a nut kid. Good-looking, wavy hair, melty eyes, about twenty-nine or thirty. He goes over big with the old dames."

"Too bad it's an election instead of a beauty contest," Skeffington said. "I'm afraid J.J. is in for a disillusioning experience. Where's the money coming from?"

"A buck here, a buck there from the old dames. But mostly it's his own, from the beauty parlors. I told you he was a nut kid. You want to know really how much a nut he is? He went two whole years to a chiropractor college."

"The most dangerous of all opponents," Skeffington said dryly. "An educated man. We'll see if we can't manage to further his education in the months to come. I hope, by the way, that he has the good sense to hold on to those initials. An Italian politician named 'J.J.' — what native Neopolitan heart could fail to respond to that appeal?"

Gorman whispered a little chuckle. "Jay Jay," he said. "Jay Jay Farinacci: oh, there's elegance for you! It's like one of our lads that comes up with the high-class middle name of a sudden. D' ye remember, years back, Frank, E. Claude Monahan?"

Skeffington nodded. "Eddie Monahan. A young man with a bright political future, until one day he decided to become E. Claude Monahan. He began to carry a cane and to bow from the waist. One Thursday night a delegation from the gasworks called on him at his home and found him all alone at the dinner table, wearing a tuxedo while eating corned beef and cabbage. He might just as well have been found going around the city streets with a rose in his teeth; from that moment on he was a dead duck. He had to flee the city; I heard later that he became a garage attendant in the Midwest and died of eating tainted fish. A humbling lesson to us all. Especially to Farinacci. And that leaves us," he said, looking at the list once more, "with three remaining candidates: Nugent, Ryan, and McCluskey. Which one do you like as a spearhead?"

The three men continued their discussion for a very few more minutes; there was the scheduled press conference to be held, and in any case, no progress was to be made in further elimination. Nugent, Ryan, McCluskey: it was agreed that if indeed there were to be a coalition with one of these at its head — and upon this point Gorman continued politely skeptical — then all were equally possible candidates. None was outstanding, and all were similarly qualified for election to the city's highest office; that is to say, all were Democrats, all were Irish, all were Catholics. It was not everything, but it was enough. As to their more special qualifications and comparative strengths, it was impossible to form an estimate at this time. All were relatively unknown and all shared the common disadvantage of political inexperience. Yet this inexperience was not exclusively a disadvantage.

"They have the strength of the stranger," Skeffington said. "They've never taken any pears because they've never been close to the pear tree. Whichever one it is — if it *is* to be one; I grant you that, John — the tactics will be more or less the same; therefore I don't think it matters a great deal which one it is. One of these three: we can forget the others. Meanwhile," he said rising, "the ball has started to roll; let's keep on pushing it. John, you'll see the precinct captains?"

"I will," Gorman said. "We'll meet tomorrow night at my place."

"Good. Tell them we'll all get together Tuesday night. Sam, I anticipate the usual financial problems; maybe you'd better have preliminary conversations with our friends the contractors this week. All except Teddy Moran and Frank Ruffino; I'll take care of them myself."

Weinberg nodded and said nothing; Skeffington said, "Fine. A good morning's work. Now: any questions? Any difficulties?"

"There's one important thing, Frank," Gorman said. "The housing development in the ward: did you speak to the banks about the money?"

"Yes. Two weeks ago I invited them to submit their bids for loaning the money to the city."

"And . . . ?"

"And," Skeffington said simply, "there were no takers. It appears that we face a conspiracy. They're out to get us by claiming the city is a poor risk under my administration. Not one of them wanted to loan the city a red cent, even for so laudable a purpose. An inhumane group, bankers: '. . . those whose hearts are dry as summer's dust.' Do you suppose Wordsworth ever had any dealings with the Consolidated Trust?"

"Now this is damn serious, Frank," Gorman said, with some impatience. He liked and admired Skeffington; he had never regretted his association with him; but there were occasional moments when he understood and even sympathized with Mother Garvey's rage at his colleague's affection for the poetic. The elusive reference, the high-flown quotation were all very well when applied to the great, nebulous issues of human rights and administrative conduct; but the matter of the new housing development was serious business: it concerned his ward. He said, "By God, Frank, we need that money."

"You'll get it," Skeffington said. "Don't worry. And you'll get it from a single source. I'm going to see Norman Cass of the Consolidated in the next week or so."

"If he's refused you once he's not likely to change his mind," Gorman said. "I know Cass: he's hard as nails."

"Well, we'll see if we can't soften him up," Skeffington said comfortably. "You'll get your money, John; the development will go up as scheduled. I give you my word. Now, if we're all set, Tom, let's get the gentlemen of the press in here. They're busy men: they have to hurry back to their papers, write their stories, and get out to the saloons. We mustn't keep them waiting."

Weinberg and Gorman left, and as he did, Gorman nodded his satisfaction; faith had vanquished skepticism. The habitual distrust he had of political promises was possible only to one who had lived long with those who made them; it did not extend to the promises of Skeffington. He knew that Skeffington would keep his word to him — although he did not know, nor did he particularly care, precisely how this was to be done — and this certitude was fortified by the further knowledge that it was very much in Skeffington's interest to do so.

Skeffington himself sat back in his chair and awaited, with pleasure, the resumption of the weekly pitched battle with the press. It was the kind of verbal infighting at which he excelled, and the fact that in such jousts his official position gave him something of an advantage did not unduly trouble him. He did not often think of politics in chivalric terms.

A<small>T</small> 7:30, Adam was waiting; Skeffington, on the other hand, was not. His unpunctuality inviolable, he was fifteen minutes late, and as the long official car pulled up he said genially, "Hop in. As a taxpayer, you're entitled to. Try the comforts of the vehicle you thoughtfully provided for me."

Adam got in. Determined to remove all mystery from the outset, he said, "By the way, when we were talking this afternoon I completely forgot to ask you where we were going."

"So you did," Skeffington said. "I took it as a rare mark of confidence; now I find it was only a lapse of memory. One more illusion lost." He chuckled and said, "Actually, we're going to a wake. Knocko Minihan's wake."

"A *wake?*"

"Surprised? I had an idea you might be: there was just the possibility that you weren't in the habit of spending your free evenings in visiting deceased strangers. But I felt that tonight it might be useful for you to come along. In its way, a wake can be quite an occasion."

"You may be underestimating me," Adam said. "I've been to a few wakes. Not many, but a few."

"I don't doubt it. Probably not exactly like this one, however. Not that poor Knocko's will be unique, but it might be a little different from those you've been to."

Adam was not prepared to dispute this. The car drove on, and he said, "His name wasn't Knocko, surely?"

"No. It was Aram. The mother was part French, and he was named for an uncle in Quebec. The old gentleman had some money, and the Minihans cherished the fond hope that one happy day it would fall into the lap of little Aram. Unfortunately there was a tragic development. The uncle went crazy and gave away all of his money to a convent outside Montreal; two months later he went to a Canadian lunatic asylum where he subsequently died. The Minihans naturally tried to prove that he'd been a madman before he gave the money to the convent. It seemed a reasonable assumption, especially when you consider that the old man suffered from the delusion that he was an air rifle and went around spitting BB's at squirrels. But as anybody can tell you who's ever tried to recover a bequest from an order of nuns in Quebec, the assumption wasn't quite reasonable enough. So no legacy was forthcoming for the little Aram. Meanwhile, of course, he'd been stuck with the name: I don't think he ever forgave his parents for that. It was a terrible start in life for a boy in this city. That's why he gladly became Knocko."

"And how did he make out after this terrible start?"

"Not too well. Save in one respect, that is. He married a grand woman who was a close friend of my wife's — your aunt's," he said. "In every other way he was a failure. He had a hardware store that he ran into the ground almost before the opening-day sale was over. Then he tried several other businesses, all of which petered out in no time at all. I don't know that people trusted him especially, and they certainly didn't like him. And neither," he said, rather surprisingly, "did I. However, *de mortuis . . .*"

"If nobody liked him," Adam said, "I imagine we'll run into a fairly slim attendance tonight."

"Not at all," said Skeffington. "The place'll be crowded to the doors. A wake isn't quite the same as a popularity contest. There are other factors involved. Ah, here we are."

They had arrived in front of a two-story frame tenement house which was in need of paint; the door on the left held a wreath with a large purple ribbon. Skeffington placed a hand just beneath this ornament and then, before pushing the door open, paused to regard the unlovely premises. He shook his head. "Charming," he said. "Come on, let's go in."

A heavy-set woman, dressed in black, and with the face of some large and extremely suspicious bird, came out of the darkness to greet them.

"Hello, Frank," she said.

"Hello, Agnes. Mrs. Burns, my nephew, Adam Caulfield. Mary's boy." There were nods, an exchange of greetings; Skeffington asked, "How's Gert taking it?"

"Pretty good. She cries a little," said the woman. Adam could not help but observe that she was herself noticeably dry of eye. In explanation she added, "She remembers all the nice things he done."

"She has a remarkable memory," Skeffington said dryly.

Mrs. Burns accepted this with a short nod of agreement, then pointed to a door on the right of the narrow hall. "He's in the parlor," she said. "I think there's no one in there now; it's still a bit early. Go right in, Frank. He looks lovely."

Adam followed Skeffington into the parlor: he saw a tall, glum room which might have been designed specifically with this melancholy event in mind. Heavy dull plush furniture had been pushed back against the walls; stretching from side to side across the room were rows of thin metal chairs, of the kind furnished by catering services. At the moment these were empty; looking at them through the gloom Adam wondered whether this was indeed due to the hour of their arrival, or rather to the simple fact that Knocko Minihan had not been widely loved.

At the far end of the parlor, decorated with wreaths and floral sprays, was a gray coffin; to Adam it seemed huge, a sarcophagus fit for a giant. He advanced upon it with his uncle; they knelt by the side of the coffin and Adam saw Knocko in death. He lay stiffly among billows of white satin, a diminutive man lost in the recesses of his mighty container. Across the top of his head occasional strands of yellowish-white hair had been combed strategically; a taut, grudging smile, which somehow fell short of suggesting an interior peace, had been worked into position. His small hands were folded across his chest, clasping a rosary, and over the coffin a large crucifix, heavily studded with rhinestones, had been suspended. Someone of ingenious mind — undoubtedly the undertaker, thought Adam — had fixed a baby spotlight so that it played full upon the crucifix; high above Knocko's final, alien smile, the rhinestones glittered and danced.

Adam said a prayer for this man he had not known. Skeffington, after a moment, got to his feet slowly, looking about him, at the coffin, at the crucifix. "A lavish display," he said. "And you couldn't get the man near a theater in his life." He put his hand lightly on Adam's shoulder and said, "Will you do me a favor and stay here a moment? I have to go in and say a word to the widow."

Adam looked up, surprised; he rose quickly. "You mean, wait *here?*"

Skeffington smiled slightly. "I'm afraid I do; it seems to be about the only place. You could wait in the car, but I've sent the chauffeur on an errand. In any event, it won't be too bad; I'll be back directly. Why don't you just sit down in one of those chairs in back? People will be coming in shortly, and anyway the whole thing is an experience you ought to have; it's a custom that's dying out. Besides, you can regard it as a meritorious act; you'll be keeping poor Knocko company."

Adam nodded reluctantly. There seemed nothing to do but agree, although he was scarcely happy over the prospect of the solitary vigil. Feeling vaguely that he had once again been outgeneraled all along the line, he moved towards the back of the room, as far as possible from the dead Knocko, the rhinestones, and the baby spotlight. Here in the dim light of the evening, he sat down to await the return of his uncle.

In the first few minutes of his wait, the quiet, as well as the gloom, became increasingly uninviting. All light from the outside seemed to fade; the macabre cruciform dazzle above the coffin dominated the room. From somewhere there came the sound of a banging door; no one entered. Adam had indeed, as he had said earlier to Skeffington, attended a few wakes, but his memory of them was obscure. Now in this silent gloom he had a disquieting recollection of a story of Synge's about a wake in the Aran Islands: the long procession of shawled and sobbing women gathering at the bier, rocking back and forth to the wail of the keen. That such a scene could be duplicated in the parlor of Knocko Minihan tonight was wildly improbable; nevertheless, Adam found himself speculating upon it in some detail. Suddenly, from somewhere to his right, there came a sound. "*Sssst!*" it hissed.

He jumped, startled. He turned and at first saw no one; then, in a corner which was darker than the rest of the room because of the shadow of a partially opened door, he saw a small, puckered woman, peering out at him with lively eyes.

"Did I *scare* you?" she said. The possibility seemed to delight her.

"No," Adam lied stoutly. "You startled me. I didn't see you come in."

"Ah, I *was* in," she said. "I was here in my corner when you come in with Frank. Are you the nephew?"

Adam nodded. It seemed to him that with the discovery of this silent little watcher of the shadows a new dimension of eerieness had entered the room. She had spoken of "*my* corner" with a proud possessiveness, almost as if she had come in with the coffin and would remain in her appointed place, firm, open-eyed and irremovable, until it was taken away.

"I'm Delia Boylan," she said. "I knew your pa and I knew your ma and I knew you when you was a baby." Pepper-and-salt eyebrows rose as she considered him now. "You was homely as spit," she said.

"Ah," said Adam. How did one respond more fully to such frankness? He had no idea. He said, changing the subject hopefully, "I'm surprised there are so few people here to see Mr. Minihan."

"Ah, they'll be in," she said confidently. "They'll all want to get a good last look at old Knocko. There's them that's been waiting for it a long time. We're early. I always like to be a bit early." She raised herself to a half-standing posture and gazed critically at the coffin. "He looks grand with the cheeks all puffed out, don't he?" she asked.

She spoke of the corpse with the nonchalant detachment possible only to those who have had vast experience with death. "He looks very nice," Adam said. He was painfully aware of his own lack of the special vocabulary of compliment appropriate to just such an occasion; he was sure that one existed. "Of course," he added, "I didn't know him when he was alive."

This, too, was maladroit; but Mrs. Boylan did not appear to mind. Her narrow little shoulders shrugged in contempt and she said, "A little runt of a man. Thin as a snake and no color to him at all. He was part French, you know."

"I know."

"That makes all the difference," she said mysteriously. "*Aram*. Ah well, that's small matter now." She spoke as one forgiving him the injury of his ancestry. "God be good to the man," she said. "He was mean as a panther, but good luck to him."

Adam said nothing. Once more, there seemed to be nothing to say. The silence was broken by the entrance of a trio of mourners who came in, looked slowly about the room, nodded to Delia, then filed up to the coffin.

"The Carmichael girls," Delia explained, "with the brother Tim. *They* come early, as a general rule." She moved abruptly in her chair, stretching out to face the door. "*Sssst!*" she hissed.

Adam followed her glance. He saw a stout, balding young man, spruce and smooth in the discreet clothing of his profession, moving with purposeful yet superlatively respectful steps towards the coffin.

"*Sssst!*" Delia said again. "Johnnie!"

The young man paused and looked in their direction; Adam thought he appeared to be annoyed. In response to Delia's frantically beckoning hand he came over to them with an obvious reluctance.

"Johnnie Degnan," Delia said to Adam, adding unnecessarily, "the undertaker. We always like to have our little talk."

"Good evening, Mrs. Boylan," the undertaker said unenthusiastically.

"Ah, Johnnie," Delia said. She introduced Adam. "Frank Skeffington's nephew, Johnnie. The sister's boy."

The undertaker brightened; he made a short, formal bow. "Very pleased to meet you, sir," he said. "I've always been a great admirer of your uncle, although I've never had the pleasure of making his acquaintance. I hope that will be remedied tonight. Ah . . . was there anything in particular, Mrs. Boylan?"

"He looks grand, Johnnie," she said, waving towards the coffin. "Just grand. Did he take a lot of doing?"

An expression of slight strain appeared on the undertaker's round face; clearly, thought Adam, questions from the laity were not encouraged. "Mr. Minihan was in remarkable condition, Mrs. Boylan, for one of his advanced years," he said. He spoke in a low voice and with extraordinary rapidity, as if in the hope that by a sudden sprint through his words he might bring this interview to a close. It was a forlorn hope; Delia had reached out and grabbed the sleeve of his coat.

"And Johnnie," she said, "you laid him out in the *big* coffin! Ah, you rascal, you!" She rolled her eyes and released a little whoop of laughter; down by the coffin the Carmichael triumvirate turned in unison to stare. The undertaker made a swift, imploring pass with his hands, and Delia lowered her voice to a stage whisper. "My God," she said delightedly, "wouldn't it kill the man if he knew!"

The undertaker gave her a look of pain. "Mr. Minihan has a very fine casket," he said, emphasizing the final word. "As I'm sure he would have wished it."

"Ah," Delia said, "but the cost of it all! The cost, Johnnie!"

"Mr. Minihan," said the undertaker swiftly, "was a very prominent figure in the community. Very prominent."

Delia nodded agreeably. "He was the cheapest old devil that ever lived," she said. "And you know it. Well, he's gone now, poor man, and you done an elegant job on him, Johnnie." As a grace note she added, "No matter what you charge."

"Ah ha ha ha," said the undertaker tonelessly, giving Adam a nervous smile, presumably meant to imply that they both were familiar with the irrepressible Mrs. Boylan. "Well, I must go now, Mrs. Boylan. Many duties. A pleasure to have met you, sir. I hope to meet your uncle." He bowed again and hurried away on muted feet.

"There's a great rogue," Delia said approvingly. "Only thirty years old and he'd steal the skin off your bones. Just give him the chance and it's the big coffin, ten limousines, and the Holy Name Choir to sing you good-by."

"And is he responsible for the crucifix?" Adam asked, pointing to the dazzling object above the coffin.

"The pride and joy," she assured him. "It all goes on the bill." She shook with a sudden rusty flutter of reminiscent mirth. "I says to him one day, I says, 'Don't you dare to stick that big sparkler over me when I'm gone, Johnnie Degnan! Don't you dare!' And he damn well won't; he knows he won't get a ten-cent piece out of me. Ah, he's a sly one," she said, "but he knows I'm on to him. *Sssst!*"

The sound, while no longer unfamiliar, was unexpected; Adam jumped again. An angular woman of forbidding aspect had come into the room and was now engaged in making hand signals to Delia.

"Aggie Gormley," Delia said. "I wonder has she news about the will? I'd best go see. I'll be back in a minute."

She hustled away with jerky, efficient steps, and Adam was alone once more. He looked at Delia, conversing with her newsy friend; he looked at the Carmichaels, talking quietly to Johnnie Degnan; he looked at the coffin and the jewelry above it. He looked, too, at his watch, and wondered absently when his uncle would return. Rather to his surprise, he did not greatly care, for he discovered to his horror that here in this presepulchral room, reserved for mourning, and in the appalling company of Delia Boylan, he was undoubtedly enjoying himself.

Skeffington, when he had left the parlor, had gone back along the hall until he came to a closed door. He knocked softly, then walked in. He was in the kitchen; on the far side of the small, neat room he saw, dressed in black, the tall, stooped figure of his wife's old friend. She was still, even now, a pretty woman, but faded, very faded; life with Knocko, thought Skeffington, must have been a fading experience. A quick rush of pity came over him as he looked at her; this was succeeded by quite another feeling, unexpected and hardly less painful: *My God,* he thought, *we're the same age almost to the day!* He shook his head quickly and said, "I'm sorry, Gert."

"I know you are, Frank." Obviously she had been weeping; now, however, she had stopped. Skeffington sat down across the kitchen table from her.

"Gert, I'm not going to commiserate with you. That'd be nice, but it wouldn't help much. But I do want to have a little talk with you on practical matters. I know you don't feel much like discussing anything like that now, but I want you to. Will you do that for me?"

There was a faint nod. "I will, Frank," she said.

"That's the girl. Now, first of all, do you have any idea of how you're situated? What did Knocko leave you? Was he able to leave you anything?"

One thin hand rubbed the narrow forehead wearily. "I'm not sure what he did or didn't leave, Frank. I haven't thought much about it at all."

Skeffington gently persisted. "Of course you haven't. But I want you to think about it now. That's why I made you promise you would. Sometimes at a time like this you need to change your thoughts every now and then. And sometimes you have to. You've got to think just a little bit of how you're going to live, Gert." He added, although he felt no confidence in this at all, "Knocko would have wanted you to."

She began to cry again, quietly. "He was a good man, Frank. You had to know him."

He let her cry, and said elusively, "I know he would have provided for you if he could. But we can't always do what we'd like to do. Now, I know he had nothing in the bank; he told me that himself. Was there any insurance?"

"There was some once," she said vaguely, "but I think it's gone. They ware charging him too much for the premiums, he said. Ah, I don't know. He told me very little about money, Frank. He had such bad luck."

"Yes." Bad luck, he thought, which had lasted no less than fifty years: a new world's record. "Any other holdings he might have had? War Bonds, for instance?"

She shook her head. "Since the store closed it seemed hard to put anything by. I know he got discouraged at times. You couldn't blame him. There was so much went wrong for the poor man."

"I know, Gert," he said soothingly, but to himself he said savagely: *and all of it of his own making.* It was tragic: this once-lively, once-lovely woman, whom he had known since childhood, who had been his wife's closest friend, now left old and beaten and penniless thanks entirely to her marriage to a dour, improvident boob! And yet she had loved him. It was utterly improbable, utterly irrational, and, he thought ironically, it happened all the time. Yet in this case it had happened to someone of whom he was fond; now it was up to him to do what the loved one had failed to do.

"Well, Gert," he said, "I guess now's as good a time as any to make good on a promise." He reached into an inner pocket of his coat and brought out an envelope. "Just before Kate died, she left me a little present for you. I would have given it to you before but there was a condition attached to it — she said I was to hold onto it until I was sure you really needed it. I guess you could say that time is now."

He handed her the envelope, and she took it silently. Still looking at him, she opened it; it was only when she felt the contents slipping out that she looked down. In her lap were ten one-hundred-dollar bills. She said instantly, "I won't take it, Frank. Thank you, but I won't."

He had anticipated this: the woman was not a fool. He reached over and took the bills in his hand. "All right," he said, "it's up to you, Gert. I'm not going to force you into anything. But I'll tell you this: The money belongs to you. Kate gave it to me to give to you, and if you don't use it, I can promise you nobody else will . . . I mean that, Gert."

She shook her head. "I saw Kate before she died. She said nothing about leaving me any money, and she knew I didn't want it. That money comes from you, Frank, and God bless you for it. But I won't take it."

It was no more than he had expected; the maneuver of the imaginary legacy was ridiculously transparent, especially to this woman who had her pride and who, moreover, knew him so well. But he had had no time; it would have to do. He said briskly, "Listen to me, Gert. I'm not an ungenerous man, but I'm not an idiot, either. I'm not in the habit of going around handing out one thousand dollars, even to old friends; it's a habit I can't afford. You can rest assured that if this were my money, no such sum would have come drifting so easily into your lap. Use your common sense, woman. But the point is that it's not my money; it's yours, that's the truth, and that's the end of it. And I tell you again that if you don't take it, I'll get rid of it, nobody'll get it. It was Kate's gift to you and you alone." He reached out and took her hand; then, extending the money towards her again, said insistently, "Come on, Gert. No false pride. Take it. It's yours. My God, woman, it's a mortal sin if you don't!"

She looked at him steadily, the tired old eyes regarding him for what seemed a very long time; then her hand reached out, touched the money, then drew back. She said, "*Was* it Kate's, Frank? *Is* it mine? Do you swear it?"

"I do, Gert," he said solemnly. And he knew that he had won.

She took the money, holding it awkwardly against her lap. Looking up at Skeffington she smiled with an odd, almost a young, shyness. "God bless you, Frank," she said.

"Why, I hope He will," he said, "but hardly for this. I'm just the messenger boy here. All blessings go to Kate, and I'm sure she doesn't need them by now." He got up and patted her on the hand. "I'm going back out front now," he said. "You ought to come out yourself a little later."

"I will, Frank." She thanked him again: for the money, for coming in to see her husband. As he was leaving she said, "Frank?"

"Yes, Gert?"

She looked at the money in her hand and said, "I still don't believe you."

He smiled. "That's your privilege as an old friend. I find that very few of my old friends ever believe me. Maybe that's how they got to be old friends in the first place." She knew, he thought, but she didn't *quite* know, and that was all right: as long as there was the doubt, her pride was saved. He had reached the door when she stopped him again, and this time there was anxiety in her voice.

"I suppose they'll come tonight?" she said. "There haven't been many up to now." She added defiantly, "He was a difficult man in his way, but he had his friends. He had many friends, Frank."

"He had indeed," Skeffington said reassuringly. "They've just been waiting for the final night, that's all. They'll be here tonight, Gert. You'll see. Your only difficulty will be to fit them all in."

As he walked from the room, he thought: Poor woman. If friendship with Knocko were to be the basis for attendance at his wake, it could have been held in a phone booth. . . . However, because of Gert, he had that afternoon taken steps to increase substantially the number of mourners tonight. He had issued an order to all department heads that delegations were to be sent; as a less compulsory, but possibly even more effective measure, he let it be known that he himself would be on hand. While walking along the hallway back to the parlor he thought of the crowded rooms, in which he would now have to remain at least another half hour; he thought of Gert; he thought, with no particular pity, of the miserable Knocko, whose death, in a sense, gave point to the evening.

To the thousand dollars he had just given away, however, he gave no especial thought, for, as Charlie Hennessey had once pointed out, the opponents of Skeffington who believed him to be an avaricious man, or one even concerned with money as such at all, could hardly have been farther from the truth.

He came in to the parlor to discover that the crowd had begun to arrive. The rows of chairs, empty before, were now rapidly being filled; as he entered the room heads turned towards him at once. He looked for Adam and signaled to him; Adam approached, only slightly behind Delia Boylan.

"Ah now, Frank," she said eagerly, "how is she taking it back there?"

His reply was brief. "As well as could be expected." He added dryly, "I'm happy to see that you're bearing up under the strain, Delia."

Once more Adam heard the derisive whoop of laughter; it rang through the gloomy room; heads turned; at his position of duty down by the coffin Johnnie Degnan frowned reprovingly and did a plump little dance step of despair. "I'll live," Delia said. "Well, me and the nephew has been having a lovely talk about poor Knocko, the old devil."

"I wish I'd been here to join you," Skeffington said. Turning to Adam he added, "Mrs. Boylan's pious reflections on the faithful departed never fail to uplift the spirit. She has a splendid attendance record at the deathbed of her many friends."

"I go to them all," she said proudly. "I don't miss a one."

"Everybody has to have a hobby," Skeffington said. "Now if you'll excuse us, Delia, I want to take my nephew into the next room and introduce him to some people. Give my best to Tom and the family."

"I will, Frank." The sharp little eyes glinted maliciously and she said, "And will I tell them you wouldn't mind hearing from them come Election Day?"

"I always treasure the Boylan vote," Skeffington said, "and yours in particular, Delia. Every time I get thinking about the wisdom of giving the women the vote I think of you and my fears become quiet."

She crowed with delight. "Ah, that's all mush, Frank. But you know we're with you every single time. The whole family."

"I do, Delia. I appreciate it. And now," he said, with no change of expression, "we'll leave you to your prayers. Good-by, Delia."

Out in the hall he drew Adam aside and said, "I hope you see how things work out for the best. If I hadn't left you alone in there, you wouldn't have met Mrs. Boylan and had your little devotional chat. Your field of experience has been immeasurably widened in the space of but a few minutes."

"I won't deny it," Adam said. "I've certainly never met anyone quite like her before. She's a fantastic woman."

"I suppose she is," Skeffington said carelessly. "I'm so used to her I don't notice any more. It takes a fresh eye to fully appreciate Delia. I may add that she's a woman it's far better to have with you than against you. She has the tongue of a cobra."

"And does she really spend all of her time going to wakes?"

"Apart from a few hours of sleep each night, I believe she does. As she said, she doesn't miss a one. You must remember that she's a singularly devout woman. Also," he said reflectively, "it's somewhat cheaper than going to the movies."

While they stood in the hall, more people came in; clearly, the wake of Knocko Minihan was expanding. As it did, Adam was struck by the altered deportment of his uncle; it was almost as if, from being one of the visiting mourners, he had suddenly become the host. He nodded and spoke briefly to all the new arrivals; without exception, all responded in identical fashion: a muttered acknowledgment of the pitiful fact of Knocko's death, followed by a perceptibly more fervent statement of good wishes for Skeffington in the coming elections. A short, round woman with a serene face approached them with slow, heavy steps; to her Skeffington spoke at somewhat greater length.

"Glad to see you, Annie," he said. "I gather that everything got here all right?"

"It did, Frank. You wanted no whisky or anything like that?"

"No. What have you got out there?"

"Coffee and tea, sandwiches, and cake. There'll be plenty for everybody, no matter how big it gets."

"Good. Where are you setting it up, in the kitchen?"

"There's a problem there, Frank. God knows there's no place else we can put it, but that's where Gert is, sitting all by herself. I don't like to bother the poor woman."

"Go right ahead and bother her," Skeffington said decisively. "That's what she needs right now, someone bustling around, something to take her mind off things for a few minutes. It's not good for her to be sitting out there all alone. See if you can't get her to come in here, just to go through the motions. If she doesn't want to do that, try to get her doing something out there. If you have any difficulty, let me know."

"All right, Frank, I will." The woman went down the hall with her calm, weighty tread, and Skeffington, who had been noting with some amusement his nephew's polite if imperfect attempt to conceal his curiosity, said, "That's a role I occasionally practice: the combination physician, caterer and master of ceremonies. It's something I might have to fall back on one day when I retire from politics."

"I am impressed," Adam said truthfully. "I hadn't realized that all this was a part of your job."

"Well, this is rather a special case. The widow's an old friend, and in her present condition she's in no shape to arrange for the usual civilities. So I just had a few things sent over." It was a detail he had taken care of that afternoon; the food had come from the ample commissariat of the Wadsworth Hospital. As this was a city institution, the food had been provided for by public funds; it was, in a word, a tax-supported wake. And all for Knocko Minihan; the beneficiary, thought Skeffington, was unworthy of the occasion. He said to Adam, "I'm not so sure that all the arrangements would meet with Knocko's approval, but then of course, when you come right down to it, he's not really in much of a position to complain, is he? Come along, I want to go in here."

They entered the next door down the hall; Adam found himself in a room which compared favorably with the parlor in its size and general hideousness, but which contained many more people and a great deal more noise. It was not until he had been in this room for a moment that he realized that there was still another difference: here, the mourners were exclusively male. To his surprise, he recognized some of them as the old familiars of his uncle's outer office. They had disdained the chairs which had been set out for them in a severe row which paralleled the wall; they preferred to stand, talking, smoking, moving, waiting. When Skeffington came in, the waiting was over. They surged around him, the noise grew, and Adam was soon separated from his uncle by a tight, struggling double ring of the self-appointed palace guard. He caught Skeffington's eye; in return he received a quick but unmistakable wink, the meaning of which was quite clear. For the moment at least, he was again on his own; Skeffington had decided that it was time for his field of experience to be widened still further.

But this widening was to be temporarily postponed, for his first encounter was with an old acquaintance who held no surprises. It was Ditto Boland. Just seconds before, Ditto had been valiantly attempting to crash through the impenetrable living barricade to gain his idol's ear; he had failed. Once more, craftier, stronger, more resourceful men had beaten him to the punch; a veteran at rejection, he had accepted defeat, and had settled for the next best thing. He had gone to talk to Adam.

"Good evening, Adam," he said, panting slightly. The heat of the evening and his own obesity had been hard on Ditto; the tiny, ridiculous head streamed with sweat, and the clothes on his huge body were rumpled and awry. "Well, well, and isn't this a grand evening, Adam. A very spirited occasion, as we say. Apart from the unhappy death of poor Knocko, that is."

For not the first time that evening, Adam wondered at this ability, apparently rather widely possessed, to separate sharply the occasion from the melancholy event that had produced it; he thought it unlikely, however, that Ditto could shed much light on the matter. And so he said merely, "Hello, Ditto. Have you been here long?"

"No, no, Adam, not very long at all. The fact of the matter is that there was a slight mixup at the Hall. An unhappy confusion, as we say. I and some of the boys were waiting there for the Governor to ride over here with him, but he got away without us being properly informed. I and the boys had to come in a taxicab," he said in an aggrieved voice. "I make no accusation against anyone in particular, Adam, but it's my personal belief that the Governor was not told I was out there waiting. There are certain confidential secretaries who are getting too big for their britches and are keeping from the Governor valuable information he'd like to hear. That's all I'll say, Adam. I make no definite charges, but all the same, Adam, I wouldn't like to be a certain high-and-mighty secretary when the Governor finds out what's been going on in Denmark, as we say."

As the pre-emptor of Ditto's position in the official car, Adam felt it only prudent to change the subject; he said, "I suppose Mr. Minihan was a friend of yours, Ditto?"

"Knocko? Oh, yes, yes, Adam. Of course he wasn't in politics like the Governor and myself, so I didn't see so much of him through the years. We weren't on the intimately bosom basis, as we say. But we were friendly. Oh yes, Adam. When he had the hardware store I was one of the very first to give him business with a purchase. I purchased a screwdriver. Poor Knocko. Gone but not forgotten. A very lovable man, Adam. Everybody loved him."

"That's curious," Adam said, "because I had the idea that he hadn't been terribly popular."

"Is that so now, Adam? Is that really so?" Circumspection had suddenly descended; it sat upon him oddly, like an ill-fitting hat. "Now isn't that interesting? Yes, that's very interesting indeed, Adam. Yes it is. And from who might you get an idea like that, might I ask?"

Rather unfairly, Adam said, "From my uncle."

"And who would know better?" Ditto said instantly. "Who would know better than the very same man, Adam? You can't beat the Governor when it comes to sizing a man up. He has a grand knowledge of the human man, as we say. I remember he spotted the mean streak in Knocko the first time he met him. He said to me personally at the time, he said, 'Ditto, the man has a bad eye.' I freely admit to you, Adam, I didn't see it myself at the time, but how right the Governor was as always was proved beyond all doubts when my screwdriver broke not a week after I made the purchase. But," he said largely, "forgive and forget: that's always been the Governor's grand motto, and mine has been as per the same. The Governor held nothing against the man and neither did I, and that's why the two of us are here tonight. Letting bygones go by the boards, as we say."

Death, then, had atoned for the defective ten-cent tool; Adam, not without some guilt remembering that it was he who had introduced the theme of Knocko's unlovelier side, switched to a less personal level. He said, "You must be an old hand at these wakes, Ditto."

"Yes, yes, Adam. I've been to some grand wakes in my time, very nice affairs. I remember the time I went with the Governor over to Danno Herlihy's wake. You remember Danno no doubt, Adam?"

"No, I don't believe I ever knew Danno."

"The Assistant Water Commissioner with the bum ear. He died of a bad appendix which the doctors couldn't find in time; it was later told to me in secret confidence, as we say, that when they took the man apart they found it around in back down by the spine. There was a grand wake, Adam. One and all had a grand time. The Assistant Commissioner was given the send-off in A Number One par excello style. There was turkey, ham, roast beef, potato salad and some lovely brisket." Ditto smacked his lips *in memoriam.* "And then of course there was the Wenatchee apples that the brandy had been put in. They were a tasty treat to the tongue, as we say. Do you know the Wenatchee apples that they put the brandy in, Adam?"

"No."

"They're big hard red apples from out West in California or Iowa or some place like that. They grow them in the apple orchards out there. You take out the cores and that leaves the empty hollow center, which you put the brandy in overnight. It all soaks up into the apple and gives people something nice to munch on the next day. A grand dessert."

"And this was the feature at Danno Herlihy's wake? A brandied apple?"

"*One* of the features, Adam," Ditto said, correcting him. "Oh yes yes, just one of the features. It was all grand otherwise as well, as we say. I remember the Governor came up to me at one point in the evening and said, 'Have you ever seen a grander wake than this, Ditto?' 'No, Governor,' I said, 'I haven't.' And it was the truth, Adam. The only bad spot in the whole entire evening came with the black sheep brother from New York. The family hadn't seen hide and hair of him, as we say, for thirty years, but he turned up the last night of Danno's wake. And what do you think he did? He got *himself* an appendicitis attack just as they were saying the Rosary! The very same identical thing Danno had died of, and he had to get one for himself just as they were saying the prayers for Danno! The family never forgave him."

"And damn well they shouldn't of," Cuke Gillen said. He had come up in time to hear the last of the story. "The bum was a flycatcher, a scene stealer. He tried to cop the act at his own brother's wake. I knew the bum years ago, in vaudeville; he played the small time with me. He used to beat hotel bills. What he'd do, he used to walk around the lobby with his tie pulled up tight around his neck, giving himself the old chokeroo. After a while his face would get all red and he'd look like a country boy. You know, a big honest hick kid. So the manager might be worried as hell about his dough, but one look at that face and he'd figure that no guy with a kisser like that could sneak his way out of the bathroom, let alone a hotel. So he stops worrying, and the first thing you know — Zing! the bum puts his cardboard suitcase under his arm, hops out of the window onto the fire escape, and it's good-by Swanee to dear old Peoria!"

"A very low type of a man," Ditto said virtuously. "You could tell it from the way he behaved himself at Danno's wake. But every other way you looked at it, the evening was a grand success for all members present, as we say." The sight of Cuke now seemed to unsettle him, to remind him of something temporarily forgotten; he glanced hastily over his shoulder at the center of the room, where Skeffington stood, still surrounded. "Did you have a chance to say a few words to the Governor tonight, Cuke?" he asked anxiously.

"Sure. I was over there shooting the breeze with him just a few minutes ago."

"Ah," Ditto said. "Aha. Is that a fact, Cuke? You were over there talking with him, were you? I'll have to go over myself in a minute. I know he's been wanting to see me." He looked unhappily at the circling, suppliant guard; there seemed to be more of them than ever. It was hard, very hard. In another moment he would try again; maybe the Governor would see him, would beckon to him, and the terrible protective lines would part. Meanwhile . . . he said wistfully, "And how is he this fine evening? In the best of fettles, I hope."

"In great shape. He was just telling the boys a minute ago about the way it looks in the Second Ward. It's looking very good. Tom Healy is coming around; at least it looks like he is. Anyway, we're putting on the heat over there next week. The Governor tells me we'll be going over there every single night for different meetings. And of course as usual I'll be right on hand with my scintillating assortment of snappy stories for young and old, rich and poor." He winked at Adam, and then, because he was Skeffington's nephew, favored him with a particularly choice specimen bit from the act: with his palms he slapped his thighs to the rhythms of "Glowworm"; he capered about and executed his celebrated off-to-Buffalo break. Adam had witnessed this performance before; he was not now greatly astonished to see that the presence of the deceased Knocko in the adjoining room in no way affected its gymnastic vivacity. "One solid boffola from beginning to end," said Cuke, coming to a sliding stop, "guaranteed to make you split your sides with good clean laughter." Smartly, he spanked his collar with a forefinger.

"There's no doubt I'll be going along with the Governor to all those meetings," Ditto said without conviction. "No, no, there's no doubt of that at all. As per always, Ditto will be ready and waiting for the Governor's beck or call, as we say. The Governor's a great one for sticking by the old and trusty friends, no matter what certain swell-headed secretaries may think. I mention no names. Was there any more news mentioned, Cuke?"

"Camaratta was talked about. Apparently he's getting smart and coming in with the boys. The Governor mentioned him in high terms."

"Oh yes, yes," Ditto said, nodding. "They're very close these days. All together in the one cause. Camaratta's done some very dirty business in the days gone by, as we say, but the Governor's not the type of man who holds onto a grudge. No no, Camaratta is sitting very pretty these days. That I know. I'm so used to the Governor I can tell how he feels towards a man by the way he mentions his name. The rise and fall of the voice. The inflections, as we say. Was there any news about Jimmy Murtagh and the Park Commission, Cuke?"

"A gone goose," Cuke said. "On account of he was caught playing easy-kneesy with Mother Garvey."

"Aha. Well well well. I could have told him that, if he'd come to me and asked me. I knew the Governor's feeling on the matter very well. Jimmy was running around on the thin ice, as we say. Oh yes yes."

Adam could not help marveling at the completeness of Knocko's failure to dominate, or even to intrude upon, his own wake. Here in the antechamber he was playing a bad second fiddle to the swapped vote and the living Skeffington; in the adjoining room, where the women were gathered before the bier, was he equally unfortunate? Presumably so: City Hall undoubtedly possessed its Ladies' Auxiliary. Yet there, perhaps the tactless presence of the casket and its contents might severely hamper political discussion; upon further consideration, however, he was inclined to doubt this. It was evident now that they had come tonight neither to bury Knocko nor to praise him; they had come to ignore him. The more one considered this neglect, Adam thought, the more callous one discovered it to be, and despite his resolutions to be prepared for all possible developments, he was somewhat shocked by this one.

Cuke and Ditto had continued to talk; they were interrupted by the approach of old John Gorman. He had been standing to the left of the ring surrounding Skeffington, talking to petitioners with more modest or more localized requests. Now he came across the room, a remarkably neat, spare old man, straight as a string; when he reached them he said softly, "Ditto. Run down to the car now and tell Patsy to take you down to Ryan's for a half-dozen boxes of cigars. He'll know the kind. You'd best go along with him, Cuke. The fresh night air will do your lungs a world of good."

The two men obeyed instantly. It was, for both, an errand of pleasure, and besides, an order from Gorman was an order from Skeffington. Gorman turned to Adam, smiling faintly.

"There's no greater turn you could do Ditto," he said. "Up in the back seat of the big black car, just himself and Cuke. Almost as good as if it was just himself. Well now, did the two of them tell you all about politics?"

"Not quite," Adam said. He was slightly abashed by the question, which seemed to place him in the undesirable relation of pupil to two such dubious tutors, and which, moreover, had come from a man for whom he had both liking and respect. He knew the regard in which his uncle held Gorman, and he could only assume, now, that Skeffington had told the old man of his nephew's proposed initiation into the campaign; the consequence had been this gently ironic question. (The assumption, as it happened, was quite incorrect. Skeffington viewed his conversation with his nephew as a peculiarly personal matter, and he was not in the habit of discussing his private affairs with his political associates. Gorman, however, had required no special information. He had known Skeffington intimately for many years, he knew of his fondness for this nephew, of his bitter disappointment in his son, of his loneliness since his wife had died. The old man could put two and two together. The answer he had arrived at now pleased him. He's a good lad, he thought, and it's a good thing for Frank.) Adam added, "Although the subject did manage to come up, Mr. Gorman. As a matter of fact, it was just about the only subject that did come up."

"Ah well, that's natural enough," the old man said mildly. "If you met the Pope you'd talk about religion."

Adam smiled. "I suppose so. Still, wouldn't we also talk just a bit about Knocko Minihan? Particularly if we happened to meet at his wake?"

"It would be the pious thing to do, no doubt," Gorman agreed. "But then if you both knew Knocko, you might damn well want to talk about almost anything else in a hurry. Out of respect for the dead, you might say."

"Yes, I see. But what I don't see is this: if Knocko was such a generally disliked man, why are so many people here tonight? They didn't come to gloat, obviously; they're not ghouls. But then why did they come?"

"That I'm not sure about. Still," the old man said thoughtfully, "I wouldn't think you'd be far wrong if you said they came as you did yourself. For the very same reason, that is."

Adam stared at him. "But I came only because of my uncle."

"So you did," Gorman said. "So you did, indeed."

"Then you mean that all these other people came because of Uncle Frank, too?"

"Ah well, I wouldn't say all; that'd be a bit of an exaggeration. You had a little chat with Delia Boylan, I hear" — suddenly and irrelevantly, it occurred to Adam that there seemed to be very little that this old man did *not* hear — "and there's some that came like Delia: they just enjoy themselves going to a wake. It's like little boys and girls going to birthday parties. Then there's some that came on the widow's account: Gert's a fine woman, and she has her friends. And there may be a few no doubt came for Knocko himself; they say," he said wryly, "there's saints amongst us even today. I don't run into many myself. But most of them that are here tonight stopped by for the one reason: they knew your Uncle Frank was to come. And that's the long and the short of it." He saw no point in mentioning the delegations from the different city departments who were here in compulsory attendance; it would only complicate the issue. The boy, he reflected, was a good boy, but young; naturally, he could have no idea of the way things were done. To tell him would be to serve no purpose save perhaps an educational one, and John Gorman was really not wildly interested in telling the young the facts of life.

"And so," Adam said, "while it's Knocko's wake, it's really my uncle who's the main attraction?"

Gorman nodded. "It is."

Adam said, "And naturally business goes on as usual? Only here instead of at the Hall?" His feeling of shock had increased; the whole business, he decided, was a really appalling mixture of hypocrisy and hardness.

"You have things a little twisty," the old man said softly, "If you don't mind me saying so." A little rap across the knuckles was in order, he decided; not a hard rap, to be sure, for he was a good lad and he was Skeffington's nephew, but a rap all the same. It was for the lad's own good; it would help to keep him from leaping about like a salmon to the wrong conclusions. He said, "You're a bit hard on your uncle, I think. The man has no need to go to wakes if he wants to collect a crowd about him; he can do that anywhere. All he has to do is stop on a street corner to light his cigar and fifty people come out of the cement to say, 'Hello Frank, and what can you do for me today?' And when he showed up here tonight it wasn't to talk politics. He can do that any minute of the day, any place he likes; he needs no dead man in the next room to help him tell Tommy Mulcahy that the polls are open from eight to eight on Election Day, and only one vote to a customer this year. What he came here for tonight is simple as simple can be: he came to bring a crowd to Knocko's wake so the widow would feel a little better. Knocko's been lying here all day yesterday, all last night, and all day today: how many people d'ye s'pose came in to see him in all that time? Maybe thirty-five, and ten of those came in to get out of the rain. Tonight there'll be hundreds here, and the widow'll think it's all Knocko's pals, waiting till the last moment to bid him good-by. But with all those people in here, and your uncle here to bring them, what in the name of Heaven are they to talk about but what they like and what they know? God knows they can't talk about Knocko. Half of them never knew the man, and the other half that knew him didn't like him. That's not the kind of thing that makes for easy conversation. And you can't keep a roomful of men talking in soft voices about what a terrible thing death is, and will he go to Heaven, and maybe is he up there this very minute looking down on us all? Those are grand thoughts, but somehow nobody is able to keep thinking them for two hours whilst waiting for the priest to get here to say the Rosary. So they have a little food and they talk a little politics, and I don't know that they do a great amount of harm with either. And then when the priest does get in at last and they all kneel down to pray for Knocko, you might put your mind to this: there'll be ten times the people here praying for him as would be here without your uncle and all the chatter about politics. I don't s'pose they'll all be praying away as holy as St. Francis, but you never know about a thing like that; maybe some of them will mean it, and maybe it'll do Knocko a bit of good. I have the suspicion that he's in no mood at the moment to throw away any prayers from friend or foe; he's likely to be needing anything in that line that comes his way." He paused; it had been a speech of fantastic length for this ordinarily taciturn old man. Still, he reflected, sometimes a bit of gab was needed to drive a point home. He wondered: had it done the trick? He hoped so; looking at the boy, he thought so. In any case, it was all he had to say on the subject. "So that being the way it is," he concluded, his mild blue eyes resting on Adam's face, and his thin old lips twisted once more into the just perceptible smile, "don't be too hard on us, boy. I don't doubt but that it's a bit different from what you're used to here tonight, but it's no terrible thing that's being done."

During the first part of this speech Adam had been surprised, then uncomfortable; during the latter part he had felt his face growing redder by the word. He could not know that his embarrassment and evident sincerity had touched the old man. It was the kind of reproof he had never before experienced as an adult; it was the admonition customarily reserved for the world of the refractory child: quiet, paternal, expressed in such simple terms that even the most backward little boy could somehow grasp the fact that he had been impertinent. It had been humiliating, but what had been far worse, it had been justified. For he had come here tonight as the alien guest; once ashore, he had lost no time in the uninformed criticism of the customs of the land in which he found himself. He had been rude, and he had been told about it: it was as simple as that. Apologetically he said, "I'm sorry, Mr. Gorman. I'm afraid I'll have to plead stupidity and some pretty bad manners."

"Not at all," the old man said courteously. "You said nothing that was so bad; just a small mistake you couldn't help but make unless somebody told you different. And who was to tell you? Ditto? You might as well go to poor Knocko for the news. And your uncle couldn't very well tell you. You could hardly expect the man to grab you by the arm and whisper, 'Come along, now, we're off to a wake. There's two main attractions, the corpse and me, but just between the both of us, the corpse ain't in it with me!' So the only one to tell you the way things stood was myself and so I did." He looked appraisingly at Adam and said dryly, "I don't think the damage was too permanent. You look like you might be able to sit up and take a bit of soup in a day or so."

Ruefully, Adam said, "Just about." But the old man's softening of the blow had left him feeling a good deal better; he said, "Anyway, I am sorry, Mr. Gorman. And thanks."

The old man moved a hand slightly. "Ah," he said mysteriously, "it's all a lot of nothing." He added briefly, "You'll do, right enough." It was a compliment, an astonishing one from the old man. But he was pleased by the way the boy had reacted; respectful, he thought, but not a slaverer. Not a sorehead, but not a ninny either. A decent lad, and good for Frank; too bad, he reflected, it couldn't have been the son. A damn shame. But that was the way it went, and a man could waste his whole life away wishing, wanting, and wondering why; John Gorman was far too busy for such waste. He considered the subject of Adam's instruction now closed. With his lips slightly pursed, he began to look slowly about the room, watching for developments that might have taken place while he had been talking. One of these was in the doorway even now. He said to Adam, "Now there's your man for you, over by the door. D'ye know him?"

Adam saw a short, stout man with oddly protuberant eyes who had paused to regard the room before entering; he was middle-aged, and dressed in a rumpled gray suit; under his right arm he carried what looked to be a small shoebox. Although he stood motionless in the doorway, there was something about him which suggested perpetual and hectic movement; one felt that to see him thus at a standstill was like seeing a hummingbird forcibly immobilized: it was somehow unfair. Or at least so Adam felt; it was the first time he had set eyes on Charlie Hennessey.

Evidently Charlie had chosen Gorman and Adam as his immediate goal. He came towards them with his curious little skating steps, and was on them even before Gorman had an opportunity to identify him for Adam. In any case, such identification would have been unnecessary, for Charlie identified himself.

"Hello, my dear man," he said to Gorman. "You're looking very well, John: a nice, even, healthy color. That speaks of a good circulation. Marvelous! The blood's the thing. And this must be Frank's nephew, Adam Caulfield by name. I'm Charles Hennessey, my dear man. I read you daily in the funny papers. Nice drawing, a good sense of humor. Marvelous! I read all the papers and everything that's in them. Well, my dear man," he said, turning again to Gorman, "I see the boss still has the touch. Oh, the grand touch! You have to hand it to the man. The most unpopular man in the ward dies and almost before he's cool there's a mob scene round the casket shouting, 'Three cheers for Skeffington for mayor!' Marvelous! Shrewd! Getting votes out of Knocko, like getting blood out of the turnip. They call it alchemy, a kind of old-time magic. And Frank's the master magician. Imagination! Foresight! The only man among us to realize that you could get a good turn out of Knocko after all: you only had to wait until the man was dead. Oh, clever! My hat's off to the man!"

Adam looked up sharply as this extraordinary man voiced what was substantially the charge he himself had made only minutes before; would he, too, suffer the Gorman rebuke? But the old man merely seemed amused; he said simply, "Ah, that's all moonshine, Charlie. All gas." To Adam he said significantly, "Charlie here is running against your uncle for mayor."

"Yes, yes, fighting him tooth and nail," Charlie said briskly. "All in the interests of decent government. And of course what I'm saying is the very reverse of gas, my dear man. All truth! It's a matter of public record that Frank Skeffington has been campaigning at wakes for fifty years. Big wakes or small ones, it made no difference. If nobody died for the six months before an election he wouldn't know where to go. He's spent half a century with one eye on the coffin! A Skeffington maxim: Never neglect the relatives, friends or enemies of the deceased. I've studied the man all my life and I'm very familiar with his methods of operation, my dear man."

Gorman said, "Charlie —"

Charlie held up a warning finger, he bounced up and down for emphasis. "Which is not to say the man does no good," he said. "Far from it. Oh no no no, my dear man! In his way he does a world of good: I freely give him credit. He comes to a wake, he draws a crowd, and he keeps everybody in the house that should be crying so busy carting sandwiches they forget to cry. Occupational therapy, my dear man! The touch of a master psychologist! Another Skeffington maxim: Stampede them! Give them no time to think! And on top of that the man is charitable. A heart of gold, you can't take that way from him. If the widow here tonight should need a little cash, she'll get it without asking. If she needs a job, there'll be one waiting for her at City Hall tomorrow morning; she can sit around all day stuffing empty papers into envelopes and mailing them to herself. Nice light work and one of the best-paying jobs in the city. Marvelous! A likable trait in the man. Not good government, but likable. Generous! But by the same token, my dear man, it's not a one-way street. Oh, by no means! *Quid pro quo*, as Julius Caesar used to say. Which means, 'I'll do fine by the wake, but it'll do twice as fine by me!' Oh yes yes! Marvelous! Shrewd!"

Altogether, thought Adam, an amazing performance; however, its primary effect had been to leave him increasingly doubtful about the necessity for his own apology. Once more he looked at Gorman, anticipating some sign of rebuttal, but apparently the old man was done with argument. He said, "Charlie. Where's your cap? The one that's made out of tar or lumps of coal or whatever it is. Did you leave it home out of respect? Could you not get a nice little one made out of black sateen you could bring to funerals and wakes?"

"Dacron," Charlie said promptly. "The cap's made out of Dacron, my dear man: the wonder material of the age. Not one head cold since the beginning of the year! You ought to wear one yourself at all times, my dear man, because of your advanced years. At your time of life even the head cold can be fatal. I'm supported in that opinion by the best of competent medical authority. Oh yes yes! Precautions, they're the thing!"

"I'll try one more year without it," Gorman said, "and see will I live." He pointed to the oblong box under Charlie's right arm and said curiously, "What's that you've got there with you? Did you bring a little present for the deceased, Charlie?"

"Better than a present, my dear man," Charlie said, whipping out the box and opening it. "A camera! A self-developer, my dear man!" He pointed it at Gorman; there was a clicking sound. "In sixty seconds exactly," he announced, "you'll have a full-fledged picture of yourself as you stand at this moment, my dear man! All done within the camera itself! An automatic process! Marvelous!"

The old man shook his head. In spite of his long experience with both Charlie and most of the varieties of abnormal behavior, he had found this demonstration slightly staggering. "And why would you bring a thing like that here tonight?" he said. "Were you out to snap a picture of Knocko in the box?"

"No, no, nothing like that. I have it with me at all times these days, my dear man. A universal benefit to modern man. Grand for use in checking up on the sick and dying, for instance. Oh, marvelous! Knocko might still be among those present tonight if they'd had the good sense to use it on him. I know what I'm talking about, my dear man!" He patted the camera affectionately and said, "Grand, grand! It gives you a permanent picture record of how the patients are doing from day to day. Marvelous! Great for people visiting their sick relatives in the hospitals. Annie Mc-Caffrey's husband Bill is over in the Simmons Memorial. I went to her the other day and said, 'Tell me, my dear woman, how does he look?' She said, 'He looks about the same from one day to the next. He doesn't change.' I said, 'That's where you're 100 per cent wrong, my dear woman. All patients change, for better or for worse. Disease isn't constant. Oh no! Your trouble is that you're relying on what the doctors tell you and your own memory. Dangerous! Don't trust the memory! You go in to see him on Monday morning and you've already forgotten just how he looked on Sunday. Does he look better or is he slipping? You don't know, you can't remember. Foolish! Take this camera along with you, my dear woman. Snap a picture of him in bed at the same time every day for a week. At the end of the week compare the pictures. Marvelous! Right before your eyes you have the day-by-day pictorial record of whether the man is picking up or whether he's slowly wasting away to nothing at all! Regular check-ups in pictures, that's the thing! Take the camera now, my dear woman, I implore you! Get over to the hospital and start snapping away before it's too late! That's the only thing to do!' Oh, marvelous!" he cried, lifting the camera high above his head, and waving it about. "Here's the thing, my dear man, the very latest thing! The greatest single development in medicine since the invention of the bandage!"

Adam was fascinated. The matter of his apology had been forgotten, at least for the moment; he was dazzled by the ghastly anecdote he had just heard and by the turbulent little raconteur who had now begun to move about rapidly, circling them as he talked. Was he serious, Adam wondered? There seemed little doubt of it. Gorman sighed and said, "Charlie, Charlie. By God, you're a wonderful comfort to a worrying woman. And did she take you up on it?"

"No no," Charlie said. "You could hardly expect her to. A simple woman of the type you can do nothing for. Backward! Retrogressive! A childish faith in the attending physician. Sad, sad! I had to let her go her way. I said, 'Very well, my dear woman, I don't want to push you into anything. Only don't come around for the camera a couple of weeks from now when he's all skin and bones and his head's all shrunk up to no bigger than a walnut! I'd let you have it, yes, yes, of course, but it'll be too late, much too late! Oh yes!' Sixty seconds!" he said, breaking off suddenly. He halted his circling movements, brought down the camera from over his head, flipped open the back of it, and tore off a small rectangular piece of glossy paper. "Sixty seconds later and there you are!" he announced triumphantly, handing the paper to Gorman. "A picture record of John Gorman as he stood in this very room not a minute ago! All taken and developed within the camera itself! A sixty-second miracle! Visualize the possibilities in all fields, my dear man! It defies the scope of the imagination!"

Adam studied the small sepia photograph which Gorman held gingerly in his hand. It was not a flattering likeness. Cloudy, out of focus, with the head remarkably attenuated to approximately the length of the trunk, it offered striking evidence that the photographer had imperfectly mastered his instrument. "By God!" the old man said, in an awed voice.

"I haven't quite got the complete hang of it yet," Charlie said, "but you see the idea. Marvelous. And only the beginning! Modern science is on the march, my dear man! We're living in a wonderful age. Another generation and everybody'll live to be a hundred and they'll all have teeth like Eskimos! The dentist is all done, my dear man. He'll go out of the picture like the bison —"

"That's the kind of talk that's sure to gain you the unanimous support of the Dental Association," Skeffington said. He had been moving unhurriedly towards them for the past few moments, stopping to talk to newcomers to the room, picking up an attendant here and there to add to his bustling retinue. "It can't miss. There's nothing people enjoy quite so much as being told they're doomed to extinction. I'm surprised at an old campaigner like you, Charlie, antagonizing the dentists like that. To say nothing of the bison."

"Facts, facts!" Charlie said. "You can't hide facts, votes or no votes. How are you, my dear man? You're looking well, very well. Better than I've seen you in a long time. No slumping of the posture, nice and firm under the chin, clear eyes: grand! Grand in a man of your years. They tell me you're on the low-salt diet. Don't put too much faith in it, my dear man. No no no! That's what Billy McGrath was on and he perspired himself to death. *The system needs salt*; that's important to remember!"

"I'd almost forgotten poor Billy," Skeffington said thoughtfully. "The only man who ever literally sweated away. He used to move about accompanied by drip pans and sponges to collect the excess moisture. I'll try to avoid that fate if possible, Charlie. How's your campaign coming along, by the way? I hear you've got the sound truck out."

"Yes, yes, telling the public the facts, day and night. I'm telling them the facts about you, my dear man, as well as about your nut-boy opponent McCluskey. I watched you on television last night, my dear man; I took down every word you said on the tape recorder. Marvelous! Verbatim! Every last word! It doesn't stand up, my dear man. A grand first impression, but when you play it all back a second or third time on the tape recorder you realize the lack of substance there. Oh, inadequate, my dear man! Grand delivery, but poverty of thought. I played it back three times on the tape recorder and realized it more each time. Yes, yes!"

"Charlie, that's unfair," Skeffington said reproachfully. "You listened.

I don't know that I like these radical departures from fine old traditions. I only hope it doesn't start a trend. Suppose everybody got the bug and suddenly began to listen to what was being said in political speeches? You're playing with fire, Charlie. You may be even tampering with the health and well-being of the nation. I listened to a political speech only once in my life and I nearly died as a result. It was twenty-five years ago. Cal Coolidge was President. I was in the hospital, recovering nicely from a minor operation, when some enemy turned the radio on in my room so that I could hear a presidential address. Well, I was weak and didn't realize what I was doing. I listened to him. I listened to every word he said for nearly five minutes and then I began to sink fast. They got me just in time. They slapped me in an oxygen tent, and while it was touch-and-go for the next few days, eventually I pulled through. A good many Republicans never forgave Cal for not talking a little faster that day. But I hope you see now how dangerous your little experiment is, Charlie, and what it might lead to: the possibility of a national breakdown. Still," he said, "it may not catch on altogether. There must be a few mossbacks in the electorate who don't bother to tape-record every political speech they hear."

There had been visible and audible signs of amusement from the crowd all through this speech; there was loud, shouting laughter at its conclusion. From the periphery of the crowd came a high-pitched laugh which carried above all other sounds. Ditto had returned with the cigars.

"Tape-record every political speech they hear!" he cried. "Oh, that's a good one, Governor! Yes, indeed!"

"Marvelous!" Charlie cried happily. "A great performance, my dear man! The born raconteur in action! Marvelous! Not a word of sense or truth in the whole performance from beginning to end, but they loved it! Oh, marvelous! A great example of crowd psychology, my dear man! I give credit where credit is due! I take nothing away from you, my dear man. I give you your due every night in the wards while I'm campaigning against you. Oh yes! I stand on the sound truck and say, 'Dear folks, don't underestimate the mayor. Don't think he has no capacity merely because the city is going to rack and ruin around us, our fine civic buildings are all held together with Scotch tape and library paste, our nice residential streets look like back alleys in South Timbuctoo, and every man among us who owns property is taxed like the Aga Khan. But dear folks, don't condemn the mayor totally for this! Be just, dear folks! Remember that while he may be a bum administrator, we have to admit two things about him. One, he has a grand heart, and two, he's the greatest orator and crowd psychologist that this part of the world has ever produced! These are facts I'm telling you, dear folks! There's no one to touch him in that department! Oh yes,' " he cried, crouching, and weaving back and forth, his hand clutching an invisible microphone, the floor beneath his feet miraculously transformed into the platform atop his sound truck, " 'there's no one to touch him at all! The last surviving member of his species! Only last week I wrote letters to the sociologists down at Yale, Harvard, and Princeton, telling them to get their best men over here to watch Frank Skeffington in action before it's too late! Oh yes! Important! I told them to get them over here and watch him set the buffoons on fire, all laughing and jumping and cheering and stamping their feet, while he stands up there nodding his head and in the big air-conditioned voice telling them fifteen lies and a bedtime story to send them home happy! Marvelous! The talent is inborn, dear folks! A terrible mayor but a great entertainer! And what's the lesson in that, dear folks? Simply this: I say to you tonight that you have to make up your minds whether or not you want an entertainer in the mayor's seat. And if you do, dear folks, if you want a good laugh while the buildings of your city are falling to the ground one by one all around you, then by all means return Frank Skeffington to office!' "

This sustained performance won more laughter and applause; Skeffington had listened, greatly amused. He liked Charlie Hennessey, and while the liking was comfortably buttressed by the knowledge that, as a rival, Charlie could do him no serious damage, still, the feeling had more genuine roots. Skeffington knew that he had much common ground with this exuberant little pepperpot. They shared the same background, the same traditions, and even, to a considerable extent, the same gifts; it was just that in one of them, Skeffington reflected, somewhere along the line someone had forgotten to tighten a necessary wire, and the result was Charlie. Charlie, with all his volcanic but essentially purposeless eloquence, his thousand and one unrelated interests, his wild undisciplined quixotic pursuit of impossible ends! Looking at Charlie in full flight was for Skeffington a little like looking into a mirror in a fun house: through the lunatic distortions, he could always manage to discern just a little bit of himself.

However scattered his shots, though, Charlie was almost always hugely diverting in process; at least Skeffington found him to be so, and he was now pleased to note that apparently his nephew did, too. He had been watching Adam with some care during the progress of Charlie's monologue; he was satisfied with the results. The boy was clearly fascinated by this extraordinary orator; now he was laughing like the rest; his earlier reticence seemed gone, he was caught up in the atmosphere of the room.

Still, while that was all desirable, Skeffington reminded himself that this atmosphere must now be controlled; otherwise it could get out of hand. And, after all, it *was* a wake, Knocko was in the parlor, and, more important, Gert was in the kitchen. He looked at Gorman, who had gone over to the door and who had been talking to the stout woman who was in charge of arrangements in the kitchen. The old man now nodded at Skeffington, and he put up his hand, slowly quieting the crowd.

"Charlie," he said, "you put me to shame. When I hear those complimentary words you've been directing to the electorate on my behalf, I deeply regret that I haven't shown the same generous spirit towards you. Maybe I can repair that deficiency in the weeks to come. Meanwhile, I hope you haven't been favoring me exclusively. I hope you've been fair enough to extend the same courtesies to friend McCluskey!"

"Never fear, my dear man!" Charlie said. "Absolute impartiality! I'm after the nut-boy hammer and tongs, yet at the same time I say a good word for him. 'Oh, dear folks,' I say, 'it's grand to see a nice, clean-living young man want to make his way into public life today! Nice! I've got respect for him. Dear folks, I don't hold it against him for a minute that the poor boy's nothing but a decoy duck for Mother Garvey as well as the power-trust gang! A duck in a double-breasted suit! It's not his fault, dear folks. Oh no! Innocent! Innocent as the day he was born! Doesn't belong in the dirty business of city politics at all; it's a shame to drag him in! A marvelous candidate for the presidency of the senior class in high school! Great at planting bushes in the school lawn on Arbor Day! Grand! Marvelous! But dear folks, a mere pawn in the hands of those that run him today! A clean-living pawn, but still a pawn! The boy's —' "

"Fine, Charlie, fine," Skeffington said, interrupting. He was enjoying what was being said, but it would have to wait for another time. "Glad to see you're giving everybody the same treatment. At the moment, however, I think we're all going to have to quiet down a bit. Knocko's window'll be in here any moment. Naturally she's distressed, and she won't want to linger, so I suggest that you extend your sympathies briefly, and then move out to the kitchen where there are refreshments. I also suggest," he said meaningfully, "that after the refreshments you stay around for the Rosary. I know that most of you intended to, but there may be a few who suddenly remembered more pressing errands. If so, I think those errands had better be postponed. A few prayers won't kill you, and some of you may actually enjoy the sensation of being on your knees for a change. The priest should be here shortly."

"Marvelous!" Charlie said. "The swiftness and dispatch of it! Marching orders! I hand it to you, my dear man. Marvelous!"

It was the entrance of the widow that returned Adam to a sense of the occasion. Guiltily he realized that he had succumbed completely to the mood against which he had protested; before the caperings of Charlie Hennessey, he had found no trouble at all in forgetting Knocko Mini-han. This feeling of guilt was heightened when his uncle, a moment later, steered him towards the widow. She was a tall, somber woman with a gentle, grief-drawn face; clearly, she had not forgotten. Contrite, Adam tried hastily to summon up some last-minute emotion more or less appropriate to death; in this he was regrettably not successful. Skeffing-ton presented him to the widow; he muttered what he hoped was an acceptable phrase of condolence; she nodded and gazed at him with a polite, dulled curiosity. He left the room quickly and joined the men in the kitchen. Skeffington remained behind while the others in the room paid their respects, quickly and quietly; then he took the woman by the arm and directed her down the hall and into the parlor itself. To Adam, it all seemed very hard indeed on the widow, and he could not imagine why his uncle appeared so determined that she should go through with it, as though it were some form of compulsory ritual. Doubtless it had its value; Adam did not know what this might be. To him, it merely seemed an unnecessary and, very probably, a peculiarly painful procedure.

He did not wait long in the kitchen. He stood by the table, talking with some of the men whom he had seen in his uncle's office; Ditto had deserted him for the moment. Soon he saw his uncle come back down the hall with the widow. She disappeared, and Skeffington came into the kitchen.

"I think we might move along up to the parlor," he said to Adam. "I saw a priest come in as I was coming back down here: I imagine they'll be saying the Rosary any moment now. We'll join them, and then we'll go."

Led by Skeffington, the men left the kitchen and trooped up to the parlor; there, at the door they were met by a priest. Or, more accurately, by a Monsignor; it was the Cardinal's secretary.

"Good evening, Governor," he said pleasantly.

"Well, well," Skeffington said, some slight surprise in his voice. "Monsignor. This is an unexpected pleasure. Nice to see you again. Are you here as an emissary of His Eminence?"

"No, no," the Monsignor said. "I'm on my own tonight. Mrs. Mini-han is something of an old friend. When I was a boy in this part of town I used to drop in to see her fairly often. Most of the children of the neighborhood did, I think."

"Yes," Skeffington said thoughtfully. "So they did. I'd almost forgotten. Poor Gert." Then, speaking less to himself and more to the Monsignor, he said, "Well, it's very good of you to remember and drop in now. Tell me, how's your boss these days?"

"Very well. I'll tell him I saw you, Governor."

"Do that," Skeffington said. "He'll be overjoyed."

The Monsignor smiled. "You may be misjudging His Eminence, Governor. It's a case of the bark being a good deal than the bite."

"I wouldn't know," Skeffington said. "I've never been bitten. There were a few quick snaps in my direction, but I managed to avoid them. However, that's neither here nor there at the moment, I suppose; there's no reason why you should be bothered with these old-time vendettas, Monsignor. By the way, have you met my nephew, Adam Caulfield?"

The Monsignor, who would have given rather a lot to be bothered about the old-time vendettas, greeted Adam with an automatic affability, but his mind was on Skeffington. The old politician captivated his imagination; he saw him a unique, a rich, extraordinary personality who contained within himself a part of local history which soon would be no more and which never again would reappear. It was a vein that called out to be tapped before it disappeared, first, from view, then even from memory; for just a moment the Monsignor thought of suggesting to Skeffington the possibility of a luncheon, a meeting, a talk. Then he thought of the Cardinal, and of the old, tough, knobby face darkening with rage and disappointment when he learned — as he surely would — of the deliberate encounter, planned by his own subordinate. It would be imprudent; worse, it would be unfair. For the time being, at least, any such meeting was impracticable; a little later, perhaps . . . And so the Monsignor, nodding towards the parlor, merely said, "I suppose we'd better go in now."

They went in, they knelt, and the Monsignor led them in the Rosary. They recited in unison the five decades of the beads which commemorate the Sorrowful Mysteries of the Church; they prayed for the immortal soul of Aram Minihan. And as they prayed, their responses low, rhythmic, and at times not quite distinct, riding high over all other voices came one which to Adam was familiar, clear, unhesitating, and infinitely fervent. It was the voice of Delia Boylan.

The Rosary over, it was time to go. Skeffington swiftly and efficiently made the rounds, saying the necessary good-bys; then he signaled to Adam, and uncle and nephew walked towards the front door together. They had almost reached the door when Skeffington, suddenly halting, said, "Hold on a minute. I want a word with that undertaker before we go."

They both turned and saw the head of Johnnie Degnan, poking out of the kitchen at the far end of the hall; obviously he had been watching their departure. Skeffington beckoned, and he came running quietly to them.

"Ah, good evening, Governor," he said, in his swift hushed tones. "A very sad occasion. I wanted to see you before this evening, to make your acquaintance, but the pressure of my duties didn't quite allow. I'm John Degnan, Governor."

"Glad to know you, Mr. Degnan," Skeffington said. "As you say, it's a sad occasion. I'm happy to see you've done your best by it, however. I've been admiring your handiwork with the deceased."

"Thank you, Governor. Thank you very much. That's nice to hear. I did my best," the undertaker said modestly. "I don't mind telling you, Governor, that Mr. Minihan presented a very difficult case. Because of the age and the sunken cheeks and the wrinkles. I'm sure you can appreciate the difficulty of the task, Governor. Everything had to be smoothed out delicately, the youthful contours restored, and so forth."

"Yes. Now, Mr. Degnan, only one feature of your work disturbs me and that is the probable cost. You don't mind if I say that I was rather struck by the fact that the coffin, and what might be called the general deathroom décor, seem a trifle splendid for someone who was in decidedly modest circumstances?"

The undertaker smiled; it was, Adam thought, a nervous smile. "I see what you mean, Governor," he said swiftly. "I appreciate that point of view. And yet I always think the family is more satisfied if the final homage, as I like to think of it, is really nice in its every aspect. Something that the deceased would have been proud of if he could have seen it."

"Why, those are the feelings of an artist," Skeffington said. "They do you credit, Mr. Degnan. I presume, incidentally, that you've discussed all this with Mrs. Minihan?"

"Well, no. Not exactly, that is, Governor. I thought it best not to in her distraught condition. Just a few words here and there. I think you could say, more or less, that it was left to my discretion, as it so often is. I always believe in taking as many worries as possible from the shoulders of the family."

"That's very thoughtful of you. Now then, you're a young man, Mr. Degnan, but I understand you've had quite a bit of professional experience. As you might put it, you've been in charge of a good many final homages. Or as I might put it, you've buried a good many people. What would you say was the lowest price you've ever buried anyone for?"

"The lowest *price*, Governor?" The smile remained; it wavered uncertainly. "I don't quite understand. . . . What I mean to say is, Governor, I don't believe that's anything I've ever quite figured out."

"Try," Skeffington urged him. "Make a rough estimate. Would it be . . . oh, say thirty-five dollars?"

"*Thirty-five dollars!*" The gasp of astonishment and pain broke through the modulated occupational tones; the undertaker looked wildly at Skeffington and said, "You couldn't *begin* to bury anyone for that price today, Governor!"

"I'll bet you could if you really tried," Skeffington said pleasantly. "I'll bet you could both begin and end. And just to prove my confidence in your resourcefulness, Mr. Degnan, why don't you do that very thing with Mr. Minihan? Let's give it a real try. I think you can do it. I'm sure the final bill won't read over thirty-five dollars. Matter of fact, I'll instruct the widow to that effect immediately."

"But Governor, you can't be serious!" Degnan cried. The smooth round face had become agonized; the soft hands were united in front of him in a tight, beseeching clasp. He looked as if he were about to hurl himself at his persecutor's feet, and Adam, who had not until a moment ago realized just what it was that his uncle was doing, now felt a sudden pity as well as disgust for this abject little profiteer. "The costs alone, Governor," Degnan moaned. "They're going up every day. I couldn't possibly do it. It's all *arranged* —"

"Fine," Skeffington said. "Then let it go through as arranged. But for thirty-five dollars."

"But, *Governor* . . ."

Skeffington pulled his watch from a vest pocket and examined it with apparent surprise. "It's later than I thought," he said. "Well, then, Mr. Degnan, it's all settled. I'll leave the details to you. A suitable funeral conducted for thirty-five dollars, with no cutting of corners. All the normal courtesies extended, the usual paraphernalia available. I'll have a few men on hand just to see that everything goes along well. I know you'll do a grand job. In any event, I'll be sure to hear about it: my observers will give me a full report."

The undertaker's face, which for some moments had been the color of putty, now had turned a vivid red. "But Governor! I hope you know how eager I am to co-operate in anything you suggest. How eager I *always* am. But what you're asking is *impossible*. . . ."

"Why, that's one of the words that doesn't belong to the bright lexicon of youth," Skeffington said reprovingly. "I've always believed that nothing is impossible when one has youth and ambition. I hope you won't be the one to shake this treasured belief. Because if you do," he said, regarding Degnan with a stare which its recipient suddenly found to be as unpleasant as anything he had ever experienced, "you might shake my confidence in you. What's worse, you might even begin to shake public confidence in you. That is a bad thing to have happen to a young undertaker with dreams, Mr. Degnan. You never can tell how far it might reach. It might even reach the members of the licensing board for your profession. You never know. But we mustn't keep you from your labors any longer. I suppose you have many things to do at a time like this. Possibly even more than you'd anticipated. Good night, Mr. Degnan. Glad you introduced yourself."

They went out the door and down the steps; Degnan's anguished voice trailed them to their car. "Thirty-five dollars!" it wailed. "Governor, I *appeal* to you . . ."

When they were under way, Skeffington said: "I hadn't planned on rounding your evening off in just that way. I hope you weren't too shocked by my treatment of the widow's helper."

Adam shook his head. "It seemed to me that the widow's helper rather had it coming. And will he do it for thirty-five dollars, do you think?"

Skeffington chuckled. "I wouldn't be surprised," he said dryly.

"And the sum? That puzzled me. Why exactly thirty-five dollars?"

"No particular reason. It seemed a nice round humiliating figure. I'm not very fond of these deathbed bandits." Especially, he reflected, when they propose to enrich themselves at his expense; for rather early in the evening it had occurred to him that the funeral would necessarily be paid for from the thousand dollars he had given to the widow. "I'd heard about this Degnan, but I'd never happened to run into him before tonight. After tonight I imagine he'll see to it that I don't run into him again. Well," he said, shifting his position and facing his nephew more directly, "I didn't think we'd be in there quite so long. I apologize to you. I only hope you weren't bored."

"No, no. Far from it." Adam thought for a moment, looking back over the evening. There were a number of questions he wanted very much to ask his uncle; the difficulty was that some of them were not so easily put. He began with one that was; he said: "Uncle Frank, what about a man like Charlie Hennessey? I mean, what is he? What does he do?"

"He runs for office, mostly. Against me or against anybody; Charlie plays no favorites. He hasn't been very successful lately, but back about twenty years ago, Charlie was considered quite a comer. He was always a great talker and he started off with a bang. He was on the City Council, a member of the Governor's Council — not under me, I might add — and he even served a term in Congress. In those days Charlie seemed to be looking into a rosy tomorrow."

"And the roses faded?"

"They did indeed. You see," Skeffington said, "they suddenly discovered two things about Charlie. First, that he was honest, and second, that he was crazy. It was the combination that killed him. Theoretically at least, an honest man can succeed in politics; and there's a considerable body of evidence to prove that a crazy man can. But a man who's both honest and crazy might just as well be a Chinese midget for all the good he'll do himself at the polls."

Adam protested. "But he's not a madman, surely?"

Skeffington shrugged. "It's a nice question of definition. He's not a certifiable lunatic, if that's what you mean, but he's certainly at that stage where a man's friends begin to call him 'eccentric.' What his enemies call him is apt to be something else again. Politically speaking, it's my opinion that Charlie is harmless except on those rare occasions when for some mysterious reason he decides to support me; then I want to run for cover. He's a dangerous man to have in your corner. He's great on the platform, but he has a crack right down the middle, and you never know when or where he's going to take off. I remember that when he first entered the City Council we were having a big to-do about a new municipal sewage system. Danny Leary was Council President, and he had Charlie all lined up to make the big speech in favor of it. Well, it was a big speech, all right. It lasted an hour and a half; the only trouble was that somewhere in the middle of it Charlie got sidetracked into talking about the marvelous advantages of having universal, compulsory fingerprinting introduced into the city, with the FBI coming in to take the prints of everybody who was still breathing. 'Not even the nuns in their convents should be exempt!' said Charlie. Naturally that made a tremendous hit with the good Sisters; poor Leary spent the next two weeks crying in convent vestibules, explaining to Mother Superiors that his own daughter was a nun, and that he himself often went to daily Mass when the weather was good. Some of us wondered, however, what all this had to do with the problem of municipal sewage, and it was just about this time I began to suspect that Charlie's political value had its limitations. It's too bad, in a way, because he's a good fellow — smart enough, and knows the local political situation from A to Z. And, as I say, he won't take a dime from anybody. Charlie's trouble is that he's not content with asking the voters to lend him their ears; halfway through the speech he starts wanting to take their pulse as well. The result is that he's the kiss of death. What was that he had with him tonight, by the way — a camera?"

Adam told him of Charlie and the self-developing camera. Skeffington listened attentively, chuckling from time to time as he heard of the photographing of John Gorman, and of the grisly potential of the camera as an instrument in the sickroom. When Adam finished the story, which seemed to him in the retelling even more improbable than when he had witnessed it in actual development, he looked questioningly at his uncle; both men broke into laughter.

"You see how it is," Skeffington said. "The authentic Hennessey touch: I'd recognize it anywhere. I wonder how the patient is supposed to react when the photographer asks him for 'just one more'? Sounds a little final, as if he were soon to be among the souvenirs. What else did Charlie have to say for himself?"

Adam hesitated. Then, because there was much he was still curious about, and because a note of comradeship, almost of complicity, seemed to have been established between them on this ride home, he decided to move into more doubtful waters. He said, "Actually, he didn't talk much about himself at all. He talked mostly about you, Uncle Frank. About you and the wake."

"Reasonable enough, under the circumstances. The wake was there, and so was I."

"Yes. The thing was that he seemed to be saying that the conjunction had a rather peculiar effect on the wake, that it changed its character pretty drastically."

Skeffington nodded. "From the funereal to the political," he said. "And what did you think of that?" Adam hesitated again, and Skeffington gave him a look of pleasant inquiry. "Go ahead," he invited. "I'll probably be able to bear it."

"Well," Adam said reluctantly, "to be honest, I had something of the same thought myself a little earlier, before Charlie arrived. I had quite a talk with Mr. Gorman about it." Now that he had gone this far, further frankness seemed unavoidable; somewhat uneasily he gave his uncle the full account of what had passed between Gorman and himself. Was it a mistake? he wondered. Probably not; it occurred to him that Gorman would himself unquestionably have mentioned it in due course.

As he talked, he kept his eyes on his uncle's face: the scrutiny proved remarkably unfruitful. The heavy features registered nothing more than a polite, unchanging interest; it was impossible for Adam to tell whether his uncle was indignant, whether he was outraged, whether he was totally unaffected. Or — in a sense, even worse — whether he was simply amused. It was most disquieting . . .

He completed his explanation. Skeffington said, "I've seldom heard of John's being so eloquent; it stands as a great tribute to your qualities as a listener. I must say he put the case for me rather well; I couldn't have done better myself. Charlie's approach, on the other hand, must have been considerably different. I imagine he probably said something to this effect." And then, while Adam stared at him, he proceeded to duplicate Charlie's speech in astonishing detail; it seemed to Adam, remembering the original, that the reproduction was virtually word for word. Finishing, Skeffington said, "Close enough?"

"Close enough," Adam agreed, bewildered. "The question is: How? You couldn't have heard it from where you were."

"Extrasensory perception," Skeffington said gravely. "A man can't go far without it today." Once again, Adam heard the familiar deep chuckle. "Of course, there is the additional fact that Charlie's principal addresses don't change very much over the years. He has the unwillingness of the artist to tamper with the perfect production. This is one of his best, a regular party piece. Or wake piece, if you prefer. I must have heard it a hundred times. It's extremely entertaining. In addition to which," he said casually, "it contains more than a little truth."

Adam looked up sharply, but his uncle seemed preoccupied in withdrawing a cigar from his vest pocket. It was long, fat, dull-greenish in color. It did not appear to be at all the same grade of cigar that had been provided in quantities for the wake.

"One over the limit," he said cheerfully, lighting it. "A happy shortcut to the Dark Encounter. Well, you see me refusing to be less than candid with you. I don't want to give you a misleading impression. I should add that while Charlie was telling the truth, up to a point, so was John Gorman. Actually, they were both right: Knocko's wake was and it wasn't a political rally. Given the circumstances, and," he added, with a faintly deprecatory wave of the cigar, "given myself, it could hardly have been anything else. You see, what you're up against here is the special local situation. To understand what happened tonight, you have to understand a little bit about that situation, and just a little bit more about my own rather peculiar position in it."

He leaned back, relaxing against the cushions; simply, detachedly, without boast or embellishment, he began to talk about himself. It was an extraordinary procedure; just how extraordinary, Adam did not realize. For while Skeffington had long studied his city and his own relation to it, the results of these studies he had been careful to keep to himself.

From the beginning of his career, he had sharply divided the private from the public side of his life. Of the many friends he had made in politics over the years, none — not Gorman, even — had been admitted to the isolated preserve of the private thought, the personal concern. His wife had been his single, ideal confidante; with her death had come a void. Because Skeffington was, literally, a family man, he had tried one day, somewhat against his better judgment, to fill this void with his son. He had talked of himself, his work, his problems and his plans, and as he talked he had gradually become aware of the look upon his son's face: that characteristic, pleasant, glazed half-smile which indicated that somewhere beneath the surface inattention struggled with incomprehension. There had been more than the look; there had been the dancing feet: they had begun an abstracted, rather complicated tapping on the floor of the study, doubtless in anticipation of their evening's work ahead. *I should have been Vernon Castle*, Skeffington had thought bitterly. He had left the room abruptly and the experiment had never been repeated.

And now, as he had one afternoon three weeks before, he talked to his nephew.

"You see," he said, "my position is slightly complicated because I'm not just an elected official of the city; I'm a tribal chieftain as well. It's a necessary kind of dual officeholding, you might say; without the second, I wouldn't be the first."

"The tribe," said Adam, "being the Irish?"

"Exactly. I have heard them called by less winning names: minority pressure group (even though they've been the majority for half a century), immigrant voting bloc (even though many of the said immigrants have been over here for three generations). Still, I don't suppose it makes much difference what you call them; the net result's the same. I won't insult your intelligence by explaining that they're the people who put me in the mayor's chair and keep me there; I think you realize that the body of my support doesn't come from the American Indian. But as a member — at least by birth — of the tribe, you might give a thought to some of the tribal customs. They don't chew betel nut, and as far as I know the women don't beautify themselves by placing saucers in their lower lips. Although now that I come to think of it," he said, "that might not be a bad idea. It might reduce the potential for conversation. However, they do other things, and among them they go to wakes. And so do I."

"Which are and are not political rallies?" Adam asked. "Or was Knocko's case a special one?"

"Not at all special, except that the guest of honor was somewhat less popular than many of his predecessors. But of course when you speak about wakes as being political rallies, that's a little strong. You have to remember something about the history of the wake around here. When I was a boy in this city, a wake was a big occasion, and by no means a sad one. Unless, of course, it was a member of your own family that had died. Otherwise it was a social event. Some of my most vivid memories are of wakes. I remember my poor mother taking me to old Nappy Coughlin's wake. We went into the tenement, and there was Nappy, all laid out in a little coffin which was kept on ice. Embalming was a rather uncertain science in those days. It was a hot day in July and there were no screens on the parlor windows; there were flies in the room. I can still hear the ice dripping into the pans underneath the coffin, and I can still see Nappy. He had one of the old-fashioned shrouds on, and he lay stretched out stiff as a ramrod. And on his head he wore a greasy black cap, which his good wife had lovingly adjusted so that the peak was pulled down over one eye. It gave him a rather challenging look; you had the feeling that at any moment he might spring out of the coffin and offer to go four fast rounds with you. My mother was horrified at the sight, and I remember that she went directly over to the widow and told her she ought to be ashamed of herself, putting her husband in the coffin with his hat on. Whereupon the widow simply said that he'd never had it off; he'd worn it for thirty years, day and night, in bed and out. So naturally she left it on, not wanting to say good-by to a stranger. However, when Father Conroy came in, the hat was whisked off fast enough. I can remember — it was my first wake, by the way — going into the kitchen, where somebody gave me a glass of milk and a piece of cake. And while my mother was in the parlor talking with the other women, I was out there with the men, just sitting around, eating cake, and listening to them talk. I hadn't the faintest notion of what they were talking about, but it didn't matter much. I was in seventh heaven. Everybody seemed to be enjoying themselves, and I knew I was. When my mother came to get me and take me home, I left with the greatest regret; I decided I'd never had a better time. Well," he said, "so much for memories of happy days. I wouldn't imagine it would sound like very much to anyone who'd been brought up today."

Adam smiled. "It sounded like a little boy having a wonderful time for himself. Although I must say that it didn't sound very much like death. Or even a political rally, for that matter."

"Matter of fact, it was the first political rally I'd ever been to," Skeffington said. "I was just too young to know it. You see, that's what all the men were talking about: politics. There was even a moment, just before I left, when Charlie McCooey himself came in: a fat man with a red face and handlebar mustache. He was the ward boss. I didn't know what that was, at the time, but I did know that the name of Charlie McCooey commanded respect and awe. I thought he must have been some kind of god. Twenty years later this childhood illusion was blasted. I gave him the beating of his life in a fight for the leadership of the ward; the vote was four to one. In the process of doing so I discovered that the god was nothing more than a dull bully-boy with no imagination and just enough intelligence to read his way through the daily adventures of Happy Hooligan. No offense intended, incidentally, by the reference to a rival comic strip."

"No offense received," Adam said. "I lack the artist's pride. Besides, I think that Happy is defunct these days." But he spoke absently, for he was not thinking of comic strips. He had suddenly remembered, while Skeffington was talking, that once, years ago, and from a source he could not now place, he had heard a series of quite different stories about the old wakes; in these, the cake-and-milk had not figured largely. He said, "But I had the idea from somewhere, Uncle Frank, that many of these wakes got to be pretty violent affairs. I know there was always a certain amount of drinking, but didn't some of them actually become brawls?"

Skeffington's heavy face assumed a mildly shocked expression. "Why, I hardly know what to say," he murmured. "I have heard that drinking men occasionally forced their way into these gatherings, but I like to believe that they were instantly sobered by the sight of decent men and women shrinking from them in revulsion." He glanced at his nephew, and his lips twitched just slightly. "No," he said, "of course you're right. There was drinking and sometimes things got a little rough. You might not have enjoyed it very much. But it's all gone by the boards long ago, and it was the exception rather than the rule; while it may seem terrible enough from your point of view today, you might reflect on the fact that there just might have been some excuse for it. I think what you have to do," he said, "is to see the wakes and everything that happened at them in the light of the times. I mentioned to you the other afternoon that life wasn't exactly a picnic for our people in those days. They were a sociable people but they didn't get much chance for sociability. They were poor, they worked hard, and they didn't have much in the way of diversion. Actually, the only place people got together was at the wake. Everybody knew everybody else; when somebody died, the others went to pay their respects and also to see and talk to each other. It was all part of the pattern. They were sorry for the family of the deceased, to be sure, but while they were being sorry they took advantage of the opportunity to have a drink and a chat with the others who were being sorry, too. It was a change, an outlet for people who led back-breaking, dreary, and monotonous lives. And if, once in a while, someone took a few too many and wanted to set fire to the widow or play steamroller in the kitchen, it was possibly deplorable but it was also slightly understandable. All in all, I've always thought the wake was a grand custom, and I still do."

"Yes," Adam said slowly. "I hadn't thought of it in that light — I mean, I hadn't thought of the wake as being a kind of *relief* from grimness. And yet I guess it must have been, all right. But what about *now*, Uncle Frank? Those same conditions don't exist, do they?"

"No," said Skeffington, "and neither does the wake. Not in the same way, that is. It's a disappearing phenomenon, like the derby hat. As the younger people grow up, the wakes are more and more changing their character: for example, they're being held now in funeral parlors rather than in the homes. The wake will still continue in some form; after all, it takes a long time to get rid of old tribal customs. And Knocko's was a bit like some of the old wakes; that's why I wanted you to see it. And as for the political discussion, that was in the grand tradition, too. By the way, did you happen to wonder why they might have been talking politics tonight?"

"Well, I naturally thought it was because you were there. But —"

"But," Skeffington said, interrupting with a look of some amusement, "was I there because they were going to talk politics? Right?" It was all too remarkably right; Adam flushed and began to protest, but Skeffington said, "A perfectly natural question. I'd be astonished if it hadn't occurred to you. The answer, by the way, is a little bit of both. I suppose I went at least partly because it was one more opportunity to keep the ball rolling. It's almost impossible for an old campaigner to avoid the occasions of sin. But whether I'd been there or not, they would have talked politics anyway. It's what interests them most. It ought to: it gave most of them everything they have. I mentioned to you the other day that the main reason I went into politics was because it was the quickest way out of the cellar and up the ladder. A good many others felt the same way. A lot of the younger men wanted a nice new dark serge suit that didn't necessarily come equipped with a chauffeur's cap. And the only way out was through politics; it was only when we gained a measure of political control that our people were able to come up for a little fresh air. They know that; they think of it as the big salvation for them; that's why they talk about it when they all get together. It's a very serious part of the business of living. And when I'm around, naturally I'm expected to talk it with them. And I do. I may add," he said, "that I don't find it a hardship."

Adam thought of one more question. "And the family?" he said. "The family of the deceased, I mean. Like Mrs. Minihan tonight. How do they feel while all this is going on? Don't they sometimes mind, Uncle Frank?"

"I know what you mean," Skeffington said, "but I think you're a bit wrong there. I don't think they mind a bit. There is a contrary opinion, however. Every once in a while I see where some advanced young public servant, who still had the ring of the pot on his seat while all this was going on, publicly applauds the passing of 'that cruel and barbarous custom, the wake.' Whenever I see that I take down my little book and chalk up a new name in the boob section. The man who said it obviously hasn't the faintest notion of what he's talking about. He hasn't the remotest understanding of the times, the circumstances, of our people, the way they feel and the way they regard death. I've seen a good many people die around here and I'll probably see a good many more. Unless, of course," he added, in another of those detached and faintly chilling parentheses which never failed to jolt Adam, "I beat them to it; there's always that possibility. But I've never seen the family that thought the wake was cruel and barbarous. They expected it. They wanted it. More than that, it was good for them: it was a useful distraction, it kept them occupied, and it gave them the feeling that they weren't alone, that they had a few neighbors who cared enough to come in and see them through a bad time. And you could say, too, it was a mark of respect for the deceased: rest assured that *he* wanted his wake. I remember what happened when the Honorable Hugh Archer died. The Honorable Hugh was considerably before your time; I don't imagine you'd have heard much about him."

"No, nothing."

"He was a prominent Republican attorney who once refused ten thousand dollars offered to him if he'd defend a notorious criminal. The noble gesture was unprecedented in Republican circles, and immediately he became known as the Honorable. It wasn't until much later that it was discovered he had asked for twenty thousand. Well, eventually he died. He was a huge man: six foot four and weighing nearly three hundred pounds. At that time, cremation was just coming into fashion, following closely upon Mah-Jongg, and they whipped the Honorable Hugh out to the incinerator on the very day he died. Old Martin Canady went to the ceremony, out of a curiosity to see how the other half died, and when he came running back to me he was literally popeyed with shock. 'By God, Frank!' he said. 'They took the big elephant before he stopped breathin' almost and what the hell d'ye think they did with him? They put him in the oven and burned him up with the Sunday papers! When the poor man finished cookin' ye could have buried him in an ash

tray! By God, Frank, I wouldn't want nothin' like that to happen to me!
When I go I'm damned sure I mean to stay around the house a few days
and nights so's some of the old pals can come in and have a drink and
the last look! What the hell's wrong with that, now?' And," Skeffington
said, "to save my soul, I couldn't think of a blessed thing wrong with it.
It's the way I want to go myself. . . . Well, here I am talking away, it's
late at night, and you're probably eager to get back in your house."

Aɴᴅ now the campaign moved from the shadows into full public view. Skeffington was busy, busier, indeed, than he had been at any time in the past four years, for the burden of electioneering was now added to the routine of each day. This burden included problems and difficulties of a kind unsuspected by Adam; it included, for example, the case of Johnnie Byrne, which Skeffington decided to settle abruptly one afternoon. He summoned Byrne to his office for a private talk.

"Good afternoon, Governor," Byrne said jauntily, so jauntily that Skeffington immediately said to himself: He's nervous. . . . Byrne was a City Councilman: a slight, pleasant-looking man in his forties with a small, pale-pink mouth and gentle eyes. "Tom said you wanted to see me?"

"I do," Skeffington said. "You've been out of the city for two weeks, Johnnie. I hear you went to Baltimore."

Byrne was nodding eagerly even before the sentence was completed. "Yes, that's right," he said quickly. "I spent a few days there. A fine city, very much like our own in most ways, Frank. That's really why I went."

"I see. Pleasure trip?"

"No no, business," Byrne said, answering as rapidly as before. "I'll tell you what I wanted to do, Frank: I wanted to take a look at their port facilities. You know the trouble we've been having around here on the waterfront. Well, I'd heard that they had their waterfront problems pretty well licked, and since they're so much like us, and have the same problems, I thought maybe I could pick up a few tips from the way they handled things. And I did, too. I came back encouraged, definitely encouraged." The small mouth formed a frank, open smile. "Too encouraged, I guess, Frank. I felt so good about it, you know what I forgot to do? I forgot to bill the city for the trip. I'll have to do that the first thing tomorrow morning."

Skeffington looked at him bleakly. "No soap," he said. "It won't wash, Johnnie."

This time the reply did not come quite so quickly. "Hah?" Byrne said.

A new expression came into the gentle eyes for just an instant; it disappeared and the frank smile popped into place once more. "What's the matter, Frank?" he said. "What's the hitch? It was official business; I'm entitled to reimbursement."

"Stop it," Skeffington said wearily. "When did you ever hear me haggle about reimbursement? We're not talking about reimbursement and you know it. You're lying to me, Johnnie. You went to Baltimore all right, but not on any trip connected with port facilities. In the first place, it would have been pointless: Baltimore's port situation isn't remotely like our own. They have an entirely different set of problems. You know that. In the second place, you'd never have gone on any such trip without getting an O.K. from me before you started. You know that, too. And in the third place," he said, "your wife has been in to see me. I know all about it, Johnnie, and so does she. You went to Baltimore to chase a girl. I knew that even before your wife came in. I can tell you who the girl was, where you stayed, and what you did. So we're all in on the little secret, Johnnie, and you can stop all this nonsense about port facilities. I don't like being lied to."

Byrne's soft, pleasant face seemed to retreat before each blunt word; panic now started in the gentle eyes. "I swear to God," he began, and then stopped, as if realizing that the rushing words of denial would serve no purpose. He was a trapped man with no defense but a last desperate show of bluster and indignation. "A fine thing!" he burst out bitterly. "Oh, a fine thing, Frank! A nice reward for loyalty! A man breaks his neck working day in and day out for you and the first time he leaves the city on a private matter of his own, you put your watchdogs on him!"

Skeffington shook his head. "Don't credit me with any fine feelings. I didn't wait that long. I put them on you right here in the city as soon as the campaign began." He gestured impatiently. "Of course I had you watched. What the hell do you think I'm running here: a political campaign or a protective association for wayward husbands? I know all about these 'private matters' of yours, Johnnie; I've warned you about them before. I don't know what's wrong with you. You've got a good wife and a fine family, yet you go chasing around after every stray skirt that passes through town. What are you after, a title? The Tomcat of the Year?"

Bluster and indignation had disappeared; Byrne said despairingly, "Ah, lay off the lecture, will you, Frank? It's all I get day and night from her."

Skeffington nodded grimly. "This is a different kind of lecture," he said. "I'm afraid you'll have to listen; it won't take long. You see, I don't like what you've done to your wife, but that's none of my business. What is my business is what you've done to me."

"What I did to *you?*" Byrne cried. Panic was crossed with bewilderment; the pale pink mouth remained open, and he looked at his accuser with a stupid agony. "May God strike me dead if I did anything to you, Frank!" he cried. "All right, it was a dirty trick on Irene, I admit it. I don't know why I did it. I don't know what comes over me, Frank." He was becoming increasingly abject; it was a turn which Skeffington did not find attractive. Byrne said weakly, "It seemed like I couldn't help myself, somehow."

"Good," Skeffington said. "Then you'll have had some experience in not being able to help yourself. Because that's just what you can't do now."

"But I swear to God the whole thing has nothing to do with you, Frank!" he cried. "Nothing! It was a private matter, a family affair. . . ."

"Cut it out," Skeffington said curtly. "I don't enjoy having people play the boob with me. You know what I'm talking about. You put me in a bad spot because of your stupidity. Everybody in your ward knows you're one of my men. Thanks to you, I find myself right over a barrel in the middle of a close election. The man who's been running up and down the ward acting as my right hand suddenly winds up in the middle of a first-class scandal right before election day; how many votes do you think I'll lose just because people want to turn against you? How many people do you think will vote for McCluskey just because they know if he gets in it's curtains for you? All this, Johnnie, because of your little 'private matter.'"

"But my God, Frank, they won't turn! Why would they turn on me? I've got the ward in the palm of my hand, you know that! I —"

"They'll turn on you," Skeffington said inexorably, "because you've done the one thing you can't do with our people and get away with it. You're a married man who's been fooling around with another woman, Johnnie, and it's all going to come out. Your wife is going to divorce you. And don't deny it," he said sharply, as the pale pink lips started to move. "She's been in here twice to see me. I know she's moved out and is living with her mother. I know she's been to see Father Casey, and I know that no matter what he or anybody else says — least of all you, Johnnie — she's fed up and she's going to sue for a civil divorce. And you know what'll happen when the word gets out. They'll repudiate you so fast you won't be able to catch your breath. Which leaves only one course open to me, Johnnie. I'm going to repudiate you first. I'm cutting you off, Johnnie."

"For the love of God!" Byrne cried. "You wouldn't, Frank . . ."

"I would," Skeffington said simply. "I just did. Now. You're through, Johnnie. I mean it."

Byrne's little puffy white hands tugged pathetically at each other; he made a curious whimpering sound. "You *don't* mean it!" he cried. "Say you don't, Frank! You've got to give me another chance, for the love of God! Anyone can make a mistake, can't he? We're all human, aren't we? Aren't we, Frank? We all have our little faults. Listen," he said, desperately shifting his approach, "listen, Frank: you've got it all wrong about Irene and me. I mean, it's not as bad as you say. I'm going to fix it up with her. You'll see, Frank. Everything will be all right. I'm fixing it up with her right away, maybe tomorrow . . ."

"You're fixing it up with nobody," Skeffington said wearily. "Stop trying to kid me, Johnnie. And stop trying to kid yourself. You're not a man who's made a mistake; you're a man who's made the same mistake over and over again, and now at last it's caught up with you. This is a long story. I warned you half a dozen times, and each time I got your promise. Well, it's too late for the promise now; I'm not buying it any more. The simple truth is this: you've become a luxury I can't afford. You're not a mean man, you're not envious, and you're not a double-crosser, but in a tight political campaign you're something just as dangerous. You're a weak sister, Johnnie, and I can't trust you any more. I'm even tired of thinking about trusting you. And so you've got to go."

He stopped, for the soft face confronting him had gone into boneless collapse, and Byrne had begun to sob. Skeffington watched him, more in distaste than in pity. He had witnessed the performance before; tears, he thought, came as readily as promises from the cornered Byrne. He could not bring himself to feel any great sympathy for him; he did not feel kindly towards either offender or offense. Like the voters who would now turn sharply against the guilty Byrne, Skeffington took a poor view of marital infidelity. Like most of his people, he did not regard it as one of the genial sins. It was perhaps the single offense with which he had never been charged, not even by opponents who were surely aware that it was the one charge which, if substantiated, could ruin him with the local electorate. But the charge had been impossible to introduce; domestically, Skeffington was unassailable. It was, he thought, another of his sources of strength. This had not been true of poor Byrne. When, some years before, Skeffington had first discovered the weakness of his subordinate, he had taken him to task sharply for it; at the same time, however, because he was above all a practical politician, he did not dream of cutting him loose. Politically speaking, there was no cause; the dismissal could only damage, however slightly, the organization, and although he thoroughly disapproved of what Byrne had done, he considered it as something quite apart from the main issue. Now, however, it was no longer apart; now Byrne's "private matter" had become public enough to threaten not only his own home but the campaign, and Skeffington himself. And so Skeffington had acted, swiftly and necessarily. The man, he reflected, had been a boob, and a boob engaged in what was essentially dirty business. As he watched the tears fall, he found that he was not deeply moved.

"All right, Johnnie," he said finally. "Stop it now. The lecture's over. That's all I want to say to you. You can go now."

Byrne stood, automatically obedient even in his anguish. "Frank," he said, and sniffled. "Frank, for the love of God. I *promise* —"

"No," Skeffington said. "I told you I meant it, Johnnie. Run along, now."

Byrne went, shuffling slowly, without another word. Skeffington sat looking at the door which had closed noiselessly behind him. He did not look long; he had work to do. It was late in the afternoon when John Gorman entered and said, "Johnnie Byrne dropped in to see me."

Skeffington nodded. "I thought he might. That's where I'd go if I were in trouble, John. And Johnnie's in trouble."

"It's a damn shame this had to happen," Gorman said. "He's a popular lad in the ward."

"He *was* a popular lad in the ward," Skeffington corrected. "Three weeks from now a gypsy could beat him. He's done. You know that, surely?"

"I do," Gorman said. "I do indeed. You did what you had to do and nothing else. Still, I hate to see a thing like this happen so soon before election. It always means a bit of trouble, no matter how you grease the ways."

"It does," Skeffington agreed. "But not too much in this case. There may be a few who'll stick with him, but Johnnie's hardly the type to breed a schism. Besides, all the sympathy will be with the wife, once the news about the divorce gets out."

"Ah, it's hard on the woman," Gorman said reflectively. "She's a good sort who deserved better than Johnnie. Now she'll be alone, she'll have the kids, and she can't marry again. Will she squeeze enough out of Johnnie to get along on, d'ye think?"

"I sincerely hope the good judge'll see to that," Skeffington said. "Meanwhile, we'd better keep an eye on her. See that she doesn't want for anything. If she needs any money or clothing or anything like that, see that she gets it. As for Johnnie," he said, "I don't know what he'll do. He's able-bodied; I presume he can go to work. It'll be a change, but he can do it."

Gorman considered for a moment. "Johnnie's a bit of a little rat, right enough," he said. "A weakling, ye know, from the very first word. And yet, in a way, likable. He was very popular in the ward. By God, Frank, I don't know where a man like that belongs unless it's locked up tight in a monastery for the rest of his days."

"Or locked up tight with a good veterinary for a couple of hours," Skeffington said, remembering his remark about the Tomcat of the Year. "I have a feeling that might work wonders with Johnnie. But enough about our former playboy; let's get down to work. We have a lot to get done before tonight."

And so the case of Johnnie Byrne had been disposed of. It was perhaps the most serious of a group of problems that had arisen, and although Skeffington had expected the usual hazards of the campaign, he nevertheless had to confront them when they arose; this made his day a long one. He rose, as always, early, but now, more often than not, he retired late. Too late, he thought grimly, as he noted that on several nights his arrival home had coincided roughly with that of his son.

"I almost feel I should apologize," he said one night, when he came in to discover that his son, for the second time that week, had beaten him home. "I hope I'm not damaging you in the eyes of your friends?"

"Damaging, Dad?" his son said, with a puzzled smile. "I don't get it. What's the scoop?"

"Well, the word might get around that you were getting in before your father. I can't believe that a whispering campaign of that kind would do an ambitious young night owl any good. I presume your crowd must have a certain set of standards about such matters."

His son laughed pleasantly, "Oh, they wouldn't care, Dad," he said.

Skeffington nodded. "Fine. They must be a tolerant group. Still, I won't push my luck too far; I'll try to get in earlier from now on. It may be a bit difficult because I'm a little busy these nights. You see, there's talk that we're going to have an election in November. If we are, I want to be prepared. I wouldn't want it to sneak up on me. I know you can appreciate my position."

Faint lines of perplexity, the blemishes characteristic of these baffling interviews with his father, now touched the boyish face. "Sure we're having an election in November," the son said. "The first Tuesday. Teddy Thornton was talking about it only tonight."

"You can't keep a secret from Teddy," Skeffington said. "Well, if that's the case, I guess I might just as well get some sleep and try to rest up for it. Good night."

"Good night, Dad."

Skeffington went to bed; once there, lying motionless under the single blanket, his bones seemed to expand and contract within his aching flesh; he felt the spasms of fatigue. He was doing too much; he knew it, but he knew too that at this point any reduction in activity was impossible. The most prudent of men where his health was concerned, he had suspended this prudence for the final weeks of the campaign. And, he thought, necessarily so, for although he had no great opinion of McCluskey as an opponent, he respected the strength of those behind him, and he had seen overconfidence obliterate the dreams of far too many of his fellows to feel at all complacent. He campaigned hard, therefore, as he always had, and reflected ironically that, thanks to such modern technological advances as radio and television, the going was immeasurably tougher than it had been twenty-five years before, when he had been twenty-five years younger.

Skeffington used radio and television and used them exhaustively, yet he considered both to be essentially secondary approaches; he did not believe in shortcuts to the electorate. He thoroughly enjoyed, but was not converted by, the spectacular success of his own recent television appearances. The rich voice, the full photogenic face, the presence of the natural actor: all these had combined to evoke an extraordinary response, far beyond political circles. To his surprise and amusement, the television professionals had been alerted; he had received several suavely worded letters from advertising executives, delicately suggesting that, in the event of unexpected political reverses, a career in television awaited. One communication, more urgent and less tactful than the rest, had come from the president of a company engaged in the manufacture of nasal ointments; it had offered him immediate and unconditional employment as the firm's television spokesman. Skeffington had been grateful for this letter; it had furnished him with useful material for further speeches.

"You see the alternative I face if you fail to return me to office," he said, addressing the television audience, and waving the letter before him. "I'll become a television announcer, the oldest television announcer in the world. Very possibly I'll wind up between the waltzing cigar and the talking beer can. That's an unhappy fate for a man of my years. I beg your assistance in preserving me from it!"

But, satisfying as he found this experience on television, and valuable though he conceded it to be, he did not for an instant consider it a substitute for the technique of personal contact which had served him so well for decades. The indirect penetration of the home via the television screen was all very well; to his mind, it did not begin to compare in effectiveness with the direct and personal visit — with the sign of recognition, the extended hand, the solicitous inquiry into family affairs, the donation of favor or promise of favor. It was this procedure, painstakingly accomplished, that had always been the heart of Skeffington's campaign; he did not change now. Instead, he added to it the newer techniques and thus acquired a schedule heavier than any he had attempted before. He felt that he was weathering it well. While, day after day and night after night, he whirled his way through the swelling, unremitting series of speeches, visits, receptions and official appointments, he found it hard but nevertheless enjoyable, a tough routine in which he somehow discovered stimulation. It was only at night, when the halt came and there was, finally, pause instead of motion, that he became fully conscious of his own exhaustion. Here, in bed, he achieved the low point of his day, and in the interval — mercifully brief — of dull, bone-aching wakefulness which preceded the regular relief of sleep, he was apt to look forward with longing to that date in November, now just a few weeks away. It was the blessed terminus, the point of time at which all would be finished.

"Probably including myself," he said aloud. It was the last sardonic tribute to the day; he fell asleep immediately afterwards. The night could be counted upon for recuperation; he awoke refreshed and began the routine all over again, not aware of weariness until, once more, he reached the late, lonely, helpless hour. In the past few weeks he had become accustomed to this ebb and flow of fatigue; it was mildly bothersome, it did not concern him greatly, and it did not interfere in the least with the progress of his campaign.

As the days went by, Adam came to spend progressively more time in his uncle's company. These meetings were, for the most part, unscheduled, and often occurred at odd hours and at a moment's notice. Skeffington would telephone and suggest that Adam, if he were interested, might meet him in fifteen minutes: there was to be some piece of campaign activity which he might find rewarding. Sometimes more warning was given, and several hours would elapse between the call and the event; more rarely, there were meetings between the two which were arranged as much as a day or so in advance. Whatever the notice, Adam responded without fail; the flexibility of his own day eliminated conflicts at the paper, and when the invitations interfered with his evenings at home — as they came more and more to do, with the acceleration of the campaign — he was troubled in his conscience by the small woeful shadow that was briefly visible on his wife's face (for in spite of her brave resolution, Maeve was imperfect at dissimulation); but then, determinedly recalling her permission, and reminding himself that in any event it would all be over in a matter of a few weeks, he felt better, kissed her, and went off to join his uncle.

Behind the swift and apparently random crisscrossing of the old and sprawling city, there was in fact a carefully worked-out plan. Skeffington, in this as in all else, had left nothing to chance. These were routes he had traveled for half a century; like a veteran guide, he knew the opportune moment for retracing old trails. The districts and quarters which were as strange to Adam as the ruins of Angkor Wat were, to Skeffington, as familiar as his own living room. Physically the city had not changed greatly since his boyhood, and the changes that had been made were largely of his own inspiring. He knew it block by block, almost building by building, and while there had been population shifts, he had noted each one in detail. As the Yankees had moved in indignant retreat before the Irish, as the Irish had done likewise before the Italians, as the succeeding if much smaller invasions of Greek, Syrian and Chinese had worked their minor dislocations, Skeffington had marked them all with sustained care, losing interest only when the migrants passed beyond the city limits, and so beyond the local vote. Adam, fascinated, watched his uncle in his tireless, accomplished conduct of these bewildering expeditions; he followed him up narrow, crooked, ill-surfaced streets into musty lodge halls, into dark little basements where a solemn Chinese shook hands with Skeffington over a partially ironed shirt, into long, narrow stores with hanging rows of salamis and herbs and cheeses, into tall, dirty, dangerous tenement buildings, bursting with families. As they left one of these one night, Skeffington said to Adam, "A place of refreshment and light, you might say. Did you enjoy it?"

Adam shook his head emphatically. "It was right out of a sociologist's casebook. Hardly the ideal place for the casual visit."

"No. Even more than that, perhaps, hardly the sort of place in which you'd like to grow up. I speak," he said, "from some personal experience. There are a good many buildings like this still around, but I particularly wanted you to see this one. Have you any idea who owns it?"

"No, none."

"Your employer," Skeffington said. "Part of the family inheritance, passed on to him by his diminutive Dad. Naturally, as a man of strong family feeling, Amos wants to keep the old place exactly as it was when it was handed down to him. He does this by eschewing the use of paint or modern conveniences. I like to see sentiment combining so happily with thrift."

Adam looked around at the whole unlovely area. "But surely something could be done about it?" he said. "Hasn't the city the right of seizure if it wants to exercise it? As a matter of fact," he said, remembering something he had recently read, "you did that, didn't you, somewhere in the city? Started a slum clearance project, I mean?"

"I did," Skeffington said. "I did it in a couple of places, years ago. I suppose I should have had the bulldozers in and cleared up the whole mess while I was at it. There's the unhappy fact, however, that things aren't done quite that easily. Rest assured that such a move wouldn't have been unopposed. And while I don't mind opposition, you have to decide whether you're ready to declare all-out war on one front, with the knowledge that if you do, there's always the possibility that you'll be murdered on another. Reformers never have any trouble with decisions of that sort. They declare war right away; they even mow down half their own side in fighting it. And that, by the way, is why the mortality rate among reformers is so high. Still," he said, more slowly, as he turned to look up and down the filthy, littered street, "I've sometimes thought that they might have had something, at that. However," he added, more briskly, "thoughts of that kind don't exactly further the present campaign effort. Come along, I want to make another visit or two before we call it a day."

In these few short weeks, Adam's knowledge of the city grew rapidly. The trips with his uncle were not limited to slum visitations; in search for the vote Skeffington penetrated all levels, revisiting old strongholds, cultivating the friendly pockets in the land of the enemy. In this way virtually every sector of the city was covered, including parts that Adam knew fairly well; even these, however, he saw now under a different aspect, as his uncle's rich stream of anecdote and information poured over buildings, statuary, landmarks and memorials which Adam may have noticed casually in passing, but which hitherto had held no meaning for him.

"Everything has a history around here," Skeffington said one night, as they were riding back through a prosperous residential area. "For example, this street we're on was once part of a battleground in the Indian wars. And over there on that corner there's an interesting plaque set into that big oak. Did you ever take a look at it, by any chance?"

"Not too close a look, I'm afraid. It's in memory of some army officer, isn't it?"

Skeffington nodded. "A major. Major George Sumner Willoughby. The story has it that back in the early days he was the saviour of the city, personally leading his troops in courageous battle against marauding Indian bands. Then early one summer he got together with a few of the Indian chieftains who, according to the story, were so awed by his fearless behavior that they dubbed him 'Big Chief Bear-Who-Thunders.' At this meeting they concluded what came to be known as 'Willoughby's Peace,' and now every year, on the second Sunday in June, we have a little commemorative ceremony, sponsored by the Descendants of the Colonial Men. They meet right in front of that plaque. I usually attend, bringing the greetings of the mayor's office and an inexpensive wreath. A delegation from the Colonial Men shows up, wearing blue flannel coats and ice-cream pants, slightly yellow with age. The pants, that is; the Colonial Men are rather nicely preserved. To make it official, they even have a genuine Indian. He's a captive Navajo they keep locked up down in the southern part of the state. Strictly speaking, he's the wrong kind of Indian — there were never any Navajos around this part of the world — but he's the best they could find; they keep him locked up, eating frugal meals and playing solitaire. Once a year they spring him; he comes to town, they give him a new deck of cards, and then they all come over to the oak tree for the ceremony. I place the wreath below the plaque and say a few words, the Colonial Men doff their hats and give the Navajo a few symbolic kernels of corn, and we all sing, 'Oh, Beautiful for Spacious Skies'! All in memory of 'Willoughby's Peace.' You ought to drop around next June and see us in action."

"I will," Adam promised. "I wouldn't miss it for worlds. Is it true, by the way? About Willoughby, I mean?"

"Up to a point," Skeffington said. "I have a few small doubts about the Major's reputed fearlessness. You see, I got interested enough to investigate the situation a few years back, and I found out that among his troops George Sumner Willoughby had been known as 'Arsey' Willoughby. It was an irreverent nickname, derived from the wounds he had received in combat. It seems that he had been wounded three times, each time in the behind. Apparently Big Chief Bear-Who-Thunders did most of his thundering in rapid retreat; I gained the impression that his orderly did very little else but pluck arrows from the Willoughby bottom. I imagine it's possible to believe that 'Willoughby's Peace' came about because the Indians simply got bored with shooting at the same old target. It's only fair to say, however, that the Descendants of the Colonial Men adopt no such cynical point of view. And I'm sure they're right; it doesn't do to go poking too deeply into our most valuable traditions."

Right or wrong, the story, like so many others of Skeffington's, fixed a point of local history firm in Adam's memory; never again would he pass by the familiar corner without glancing at the plaque and thinking of the long-dead Big Chief Bear-Who-Thunders, scrambling back towards his own lines in the heat of battle, his rear bristling with the feathered mementoes of the enemy.

As Adam's knowledge of the city increased, so too did his appreciation of his uncle's task. Accompanying Skeffington on these varied expeditions across the city, he soon saw that campaigning, even for one of his uncle's great experience, was far from being an automatic or an easy matter. From each separate trip Adam gained some small idea of the labor involved, but it was not until he accepted Skeffington's sudden invitation to spend an entire day with him on the campaign trail that he began to realize its extent.

On this day, he went to Skeffington's house shortly after an early breakfast; he arrived in time to see the front door opening to admit the line of supplicants. From a chair in a corner of the library, Adam watched with wonder as his uncle, seated at the long table with two secretaries, handled the petitioners as they filed up to him, one by one; he seemed to listen to them with patience, attention and courtesy; more remarkable still, he seemed to satisfy their wants. Adam carefully observed this queer parade of the aged and the middle-aged — there were, he noticed, few young people among them — as they approached his uncle and as they left; without exception, they left with lighter step. The placation and encouragement of so many people could not have been a simple job, Adam thought; his uncle had accomplished it without apparently turning a hair.

These interviews over, the two secretaries went directly to City Hall. Skeffington did not; in these final weeks he had interrupted his habit of swooping down on the city each morning; he went, instead, to a radio station. Here, every day, he delivered a mid-morning broadcast to the housewives; it had been a valued tactic for years. Entering the studio from which the broadcast was to originate, Adam saw that his uncle's chief secretary had arrived before them; he was arranging a series of papers across the table on which the microphone rested.

"The script?" Adam asked his uncle.

"No, no," Skeffington said. He pulled from his pocket a couple of newspaper clippings, torn from the morning's papers. "These'll do for a script. We don't want to get too formal. Those are just official papers I have to sign; it seems that the city has to conduct its business even during a campaign."

The radio studio, then, had become a temporary adjunct to the mayor's office; Adam watched while his uncle seated himself and began to read and sign the papers rapidly. One he lifted and gave back to the secretary, saying cryptically, "Not a chance." He then resumed his work. Adam looked at the clock. The broadcast was to begin at 11:00; it was now 10:58, and there were no signs of preparation. He heard a tapping sound on a large studio window which faced into an anteroom for spectators; looking around, he saw Ditto Boland waving anxiously. Ditto, at least, was ready. With him had come three more members of Skeffington's unofficial entourage; somehow, framed by the studio window, their devoted and slightly grotesque duplication of their idol seemed slightly more emphatic. Skeffington nodded briefly at them and continued to work; promptly at one minute before broadcast time, he passed the last paper over.

"All right," he said. "Now: we go to the docks after this?"

"That's right, Governor. Then lunch at 12:30 at the Abington Park with the Audubon Society."

"It's a shame that robins haven't got the vote," Skeffington said. "I'd be in in a walk. Did Sam get back from Washington?"

"Just about an hour ago, Governor."

"Did he see McArdle?"

"Yes, apparently everything went very well. I've tentatively arranged for both Sam and John Gorman to come in at 2:30 this afternoon. Will that be all right?"

"Yes, fine." He glanced at the clock for the first time. "Well," he said, standing, "we'll let everything else go until after lunch. I guess we're just about set to say a few words to the good ladies." He walked over to a microphone in the center of the studio, and placed the two ragged newspaper clippings on the reading stand which was next to it. Pointing to them, he said to Adam, "You see there a mark of distinction: I'm the only politician in the country whose broadcast addresses have weather reports and necktie advertisements printed on the reverse side."

An announcer hurried in and greeted Skeffington; Adam slipped out of the studio and into the anteroom, so that he might better hear his uncle. Ditto and the others welcomed him hastily and then fell into silence; clearly, they did not want to run the risk of missing a word. The announcer made his brief introduction; Skeffington was on. He stood easily at the microphone, his hands in his pockets. He spoke without written assistance of any kind; for the moment, even the newspaper clippings were ignored.

"Good morning, ladies," he said. "I almost hesitate to interrupt you; I know how busy you are with your household chores. But I thought that perhaps you might welcome a few moments rest from your labors before the children come in from school, and your good husbands come home for lunch. I thought you might like to hear just a few words on the progress of the current political campaign. I like to talk to you on this matter because I know you're deeply interested. Some people seem surprised that the womenfolk have such concern over political affairs; I notice that a young opponent of mine only the other evening expressed his astonishment over the large number of women at the last meeting of the Women's Democratic League. I must say that I myself wasn't a bit astonished. I might even go so far as to say that I was a little shocked that any man — especially a young man — *would* be astonished by the fact that a great many of our wives and mothers cared enough about the civic problems that affect them and their families to go to a meeting and discuss those problems. A man who's astonished at that, in this day and age — particularly if he's a young man — is something of an anachronism: he has a nineteenth-century mind in a twentieth-century body. He probably thinks that a woman's place is standing barefooted and subservient in a basement, breaking her back over a washtub. He probably thinks, to use that terrible phrase of Kipling's, that a woman is no more than 'a rag, a bone, and a hank of hair.' Now, I don't say that my young opponent, if he believes this, is at all malicious about it. I'm sure he's a fine young man who doesn't mean any harm. I think it's rather that, being so young, he hasn't had a great deal of opportunity to see for himself the magnificent things that women have been doing in the world of public affairs. Matter of fact, I think he probably relies a good bit on what his older advisers tell him. I'd like to remind you in this connection of something I mentioned the other morning: that two of his most prominent advisers were years ago the leading opponents of woman suffrage. I suppose it's a bad thing for an impressionable young man to fall into hands like that; I suppose he can hardly avoid picking up some of that evil philosophy." He paused to pick up one of the newspaper clippings. "And speaking of my young opponent," he said, "I saw on the front page of a newspaper of small circulation this morning that he had addressed an 'overflow gathering' last night in the Jewel Room of the Kilgore Hotel. Well now, that sounds impressive. Everybody in public life enjoys speaking to overflow gatherings. However, in this particular case, what the newspaper neglected to mention — and I'm sure it was an oversight: I can't believe that it intended to deliberately delude the public — was that an overflow gathering in the Jewel Room of the Kilgore doesn't necessarily mean very much. I know the Jewel Room well. It's the smallest hotel assembly room, not only in the city, but also in the state. Legend has it that it's the only hotel assembly room in the world that was once a closet. I would guess that the total capacity of this mighty chamber is three adult males and a puppy dog. And it's not at all difficult for me to believe that my young opponent addressed an overflow gathering there last night, for the reason that if he took the simple precaution of bringing only the members of his own immediate family, he was assured of one."

In the anteroom there was delayed laughter: a giggle exploded from the small head of Ditto Boland. "Oh by God!" he said admiringly. "That was a good one, one of the Governor's very best. Three adult grownups and a puppy dog!"

There was hasty assent to this from the others; they then sank back into their attitude of undeviating audition. Yet despite the apparently rapt attention, Adam had a curious feeling that he had experienced more than once in the company of these followers of his uncle: he felt that he was being watched. He looked around quickly; four pairs of eyes seemed to shift slightly. Once again he realized that as his uncle's emissary, his reaction was being observed. His reaction, that is, to *their* reaction: he knew that it was hoped that he might carry back the report of dutiful behavior. Once again he was baffled and slightly awed by this relentless compulsion to demonstrate fidelity.

Skeffington continued to talk. He read the other newspaper clipping; he recited from Wordsworth:

> *A perfect woman, nobly planned,*
> *To warn, to comfort, and command!*

As the fifteen-minute period was nearing its close, he cast one eye at the clock, and finished precisely on time. The broadcast over, the retainers flooded from the anteroom to congratulate him. Skeffington welcomed them briefly, nodded to Adam, and uncle and nephew walked out of the studio together, down the corridor which led to the street door. Skeffington's secretary was already waiting in the car; Ditto and the others crowded close behind.

"We're off to the waterfront," Skeffington said to Adam. "Here you'll notice that I have to use a slightly different approach. The fishermen and stevedores prefer a somewhat more robust delivery than do the ladies of the radio audience."

"I think the ladies must have enjoyed especially your reference to the 'perfect woman, nobly planned.'" Adam said.

"Yes, it gave them the feeling I was talking about them as well as to them, you see. I always like to use a little poetry in talking to the ladies, although sometimes there's the temptation to use the wrong kind. The thought crossed my mind as I was talking to them just a moment ago that there's a charming verse by Tom Moore about women:

> *Ask a woman's advice, and whate'er she advise,*
> *Do the very reverse and you're sure to be wise.*

"Now that more or less sums up my own sentiments rather neatly," he said, getting into the car, "but I'm a little doubtful about its value as a vote-getter. Just suppose some of the good ladies took it the right way?"

The car started off; the addition of Ditto and friends made for cramped space, but Skeffington did not appear to mind. He talked briefly to his secretary; the car stopped at City Hall and the secretary got out. Then they were on the way to the waterfront. Ditto said, "The boys and I were wondering, Governor: when we get down to the docks will you be giving a speech to Camaratta's longshoremen?"

"Among others," Skeffington said. "We'll do that later. First I want to stop at Fleet Pier and say a few words to the fishermen."

"A very loyal group, the fishermen," Ditto said approvingly. "Right behind you every solid inch of the way, Governor. I always said there was nobody like the fishermen," he said, turning to the others, "for sticking to the Governor through thick or thin, as the case may be. Many's the night I stopped by Fleet Pier on the way home of an evening and got myself a nice piece of swordfish or a little bit of haddock. And all of it free-for nothing, as we say. Absolutely positively on the house. Jumbo Jim Kilcullen would see me coming and he'd hand me the fish right off the boat. 'Here Ditto,' he'd say, 'take this home to the missus with my compliments.' Oh it was very tasty fish. A grand man, Jumbo Jim. A heart as big as the State House. You remember Jumbo Jim, Governor? The big man with the one lung and the cock eye?"

"I remember him well," Skeffington said. "I have every reason to: he double-crossed me three times in a single year. However, I admit that I look at him in a rather peculiar way: I keep on forgetting to measure his loyalty by the number of free flounders he passed out."

"Oh, you're right there, Governor!" Ditto said quickly. "One hundred and ten per cent on the bull's-eye target, as we say. You couldn't *trust* Jumbo Jim. What I meant was, he was a great hand with the free-for-nothing fish, but you wouldn't trust him with a ten-cent dime! Oh, you're right enough there, Governor! Yes, yes, yes!"

They had reached Fleet Pier; the car turned in through the gates and they rode to the very end of the pier. All along both sides were strung the vessels of the fishing fleet. Adam had seen this fleet only once before. It had been on a holiday: a Sunday in summer by tradition reserved for the official Blessing of the Fleet by a prelate. Then the vessels, newly painted and gay with flags, had presented a colorful sight as they sailed around the harbor in long parade; now, on a rather forbidding day in late October, stripped of their gaiety and in their workaday surroundings, the aspect was decidedly different. The ships seemed small, soiled and dingy; the men who came from them, one or two at a time, seemed suspicious and resentful. The outlook, thought Adam, was surely not promising, but Skeffington reassured him.

"Believe it or not," he said in a low voice, getting out of the car, "we're among friends. Just sit tight and see what happens."

Adam sat tight, as did Ditto and his friends. Skeffington walked alone out onto the pier, making towards a squat, dark man who sat on a piling near one of the boats. The two men shook hands; fishermen from the other boats began to gather around slowly. Skeffington moved among them, shaking hands, exchanging greetings. The atmosphere seemed cordial enough, yet there was a curious reserve; there was, certainly, none of the rapid dissolve into high spirits, into the boisterous good fellowship which Adam had seen on display at meetings where Skeffington was greeted by his own. Adam knew nothing of the fishermen; clearly they constituted a group of substantially lower volatility. Skeffington continued to talk to the men one by one; finally someone placed a small box next to him, and he stood on it and began to talk more generally. The men converged upon him in a grave, attentive circle; Skeffington spoke with increasing emphasis, repeatedly pounding a fist into an open palm. Adam heard very little of what was being said, for although his uncle spoke loudly, the damp wind which now came in steadily off the harbor carried most of his words away. It was, apparently, a serious talk; no one at any time laughed; there seemed to be no jokes. Occasionally the wind slackened and Adam caught an isolated phrase: ". . . meet the rising menace of cutthroat Canadian competition . . . ," ". . . experienced man to protect your interests, one who can go to Washington in your behalf . . ."; twice, unless he were mistaken, he heard mysterious and laudatory references to Portugal. Skeffington talked for perhaps ten minutes; it was a most unusual talk for him in that at no time had he been interrupted by cheers, applause, or laughter. He finished abruptly; rather to Adam's surprise, the silent men now burst into applause; they clambered about Skeffington, shaking his hand. Obviously, thought Adam, the talk had been a hit after all.

Skeffington came back to the car. "Take her around to the Morgan docks," he said to the chauffeur. To Adam he said, "A good few minutes' work. Could you hear anything at all?"

"Very little," Adam said. "The wind took most of it away. But did I hear you mention Portugal a couple of times?"

Skeffington nodded. "Foreign policy," he said gravely.

"*Foreign* policy?"

"Very important. A man can't run for mayor on the domestic issues alone. Not in this day and age. We all have to cultivate the wider vision."

"You mean that in a local election you have to talk about, say, Russia?"

"No. That's one of the great handicaps for the local politician: he can't call his opponent a Communist. It's a shame, but there you are. Of course you can *call* your opponent a Communist if you really want to, but it won't do you any good; nobody'll believe you. They all know he goes to Mass on Sunday, so he can't be a Communist; you might just as well say that the Cardinal and the Kremlin exchange pen-pal letters. No, Russia and Communism never have been much of an issue around here. We're under the disadvantage of having to evolve a foreign policy that meets local requirements."

"Which includes what?" Adam asked. "Portugal?"

"You'd be surprised how important Portugal becomes," Skeffington said, "when you're speaking to the Portuguese. These fishermen, almost all, came originally from the Portuguese mainland or the Azores. I find they appreciate an occasional reference to the glorious country of Henry the Navigator. I've been trying to find a more contemporary figure than Henry, but with Portugal that's not so easy. However, it isn't a major point. There aren't enough Portuguese. When you come right down to it, there are only two points that really count."

"Such as . . . ?"

Skeffington held up two fingers. "One," he said, ticking the first, "*All Ireland must be free.* Two," he said, ticking the second. "*Trieste belongs to Italy.* They count. At the moment the first counts more than the second, but that's only because the Italians were a little slow in getting to the boats. They're coming along fast now, though; in twenty years the Irish issue will be about as burning as that of Unhappy Ethiopia. Fortunately, I don't expect to be among those present at the time."

The car drove back through the gates and turned right; after a moment Adam said, "But is that sort of thing really so important today? I had an idea that the old emotional appeal to the homeland was dying out. You know, as the younger generation came along."

"That's what the books say," Skeffington said. "I must say, however, that I haven't noticed it myself. Maybe the books are all written by the younger generation. All I know is that just before midnight in Hibernian Hall, when the tenor starts to sing, 'I'll Take You Home Again, Kathleen,' young tears fall as freely as old. So if it's dying out, at least it's dying out moistly. Meanwhile, no matter what its state of health, I intend to see that it's not neglected."

They had reached their destination: a long pier, larger than the first. Here there were no fishing boats; a large ocean liner was berthed alongside. There were no signs of activity, either on the ship or the pier, and as the men got out of the car, Adam saw that this was not, apparently, to be another open-air address; they were going inside to talk to the dockers. Led by Skeffington, they marched into a large and barren hall. Here, burly men stood around in groups of three and four; *in toto*, thought Adam, they looked like some extravagant sub-species, an unacknowledged breed of giants. While Adam, Ditto, and the others remained in the back of the hall, Skeffington went directly through the suddenly silent groups of men, nodding to left and right, and stopped before a large, swarthy, smiling man.

"Hello, Camaratta," he said. "Good to see you again."

"Sure," Camaratta said. He winked one eye and laughed loudly. "Camaratta's a real nice fella. Everybody likes Camaratta around election time, huh?" He laughed again and said, nudging Skeffington, "Only a joke, boss. Camaratta likes his little joke. It's good to see you, too. Real good." He laughed again.

The poor fool, thought Skeffington without compassion; *he'd better laugh before the bomb goes off*. For the method of disposing of Camaratta had now been worked out; all that remained was its proper execution. It was towards the furtherance of this end, rather than that of securing the longshoremen's vote, that he had really come to the pier today. He said aloud, "I'm glad you're fond of jokes, Camaratta. A sense of humor's a blessing from above. 'Given to jest, yet ever in earnest': that's what they used to say of Lincoln. I'm happy to be able to point out the parallel between yourself and the Great Emancipator. By the way, speaking of jokes and laughter, how is Johnny Nucatolla these days? Is he laughing much?"

"Poor Johnny," Camaratta said regretfully. "A sweetheart of a kid. A real nice fella. He wanted to be mayor real bad. But I guess he just couldn't get the dough up. I hear some guys he figured he had in his pocket backed out on him. Too bad. I hear it broke the kid's heart."

"I see. Then I don't imagine he's laughing too much, after all."

"Nah. It's a shame," Camaratta said. "A real shame. A nice kid like that. Well," he said, looking around the room, "you wanta chew the fat with the boys, huh? Okay, come on over here. I'll interduce you myself, real pretty." Again he laughed.

They walked over to the small platform at the far end of the hall; jumping up on it, Camaratta yelled for attention, and then embarked upon a long, illiterate and — to Skeffington — decidedly unpleasant introduction. He heard the note of insolence in it; there was at least the firm yoking of his name with that of Camaratta, somewhat to the latter's advantage. During this introduction, Skeffington derived considerable comfort from the thought that, all unsuspected, this was one of the orator's final public performances.

At last Skeffington began to talk; he did so vigorously but simply, confining himself to the usual remarks about backbreaking toil being unaccompanied either by sufficient safeguards or appropriate reward. It was a speech he had given many times before on the waterfront, and he did not change it now, for he felt that even the slightest alteration in the anticipated pattern would arouse only suspicion in the slow bosoms of these hulking men. (As a group, he did not hold the stevedores in high regard; once, in a moment of irritation, he had expressed himself on the subject to John Gorman. "Pinheads and troublemakers," he had growled. "The only difference between them and a bunch of orangutans is that orangutans don't spend all of their time out on strike!")

As he talked, he did not give his entire attention to his words; his eye scanned the audience, from his nephew and Ditto in the rear of the hall down to those longshoremen who were stolidly bunched a few feet from him. He was looking for someone; at last he found him. He was standing by himself in front of the large bulletin-board, his huge hands folded across his belt buckle. He was a tall, big-boned, angular Scot with a harsh, watchful face; his name was Macpherson. Skeffington knew him slightly: he was a person of consequence among the stevedores, and after some weeks of careful preliminary investigation, Weinberg had reported that here was the instrument for the destruction of Camaratta. Weinberg had talked to him, at first circumspectly, then more boldly; he had discovered that here, indeed, was a spirit ripe for revolt. And so Skeffington had come down to the pier to see for himself, to carry proceedings one step further. He watched Macpherson while he talked; he would have to speak to him alone for just a moment before he left the pier. The problem was to do this without awakening the suspicions of Camaratta. It was only during the last few seconds of his talk that Skeffington discovered the perfect way out. It was so perfect, indeed, that he almost smiled at the very moment he was reciting, in tones of some passion, the melancholy catalogue of miseries that were the unfair lot of men who worked the waterfront.

Finishing his speech, he was applauded. He left the platform, Camaratta glued to his side; he did not stop to talk to the longshoremen, but walked quickly to the back of the hall. It was one of those extraordinary moments when he was grateful for the presence of Ditto Boland. He introduced Camaratta to Adam, then said easily, "Everybody else you know. As a matter of fact, Camaratta, it's a happy coincidence that we're all here together today. I want to discuss something with you, and Ditto can be of some help. I've been thinking lately that perhaps the city should pay some sort of municipal tribute to these longshoremen of yours. Possibly an annual ceremony, honoring those hardy men who have died in the performance of their arduous duties. How does that strike you?"

Camaratta nodded languidly. "Great," he said. "Real great. And about time. There's men died like rats down in them holds. Loadin'

patriotic stuff for their country, like dynamite and bombs, and —
whoom! Like rats."

"Exactly. It's high time the city recognized these dedicated men officially. I suppose we might annually honor an anonymous longshoreman,
as the nation does its soldiers each year at Arlington Cemetery. We
could pay our respects to the Unknown Stevedore. Or," he said, "we
could honor a different one each year. I suppose he might be subject to
your designation."

"Yeh," Camaratta said instantly. "I like that. I'll designate."

"Splendid. Now we have a little ceremony we perform each year in
memory of the heroic Pilsudski. A wreath is cast upon the waters, and so
forth. I thought something similar might be done for the longshoremen.
And as Ditto, who's our authority on the Pilsudski ceremony, is right
here, I think I'll have him fill you in on the details and see what you
think about it. Maybe you'll have some suggestions for improvement.
Meanwhile," he said, backing away slightly, "I can make my farewells to
your men."

Camaratta's eyes narrowed. "Hey," he said, moving forward a step.
Then he hesitated, momentarily irresolute, halted both by the eager,
confronting mass of Ditto Boland and by his own cupidity. From the
words of this fat man could come profit; he shrugged and said, "O.K.
. . . What's the pitch?"

"What the Governor and I do every spring for the memory of that
grand Polish hero Pilsudski is a lovely thing. It warms the cockles of the
soul, as we say," Ditto began enthusiastically. Skeffington moved off,
pleasantly aware that the swarthy deceiver, caught in the web of Ditto's
intricate narrative style, would be held fast for some time to come.

He greeted the stevedores singly and in small groups, pausing to say a
few words to each. As he had expected, Macpherson had arranged it so
that he would be standing alone. Skeffington spoke to him no longer
than he had spoken to the others; only the content of his message was
slightly different.

"Glad to see you again, Mr. Macpherson," he said. "Sorry it has to be
so briefly. I understand you have some interesting ideas about the waterfront. I wonder if you'd care to discuss them at some future date?"

Macpherson looked at him with light, almost colorless, gray eyes
which blinked slowly in the harsh face. "Aye," he said.

"Good," Skeffington said crisply. "Tomorrow night at ten, at my
home. You know where I live."

Macpherson smiled tightly. "I'll find ye," he promised.

"Splendid. Until then, Mr. Macpherson."

And he continued on his rounds, satisfied. Weinberg had been right;

Macpherson was his man. Tomorrow night would mark officially the beginning of the end of Camaratta's unsavory parochial regime; the thought heartened him immeasurably.

Adam had made very little out of all this. He had disliked Camaratta on sight; he had disliked him more as the moments progressed. In the car, leaving the pier, he said to his uncle, "Who is he, anyway? Does he really control things so absolutely down here on the pier?"

"Camaratta? One of Nature's noblemen," Skeffington said. "I believe his friends like to think of him as a diamond in the rough." The rest of his nephew's question he answered as truthfully as caution would allow; he said, "He's controlled things down here for many years. Did you find him at all engaging?"

"Not very, no. Is he generally regarded as such?"

"He's irresistible," Skeffington said dryly. "Obviously. Ask Ditto." Turning in his seat he said, "Was he an attentive audience, Ditto? Did he listen with interest to the tale of Pilsudski?"

"He was all ears and eyes, as we say, Governor," Ditto said promptly. "You never saw a man more interested in the facts and the figures and the et ceteras and so forths. I informed him to the fullest on all the details. He even wanted to know what happened to the beautiful wreath after we threw it out on the river. I told him it got all bashed up by the stones down by the dam, or maybe it got water-logged and sunk to the bottom of the river like a heavy stone, as we say. And he had a great idea as per this respect, Governor. He said why didn't we use a rubber wreath or a plastic one? He said that's what he'd use: a nice big wreath with maybe nice rubber roses and ferns. That way it wouldn't sink to the bottom and you could fish it out and use it over again."

"The ideal memorial to the Unknown Longshoreman," Skeffington said. "The floating, waterproof, retrievable wreath. Camaratta must be among the most sentimental of living men."

"A very nice man," Ditto said. "Oh, you're right there, Governor. I remember the time I didn't used to think so, but that was before he got smartened up, and learned that you had to take the bittersweet, as we say, and made up his mind to join up on the right side of the fence. You wouldn't find a nicer man today. And he's happy as a singing bird about the nice ceremony you're arranging for the longshoremen, Governor. He can hardly hold his horses till we throw the wreath out. Oh, that'll be the day for him!"

Skeffington agreed. "Yes," he said, "that'll be the day."

They returned to City Hall. Adam went with Skeffington up to his office; somewhere in the tangle of corridors they disengaged themselves from Ditto and his friends.

"We'll only be up here a minute," Skeffington said. "We have to hurry along to this luncheon with the Audubon Society."

Adam demurred. "Do you think I should go? I thought that was more or less a private affair. I mean, I didn't think it was political, as the other things I've been to were."

His uncle corrected him. "Everything's political," he said. "At this time of year, when I blow my nose it's political. I'm very probably appealing to the victims of hay fever. Come along, you'll enjoy yourself. You can chat about the speckled grackle to your nearest neighbor."

They entered his office, not through the private door, but through the more public access of the reception room. It was, as always, crowded; Skeffington moved slowly through it, nodding, bowing, responding by name, but never quite pausing. It was a remarkable technique, Adam thought, as he trailed his uncle; apparently the problem was to be seen by all yet stopped by none. Skeffington seemed to have solved it admirably.

His uncle disappeared; Adam sat down to wait for him. He did not wait long; in a remarkably short time he was summoned into the private office; Skeffington was ready for departure. "Come along," he said, smiling, "I think we're about a half-hour late as it is. I never like to keep a bird fancier waiting too long for his fruit cup; it's apt to make him snappish."

They went to the luncheon. It was a small gathering; protocol demanded that uncle and nephew be separated. Skeffington was given a central spot at the head table; Adam sat at a small table in the center of the room, feeling some doubt of his ability to maintain suitable conversation: he had no bird-talk. As things turned out, he need not have worried. The seat to his left was empty and remained so throughout the meal; that to his right was occupied by a frail old man with a very large hearing aid. Adam spoke pleasantly to him; as there was no sign that he had been heard, he concluded that the enormous instrument was nonfunctional. All during the meal the old man ate voraciously, keeping his eyes fixed on the head table and, in particular, on Skeffington. Three times he spoke aloud.

First he said, "That man is a disgrace!"

Later he said, "He has *two million dollars* secreted in vaults in Mexico City! It is a matter of public knowledge!"

Still later he said, "A man like that does *not* like birds!"

Each statement was firmly delivered in clear, cavernous tones. It was evident that no response was required, none was desired, and — more to the point, thought Adam — none was possible. His companion enjoyed the immunity of the totally deaf.

When the luncheon was over, Skeffington spoke briefly. He gave what seemed to Adam an extremely curious talk, establishing a parallel between the commuting businessman and the migratory fowl. It was the ornithomorphic view of man; although Adam had never before heard it expressed, there was no doubting that to Skeffington's present audience it was a most welcome one. Only the old man with the hearing aid remained unmoved; sitting in motionless, mute inaudition, he said suddenly and loudly, "*Mexico City!*"

Adam went to join his uncle at the door; he heard him saying to an elderly lady, "Madam, I agree with you wholeheartedly. And not alone to the birds: sometimes I even think that *Felis domestica* is an enemy to us all."

In the car, Adam told Skeffington of the table talk of his companion. Skeffington listened with amusement and said, "Your friend took the southern route that leads to Mexico City. There's an alternative, you know; it's permissible to hold that the money's in Montreal. For some reason, however, the sum seems to be fixed; it's usually two million dollars. Exactly why that should be, I haven't the slightest idea. By the way," he said, "I was thinking that this has been a pretty heavy schedule for you; you deserve a bit of a respite. As a matter of fact, now might be as good a time as any. I have to go back to the Hall to straighten out a few details. It's nothing that would interest you at all, but it'll probably take me an hour and a half or two. Do you suppose you could occupy yourself for that length of time without inconvenience?"

"Yes, easily." The return to City Hall, he knew, was for the meeting, earlier mentioned, between his uncle and Gorman and Weinberg. Adam was by no means sure that this would be of no interest to him; he was altogether sure, however, that it would be considered none of his business. And so he said, "Actually, it fits in very well. I have a few things to do at the paper."

"Fine. I'll drop you there." He consulted his watch. "It's a quarter of three now; supposing you come by the Hall at about 4:30 or quarter of five? By then I'll have all the underbrush cleared away, and we can get moving again."

Adam agreed. In a few moments, the car pulled up in front of the newspaper building; Skeffington said, "My compliments to the management. Tell them I think they're doing a grand job. You can also tell them I just noticed that their side door opens contrary to the fire laws. In other words, it's not an accredited egress. I wouldn't be surprised if they had a little trouble with the building inspectors shortly." And, with a cheery wave of the hand, he was gone, the long car speeding towards City Hall and the rendezvous with his two chief lieutenants. Adam watched the departure with regret. He knew that the role of the observer was a limited one; he reminded himself that he had been eager for his uncle's promise that he should in no way be implicated in the campaign. All the same, he found himself wishing that his uncle's attention to his promise might be somewhat less scrupulous; he would have given much, for example, to be allowed within earshot of this particular council of war this afternoon. And then, even as he thought this, there came the more sensible reflection that it was not a matter of the promise at all. For, promise or no promise, he believed it extremely unlikely that Skeffington would have admitted any outsider — even though that outsider might be a favored nephew — into such an important and secret deliberation.

In this belief, Adam could not have been more right.

He went to his office and began to work on his comic strip. Little Simp had been neglected of late. While Burbank no longer shared the office to serve as a distraction, there had been the disruptive force of the campaign. For the past two weeks Adam had done his work, but he had done it at odd hours and in fits and starts. He had managed to extricate the little boy and his companions from the Argentine predicament, but now a new adventure was begun; so far, it was not going well. Now, taking advantage of the unexpected hour of grace, Adam resumed where he had left off the day before. He had been working only a few minutes when the door opened and the managing editor came in. He was, these days, a man of altered appearance: he was thinner, appreciably so; his eyes had acquired the habit of blinking with great rapidity. As he entered the office now, he turned to glance nervously over his shoulder; it was as though the old, irascible, merciless voice which trailed him so constantly down the corridors had suddenly become a visible thing. He had expected to live a life of terror in these weeks of pre-election; his expectation had been more than realized. Adam pitied him; he knew that he came into this office, not to see its occupant, but merely because it was a place where Amos Force was not.

Adam went on working. The managing editor stood silently behind him, looking over his shoulder; after a moment he said dully, "Where's the chipmunk?"

He was observant in his misery; the companionable rodent was no longer perched on Little Simp's shoulder. "He's in the hospital," Adam said. "I've put him there until his fur grows back."

"Is that what eating the cornflakes did to him?"

Adam nodded. Recently, Daddy the Chipmunk had performed with heroism. An agent of Big Boris, aware of the dietary habits of Little Simp, had cunningly secured employment in a neighborhood supermarket; there, one afternoon, he had sold the little boy a carton of poisoned breakfast food. The next morning, at the breakfast table, wise Daddy, scenting danger, had sprung from his little master's shoulder and had devoured several of the lethal flakes, subsequently collapsing in agony. Fortunately the poison, while fatal to humans, was less effective against the rodent; it acted merely as a particularly painful depilatory. And so Daddy, alive but hairless, had been necessarily confined.

The managing editor made conversation. "I should think you'd draw him in anyway. Even without the fur."

Adam objected. "It wouldn't be especially appealing, would it? He'd look rather thin and shiny, like a young rat. I couldn't have anything like that on Simp's shoulder. The readers would object."

"I suppose so," the managing editor said gloomily. After a while, he said, "Where are you sending the kid this time? Abroad somewhere?"

"Yes. Rotterdam, I think."

"Rotterdam, hey?"

'Yes, Ralph, Rotterdam."

"Well well," he said hollowly. Then, suddenly, the name of this faraway city recalled a vivid memory, and for a moment he spoke with some animation. "We sent a reporter to Rotterdam once. Seven years ago. The whole thing was a hell of a mistake. The paper got an awful sticking on the deal. It was a two-week junket, run by an air line; our understanding was that they would take care of all expenses. Well, they didn't. They weaseled out of it. They claimed they promised to take care of only the *basic* expenses. So the paper was stuck with the rest. It cost us roughly $7.25 a day. Multiply that by two weeks and you get some idea of the total cost to the paper. We laid out a cool $101.50 just to let this fellow have a close-up view of a couple of dikes. Never again!"

"Once bitten, twice shy," Adam said. He went on working.

"You said it," the managing editor said feelingly. Then, as suddenly a it had come, emotion waned. His shoulders slumped, he gazed about him dejectedly, he looked with glum, unseeing eyes at the comic strip in progress. In a slow, grudging voice, he asked, "How's your uncle?"

Adam recognized it as a question torn from him by the demands of duty. Reluctant to introduce a subject which caused him daily pain, he was compelled to do so by loyalty.

"He's very well, thanks, Ralph."

The managing editor went on gamely. "That's good. Because he'll need his health. It's all he'll have left after the election. You can tell him that for me."

"Which reminds me," Adam said, "I have a message from him to you." He told what Skeffington had said about the side door of the building in relation to the fire laws. "He mentioned some potential trouble with the building inspectors," he concluded. "Is that a possibility, would you say?"

"Oh my God," said the managing editor, sagging further. "How the hell do I know? Don't I have troubles enough as it is?" He thought of the defective side door; he thought of Skeffington; he thought of expense; he thought, finally and inevitably, of Amos Force, even now waiting for him in his office. With a little moan he disappeared through the doorway.

Adam worked for another hour, then left the building for City Hall. The conference was over; Weinberg and John Gorman had gone. Skeffington joined him without delay, and together uncle and nephew once more took to the campaign trail. Here, in these hours of late afternoon and evening, Adam saw his uncle shift gears: perceptibly, the pace quickened, the routine became more complex, the burden heavier. In between the hours of five and midnight, when Skeffington decided to call it a day, they passed, almost without pause, through a swift, bewildering succession of widely scattered appearances, speeches, and presentations. And when, the night over, the two men at last were on their way home, Adam dazedly looked back over the day, and found that he was hopelessly confused. There had been too much of everything; it was only with difficulty that he could separate one event from the other; succeeding in the separation, he could not be at all sure of the sequence, especially during the later hours. There had been an open-air meeting in the West End; Skeffington had talked of a reduced tax rate, cheaper public transportation, and a proposed statue to honor the memory of Christopher Columbus. Across the city, they had gone indoors; there had been a tea party; over the teacups, and to the exclusively feminine audience, Skeffington had talked quietly of home, poetry, and the necessity of the experienced hand in guiding the body politic. They had visited a hospital; Skeffington had toured the wards, stopping by the bedsides of patients to tell a joke, to murmur encouragement; here he did not ostensibly electioneer. They had gone to not one dinner, but two. Both had been huge affairs at which Skeffington had been the principal speaker; Adam could not remember what he had said. He could remember vividly, however, that at these banquets he himself had eaten little, upon Skeffington's recommendation.

"The best advice I ever received as a young politician came from old Martin Sullivan," his uncle had said. "He said, 'Go to all the dinners, but eat none of the food. That's the stuff that kills a man!' He was right, too. Occasionally I've forgotten myself long enough to experiment with the food; always regretted it. I'm not sure where they get the meat for these ceremonial dinners, but I've suspected it comes from a kind of inedible beast especially bred for the occasion. Probably a banquet variety of yak. Anyway," he had concluded, "a word to the wise: *Don't go near it.*"

Adam had not. Hungry, after the banquets — or had it been *between* banquets? — they had gone to a television studio. Here Skeffington had talked for a quarter-hour; as Adam remembered it, it had been the grave and kindly talk of an elder statesman who, rather against his will, has been compelled to dwell at some length upon the appalling deficiencies of his opponent. Then there had been the house parties. There had been two of these: the houses of old friends had been thrown open for Skeffington's purposes; here, in the living room and library, over opulent buffet spreads, Skeffington had welcomed those of the neighborhood who had come trooping in. Here he had been among his own people, and Adam had again noticed the change of approach, the hearty camaraderie with which he greeted those who, regarding him as in some manner uniquely theirs, proudly employed his Christian name as a badge of confraternity.

Of these parties Adam remembered chiefly hilarity: his uncle standing there, telling anecdote after anecdote, mostly about politics and politicians who seemed to be familiar to them all. He recalled few details; now, weary, he did recall that he had enjoyed himself completely.

Throughout these later hours, Ditto and the rest of the entourage had made their mysterious entrances and exits; once or twice they traveled from place to place with Skeffington and Adam. Then, suddenly, they would fade away, to reappear in half an hour in quite another locale: Adam, in the course of the evening, had seen Ditto on at least six different occasions. It was apparent that although this ridiculous cordon sometimes slipped from visibility, they were never far from their protector.

In the car now, riding home, he said to Skeffington, "I don't see how you stand it. Is it like this every day?"

"Pretty much. Sometimes more, sometimes less. You have to remember that we're coming to the end of the trail now; things naturally bunch up at a time like this. As a consequence, I manage to keep busy."

"Conceded," said Adam. He glanced wonderingly at this septuagenarian, relaxed so casually on the seat beside him; he looked considerably fresher than Adam felt. Curiously he said, "What about the effect of all this on you, Uncle Frank? Doesn't it tire you, really? I'm exhausted, but you look as though you were good for a few hours more of the same thing."

Skeffington regarded him with amusement. "I have to," he said simply. "In politics, only a young man can afford to look tired. He doesn't have to prove he's young enough for the job, you see. On the other hand, if a man well along in years still wants to be elected to office, he has to demonstrate that despite the actuarial tables, he's in the prime of life. It's very important; some men go to rather extreme lengths in their demonstrations. I remember that when Arthur Grigsby Powell first ran for the United States Senate, he had his picture taken chopping wood. He won, and that became his trademark; every election thereafter he had to swing the axe. The last time he ran he was close to eighty, and he hadn't lifted anything heavier than a soup spoon for five years, but he didn't dare give up the demonstration. They taped the axe in his hands, and they held up his arms with guy-wires while a friendly photographer snapped the picture. He won, too. And to give you a more recent example, just a couple of years ago, one of our respected elders who wanted to be President went out to the Convention in Chicago, jumped off the train at the station, and raced the reporters on foot to his hotel. The hotel was two miles away, but he was out to prove something, you see. He had to. And," he said, "so do I. Except that I don't chop wood, or wear a wig, or trot along the streets at Scout's pace. I merely concentrate on not looking tired."

All of which, thought Adam, did not really answer the question of whether or not he was tired. He looked at his uncle again and concluded that, incredibly enough, it was quite probable that he was not, that somehow the long years of campaigning had left him conditioned for the effort, that the habit had in fact provided a sheath against fatigue. It was a conclusion which, though quite inaccurate, paid tribute to Skeffington's powers of concentration.

The car drove on, and Adam was silent as he reflected upon still another aspect of the day. He had realized, for the first time, something of the tactical skill of his uncle at handling the voting public. In traveling back and forth across the city, he had observed that no two of Skeffington's expeditions corresponded exactly; each had its distinct object, each was aimed at a special group of the electorate. What had astonished Adam was not that such special groups existed, but that they existed in such numbers. They were divided not only along the broad lines one might have anticipated: race, religion, national background, sex, capital and labor; inside whichever category one chose, it seemed that there were limitless special cells, each of whose concerns appeared to be in direct opposition to those of every other cell. Adam was staggered by this multiplicity of minority interests. For the first time he was witnessing directly the chaotic diversity of the democratic process in action, and he was amazed that his uncle could move so confidently and unwaveringly among the warring elements. He mentioned this to Skeffington now, and added, "It's all too complex for me. As near as I can figure it, what you really have to do is be all things to all people."

"Not a bit of it," Skeffington said imperturbably. "I only want to be one thing to them. I want to be their mayor. This involves a little juggling here and there, of course, and sometimes you have to keep half a dozen balls in the air at the same time, but it's no great trick once you're used to it. It's mostly a matter of practice. That, and of knowing what each group really wants. There's a considerable difference between what they *say* they want, and what they'll really settle for. You can promise them the first, but you only have to deliver the second."

"Yes, but they all seem to want so many things! And sometimes one group wants exactly the opposite of what the other group wants. How do you keep everybody happy in *that* situation?"

"Why, that brings us to man's best friend," Skeffington said. "The compromise. I'll give you a small illustration based on something you saw only this afternoon. You remember we were in Ward 5: it's an Italian district all the way through. You may remember that I spoke to a crowd of people in that little plaza opposite the Vocational High School. I spoke about a statue soon to be erected on the plaza."

"Yes. A statue of Columbus."

"His name was mentioned," Skeffington said dryly. "I think I should explain to you, however, that this afternoon's audience consisted exclusively of members of the local council of the Knights of Columbus. But there are certain practical objections to putting up a statue of Columbus. In the first place, the city is already loaded with statues of Columbus; he's vulgarly known as the Pigeons' Friend. Secondly, there's a good deal of opposition to it within the ward; other groups want other statues in the plaza. The Sons of Italy have been shouting for a statue to Charlie di Mascolo, who was their head man around here for years. They'd really like it chiseled out of the side of Mount Rushmore, but failing that, they'll take the plaza. A small band of lunatics wants a statue to Roosevelt. A substantial group, headed by the venerable Monsignor Tancredi, is rather partial to a statue of Monsignor Tancredi. Feelings on the matter run high and the erection of the statue can't be postponed much longer. As the plaza's city property, it's pretty much up to me to decide. And to decide without making enemies forever. That's where the compromise comes in: I'll announce it right after the election."

"And what is the compromise?" Adam asked, curious. "Who is it to be?"

Skeffington chuckled. "Mother Cabrini," he said.

"*Mother Cabrini?*"

Skeffington nodded. "Italian born, and the first American saint. Let's see them get out of that. The first man, woman, child or monsignor who objects will be stoned out of town. That's what I mean by compromise. Well," he said, as the car slowed, then stopped, "here we are, safe and sound. It's been a long day; did you enjoy it at all?"

"Very much," Adam said truthfully. "Many thanks, Uncle Frank."

"I hoped you might; I'm glad. I'll give you a ring as soon as something else breaks. Good night, my boy."

"Good night, Uncle Frank."

The car pulled off again for the last time that day. Adam went slowly up the front walk, thinking of his uncle. Mother Cabrini! The compromise was cynical, outrageous, reprehensible; nevertheless, as Adam let himself into the house, he found himself laughing. He thought again that his uncle was a most extraordinary man.

Benjy

BENJY is a broad satire, written for children, on good little boys and their dreadful mammas. Illustrated with sophistication and brio, chiefly in pink and orange, by Ati Forberg, BENJY gained a handful of devoted admirers, mostly children, but had no popular success and is now out of print.

In the following selections, Benjy is introduced, meets a Good Fairy, makes a wish, and gets it.

Once upon a time, not so very many years ago, there lived in a small town called Smiles, Pennsylvania, a little boy named Benjamin Thurlow Ballou. He had no brothers and no sisters. He lived all alone with his mother, his father, and his doggie. His mother, who was a college graduate, was named Mummy. His father, who was a television repairman, was named Daddy. And his doggie, who was an Airedale, was named Sid.

They all lived together in a nice little house, and they were very happy there.

———

It happened one afternoon, just after school was over for the day. Benjy was going along, hoppity-skip, on his way home to his Mummy and his jelly sandwiches, when from out of nowhere someone suddenly appeared before him, right there in the middle of the sidewalk. And this was the Good Fairy!

Of course Benjy did not know right away that he had met a Good Fairy, because he had never seen one before. Good Fairies did not visit the little town of Smiles very often, and Benjy had had to learn about them from stories and pictures in his little books. And *these* Good Fairies had not looked at all like the one standing right in front of him on the sidewalk. They had all been pretty ladies with beautiful smiles who floated through the air with wands in their hands and stars over their heads, and had lovely tinkling voices.

But the Good Fairy who was right there in front of Benjy was *not* a pretty lady. No indeed! He was a man: a big fat man with little eyes and a big red bulby nose. And he wore, not lovely robes, but a baseball suit, with a baseball cap tilted to one side of his head. And what do you think he carried in one hand? A wand? No! He carried a big cigar! And when he started to talk, his voice was not at all beautiful or tinkling, but it was loud and hoarse and full of big coughs. So you can understand why it was that little Benjy at first did not quite believe the Good Fairy when he looked down at Benjy and said in his hoarse voice, "Whaddaya say, kid? I'm ya Good Fairy!"

What kind of Good Fairy talk was this? Little Benjy, even though he was a very brave little boy, was almost frightened and began to back away, but the Good Fairy nodded his head and said, "I know, I know. Ya don't belee me. None o' you wise little kids ever do. But look here and I'll prove ya somethin'."

And with that the Good Fairy lifted his cigar up in the air and waved it around, and right before Benjy's wide little eyes, what do you think the cigar changed into? A *baseball bat!* And then the Good Fairy put his other hand up in the air and snapped his fingers, and into the hand popped . . . a *baseball!*

"Okay?" said the Good Fairy. "Now I'll hit a fungo." And he swung his bat and hit the baseball far far away, right over the tops of the houses. "That woulda been right outa the Stadium," said the Good Fairy. "Center field at that. Well, whaddaya say now, kid?"

And of course, after this, what could a polite little boy like Benjy say except, "Excuse me for not believing you, Mister Good Fairy."

"Okay," said the Good Fairy, waving his arm and changing the baseball bat back into a cigar. "Now less get down ta business."

He pulled an old-looking notebook out of his baseball pants pocket and began to thumb through the pages, and as he did so, little Benjy could not help but notice that not all Good Fairies had very clean thumbs.

"Lessee, now," said the Good Fairy, "you're the Ballou kid, ain't ya?"

The Ballou kid! How very strangely Good Fairies talked!

"Why, Mister Good Fairy," said Benjy, "I'm little Benjy. My full name is Benjamin Thurlow Ballou."

"Okay, okay," said the Good Fairy very quickly, almost before Benjy had finished what he was saying. Then the Good Fairy gave some big coughs and shook his head, and Benjy could see that his eyes were all watery and red. "Whoo!" said the Good Fairy. "What a night! Never again! Well, anyways, kid, the thing is this: ya got a wish comin' to ya."

"A wish, Mister Good Fairy?" said Benjy. "You mean for being such a good little boy?" For Mummy had told him many times what kind of little boys got wishes granted to them by the Good Fairies, and so now he was not at all surprised.

"Yeah, yeah," said the Good Fairy, just as quickly as before, and making such a terrible face that, if Benjy did not know better, he would almost have thought that the Good Fairy did not really like him at all.

"Nowdays," said the Good Fairy, "it's gettin' so every little crumbcake that goes around blabbin' baby talk and squealin' on the other kids winds up gettin' a wish. It's a real foul-up, Buster, but it ain't none o' my business. I don't shake the dice in this league: I'm oney the mailman."

And then he stopped because he had to cough his big cough and shake his head some more.

"Whoo!" he said finally. And then he looked at Benjy with his watery red eyes and said, "Well, whaddaya say, kid? What's ya wish?"

"You mean I can wish for anything I want, Mister Good Fairy?" said Benjy, for that was how it had been in the books.

"Yeah, yeah," said the Good Fairy. "But hustle it up. I can't hang around here all day. I gotta deliver a singin' donkey to some nut kid out in Hollywood. So come on, snap into it. Whaddaya want?"

"I really don't know, Mister Good Fairy," said Benjy, and he looked ever so seriously at the Good Fairy, and put his little finger in his mouth. "All I want is for everybody to love Benjy and be happy."

"That ain't no kinda wish!" shouted the Good Fairy, and he almost seemed cross with little Benjy. "It ain't legal, like. Ya gotta wish for somethin' *special*. Look, I'll help ya. Howja like ta be a big athalete some day? Maybe a big leaguer like the Babe, or Ted Williams? Or," said the Good Fairy, with a modest look, "like *me*? Hey? What's wrong with that, kid?"

"No thank you, Mister Good Fairy," said Benjy, smiling his very politest little smile. "That would be very nice, but my dear Mummy wouldn't want me to grow up and become a baseball man."

"Whoo!" said the Good Fairy, hitting himself hard on the forehead with his hand. "Whoo! What a cornball! Okay then, kid, howsa bout becomin' a fighter? Heavyweight champeen o' the world, maybe? Goin' around drivin' a Caddy, eatin' big steaks, knockin' other guys out: that's the old fun, hey? What kid don't want that?"

"Oh no, Mister Good Fairy!" said Benjy, his pretty blue eyes all roundy-wide. "I don't want to hit anybody, ever ever. I just want to be happy friends with people."

"Whoo!" said the Good Fairy again, and he stood looking at little Benjy with his hands on his hips. "I seen some queer ones in this racket, but you take the biscuit, Buster. Okay then, what *do* ya want? Hurry it up. I gotta get out to this little bum in Hollywood before dark, and that ain't no cinch when ya got ya two arms full o' donkey. So come on, kid, spit it out!"

But now little Benjy was all happy-jumpy with excitement, for while the Good Fairy had been talking, Benjy's little brain had been hard at work, saying. "Think think, little Benjy!" and all of a sudden he had had a beautiful idea for the very best wish in the world.

"Oh Mister Good Fairy," he said, "do big and marvelous things happen to good little boys who get wishes?"

"Sure, sure, sure," said the Good Fairy. "Alla time. Come on, quit stallin'. What's ya wish?"

"Well then," said Benjy, his eyes shining like two little stars, "I make a wish that whatever big and marvelous things happen to little Benjy, the very same big and marvelous things will happen to his dear Mummy, too!"

Who else but little Benjy would have thought of such a beautiful wish as this? And were those tears in the Good Fairy's eyes as he listened to Benjy's little voice? No they were not, but that was only because the Good Fairy was busily working away, writing down Benjy's wish in his notebook. The Good Fairy did not seem to be a very good writer, as he had to print his letters very slowly and kept licking the tip of his pencil with his tongue, but at last he finished and put the notebook back in the pocket of his baseball pants.

"Okay, kid," he said. "Toot finee. That's French for Roger Dodger." And, pushing his baseball cap back toward the back of his head, he stood there looking at Benjy for quite a long time.

"Some wish!" he said. "And some kid! Belee me, Buster, if you was mine I'd put ya behind chicken wire and charge admission!"

But little Benjy did not hear the Good Fairy's funny words, for he was thinking about how nice it was that he was the kind of good little boy who would make such a lovely wish.

"Mister Good Fairy," he said, "will it really come true true?"

"Whaddaya mean, *true true?*" said the Good Fairy. "What kinda talk is that? *True true!* If ya mean are ya gonna get ya wish, the answer is yeah, sure. Whaddaya think I come all the way down here for: to fob off phony wishes? The oney thing is, Buster, ya gotta keep ya trap shut. One little word from you about meetin' me today, or about gettin' the wish, and the whole deal's off. That's a rule they got. Don't tell nobody. Understand?"

What a blow this was to Benjy!

"But Mister Good Fairy!" he pleaded. "Not even my *Mummy?*"

"Not even *nobody,*" said the Good Fairy. "Or else the wish goes down the drain. What's more, ya'll break out in spots. So be smart, kid, and zip the lip. And now I gotta get outa here if I'm gonna beat the rush hour traffic. So long, kid. See ya in the funny papers!"

And how swift the Good Fairy was, for before Benjy could even say, "I want to thank you, Mister Good Fairy, for the beautiful wish you gave me today!" he was up in the air and out of sight, leaving behind him on the sidewalk only a little cloud of smoke that smelled like old cigars.

And so little Benjy walked the rest of the way home, thinking hard about his wonderful adventure, and about what a bad shame it was that he could not tell his dear Mummy how he had made his wish all for her today. But then, before he reached his house, he cheered up, and a sunny smile chased away all the little frowny lines on his face, for Benjy boy was never very long without his little smile, and besides, he knew that Mummy was so clever that someday she would find out who did all the beautiful things for her, and oh, *then* would there be hugs and kisses!

And, during the next few weeks, how many times do you think that big and marvelous things happened to little Benjamin Thurlow Ballou and his darling Mummy? Fifty times? Ten times? Five times?

No. *No times.* No times at all!

How very strange this seemed to Benjy! For he knew that, though he had always been a lovely little boy, ever since he had made his wish he had been even lovelier. In school, he had helped Miss Teacher so much that there was not a single minute of the day when he was not right by her side. Even when she went to meet her friend, Mister Man Teacher, to go for their little walks together, Benjy would go along too, and he would keep right up with them, even when they walked fast fast. What a scowly face Mister Man Teacher had on these walks! He was so scowly that there were times when little Benjy almost thought of not helping him any more.

And at home, Benjy helped his dear Mummy more than ever before. Every morning he woke up singing like a happy little robin, and he woke everybody else from sleepytime with his nice first grade songs like "The Goldenrod Is Yellow" and "Bunny's Tracks Are in the Snow." Then he would help Mummy get the breakfast. Benjy was such a good little cook that pretty soon Mummy let him make Daddy's coffee every single morning. And what good coffee he made! It was scarcely brown at all! By the time he was ready to march out the front door for the Little Red Schoolhouse, he had helped out so much that Mummy could not help hugging him and kissing him and saying in a very loud voice that it was nice to have a man in the house at last!

But even though he had been so extra-special good, nothing big or marvelous had happened. Whatever could the matter be? Of course Benjy was too good to think bad things about Mister Good Fairy and his big friends up in the sky, but sometimes he almost wondered if Mister Good Fairy had not told him a little fib! But he did not wonder this very much, because as soon as he did the bad cigar smell would come back into the room very quickly, and Mummy would jump out of her chair and start shouting at Daddy again, and Benjy knew that Mister Good Fairy was there. Then Benjy would be frightened and he would whisper very fast, "Little Benjy believes you, Mister Good Fairy! Honest and true true!"

And pretty soon the bad cigar smell would go away, but even when it had gone, nothing big or marvelous happened; and the days went by, one after another, and still nothing happened, and all of a sudden it was time once again for Daddy's Birthday Picnic.

What a great day this was in the little house! How Mummy and Benjy loved picnics, and what a treat it was when, every year, they all went off on a picnic on Daddy's Birthday! It was not quite as big a treat for Daddy, because he did not really like picnics very much, but he had to go because this was Mummy's special birthday present every year.

So off they drove in their little car, with Mummy up in front in the driver's seat, with little Benjy by her side, and Daddy sitting all by himself in the back with the lunch basket.

"You don't deserve it this year," Mummy said to Daddy, talking back over her shoulder, "because of those cigars! I just hope you realize how lucky you are, going off on a nice time like this in spite of everything! Don't touch that lunch basket!"

"No dear," said Daddy, although to tell the truth he had been just about to peek in under the cover, for he was very hungry. "We got a nice lunch today, dear?" he said.

"We have no cigars, if that's what you're driving at," said Mummy. "No, I'm afraid I didn't include any of your famous filthy cigars on our luncheon menu today. But for those of us who can manage to exist for five minutes without tobacco, it will be a delicious lunch. We'll have all the usual sandwiches: cucumber, egg salad, tuna fish, and peanut butter and jelly. And of course what my baby boy likes best in all the world: toasty marshmallows!"

"Oh, Mummy!" cried Benjy. "Mmmmm!"

"Joy joy, little Benjy?" said Mummy, giving him a fond little squeeze.

"Joy joy, Mummy!" said Benjy, smiling up at her.

"And," said Mummy, talking to Daddy, who was looking very hungry, "there happens to be an extra surprise for you this year. I just hope that you can appreciate it. Your little son has brought along a big Thermos bottle filled with the coffee he makes especially for you!"

"Oh boy," said Daddy very quietly. "Wow."

What a Happy Birthday Picnic it was going to be for Hungry Daddy!

And pretty soon Mummy turned the little car off the main road, and up another road, and then they reached the Picnic Place. This was a lovely meadow with plenty of big rocks and trees, just halfway up the side of Mount Laugh, which was the only mountain in Smiles, Pennsylvania. And when they got there, who should be waiting for them but Sid!

Sid knew where they went every year on Daddy's Birthday, but he liked to get there first to fix his own lunch, for he was only a dog and did not like the kind of nice food Mummy brought. And how Daddy looked at Sid's big pile of bones with the pieces of meat still on them! Funny Daddy! Whatever was he thinking?

Then Daddy carried the lunch basket over to a side of the Picnic Place which was far away from the other people who had come up to picnic, or maybe just to walk around, but whom Mummy did not like because they were common. And how beautifully Mummy and Benjy ate their sandwiches with their lovely manners! But how strange it was to watch Daddy eat his in great huge bites, swallowing them very quickly almost as if he did not want to taste them!

"Happy Birthday, Daddy dear!" said little Benjy, running up to him and pushing something small and wrinkly and black at him on the end of a stick. "Here's a pretty toasty marshmallow for my Daddy!"

"Owp!" cried Daddy, for Benjy put it right in his mouth for him, and it was all very hot and hard and gave his tongue a very bad burn. "For crying out loud," he said.

"Pull in your tongue this second!" said Mummy. "A grown man sitting there with his tongue lolling out! What will people think of me? And drink your coffee!" she said, pointing to the Thermos bottle, which Daddy must have forgotten because he had not even touched it. "Stop whimpering and drink the coffee your little son was good enough to prepare for you with his own little hands! At least try to act like a decent parent on your birthday!"

"Benjy gave up his playtime to make Daddy's Happy Birthday coffee, didn't he, Mummy?" said Benjy, with a tender look.

"Sweet boy!" said Mummy, patting his cheek. "Indeed he did. And Daddy is going to drink his Happy Birthday coffee, every single drop, just to show his little son how much he appreciates it. All right!" she said in her special voice to Daddy. "Drink up!"

So Daddy drank his Happy Birthday coffee, mostly in great big gulps, stopping to put his tongue out in the air to cool whenever Mummy was not watching him, which was not very often. And Benjy watched his Daddy drink coffee for a while, and then he got up and began to run around and play by himself over by some big rocks at the far far edge of the Picnic Place.

All of a sudden Mummy was interrupted in her watching of Daddy by a big yell from the far far edge, and she quickly turned around to see little Benjy jumping up and down and waving his arms and yelling, "Mummy! Mummy!"

"A rattlesnake!" cried Mummy, leaping up. "My own little boy has been bitten by a rattlesnake! I know it! Get up on your feet!" she shouted at Daddy. "Your little son is dying of rattlesnake bites and you sit there like a lump swilling down your precious caffein!"

"But dear," said Daddy, pulling in his tongue to talk, "how could he get bit by a rattlesnake? I mean, there's no rattlesnakes around here, dear. There's never been. Holy smoke, dear."

"Don't use your oaths on me!" said Mummy. "I'll holy smoke you!" And, reaching down, she pulled Daddy to his feet so fast that he spilled quite a bit of his Happy Birthday coffee all over himself. "You'll come along with me and save your dying son whether you want to or not!" said Mummy.

And, pulling him after her, she ran across the Picnic Place to her Benjy boy. As she ran, she reached over and tore Daddy's new birthday tie right off his neck.

"A tourniquet!" she cried. "We'll need a tourniquet!"

But when they reached little Benjy, they found they did not need a tourniquet at all, because he had not been bitten by a rattlesnake at all! He had not even been bitten by *anything!* He was shouting and jumping up and down, not because he was sick, but because he had found something so exciting that he had to show it to his dear Mummy right away! But Mummy was so happy to see her Benjy without any rattlesnake marks and not all swollen up and blue that he could not show her anything at all until she had picked him up in her arms and covered him with lovely Mummy kisses.

Then, when all the good kissing was over, Benjy took Mummy by the hand and they ran fast fast to see what he had found. Daddy came too, only not so fast, because he still had a sore tongue, and then after Daddy came Sid, who was slowest of all because he had eaten such a big lunch.

And what do you think it was that Benjy had found, all by himself, hidden away in the big bare rocks at the far far edge of the Picnic Place?

A secret cave? A pirate treasure? A space ship? No. He had found . . . a NEST! A *bird's* nest! But it was not in the least like an ordinary bird's nest, which is little and neat and made of twigs and mud and bits of string. *This* nest was huge and very untidy, and made of rough branches and hunks of rope and even pieces of wire. You might even think it had not been made by a bird at all, except that right in the middle of it was . . . an egg! And what an egg! It was about as big as a coconut, and it was a shiny black color, with one bright red spot on one end and one bright green spot on the other! And for just a moment everybody looked at the nest and then at the egg and they could not even say a single word!

"Boy," said Daddy, at last. "Boy. How'd that egg be all boiled up for breakfast, hey?"

"Predictable!" said Mummy, putting her hand over her eyes. "Forever the Philistine! You've never heard of the word 'beauty,' have you? You can't begin to realize that your little son has discovered something rare and lovely, can you? Boiled up indeed!"

"It's all cold, Mummy dear," said Benjy, who had gone over to the nest and was stroking the egg with one hand. "It feels all cold to my little touch."

"That's because it's an *abandoned* eggie, sweet boy," said Mummy. "That means there are some Mummy birds who are very bad Mummy birds who don't love their little eggies, and who fly away and leave them so that they can never hatch into lovely chickabiddies."

"Boy," said Daddy, giving a little laugh. He did not laugh very much, but when he did it was a coarse little laugh that always made Mummy ashamed of him. "Boy," he said, looking at the big egg, "I'd sure hate to meet the chickabiddy that hatched from *that* egg. Some real king-size chickabiddy."

Then, seeing the way Mummy was looking at him, he said, "Just a little joke, dear. It's a nice egg. A real pretty egg. It sure took a whopper of a bird to lay that pretty egg." And then Daddy suddenly looked up over his shoulder into the sky just a little bit uneasily and said, "Maybe the big bird didn't go away. Maybe she's still hanging around. Behind a cloud or something. Maybe we ought to get out of here, dear."

"A craven!" said Mummy. "I've married a craven! And of course you want us to leave the egg behind! You're all for giving up this precious jewel of an egg that your own little son was the first to discover, aren't you? Of course you are! That's my husband! I'm the only woman in the world married to a man who's afraid of an egg!"

"Oh Mummy dear!" cried Benjy, in his very special sad-little-boy voice that almost made Mummy want to burst right into big tears, and even made Sid the Airedale want to stuff his ears with dirt and pound his head hard on the ground. "Oh Mummy dear, don't take Benjy's eggie away! It's not the Mummy bird's eggie any more! It's little Benjy's eggie now!"

"Don't worry, sweet boy," cooed Mummy. "Of course Benjy can keep his eggie. Mummy and Benjy will take the pretty eggie back home to the little house no matter what fraidy-cats say!"

"Oh Mummy!" said Benjy, clapping his hands. "And maybe Benjy and Mummy can *hatch* the pretty eggie! They can take turns! Then we will have a little Benjy-bird!"

"Oh, he has his Mummy's imagination!" said Mummy happily. "The divine spark! I only hope he doesn't make the same sorry mistake his Mummy made! Just see to it, sweet boy, that you don't throw away your gifts as I've thrown mine! I've given the best years of my life —"

"Hey hey hey!" said Daddy suddenly, interrupting Mummy. He almost never interrupted Mummy, but he interrupted her now. "Hey," he said, looking anxiously at Benjy, "no kidding. You better put that thing down."

For Benjy had put his two little hands underneath the pretty egg and was lifting it right out of the nest!

"Once and for all, YOU LEAVE THAT SWEET LITTLE BOY ALONE!" said Mummy, talking in her through-her-closed-teeth voice. "Don't try to infect him with your silly fears! Don't try to make a craven out of my son!"

"I'm a brave little boy, aren't I, Mummy?" said Benjy with one of his brightest smiles. "And now I have my very own eggie, and the bad old Mummy birdie hasn't got it any more!"

"Hey hey hey!" said Daddy suddenly, in the loudest voice he had ever used. "WATCH IT!"

For something was happening! The pretty egg was very heavy, much *much* heavier than it looked, and Benjy, when he started to carry it across to his dear Mummy, found that it was so heavy he could not hold it tight at all! And it began to slip, and the next thing you know it had slipped right out of Benjy's hands and crashed down onto a big rock at his feet.

"BONG!" it went.

It did not sound like an egg at all! It sounded like a great mad gong! Then it bounced straight up in the air two times, and each time it came down on the rock again it made the same sound.

"BONG! BONG!"

It was a sound you could hear for miles! And then it bounced up in the air once more, and this time, when it came down, it did not go "BONG!" but it broke on the rock and split all apart, and a great black yolk came spilling out, covering the ground in a big inky pool!

"Wow!" said Daddy, and he was the only one who said a word. Mummy and Benjy just stood there with their eyes wide open and their mouths wide open, and Sid went and hid behind a rock.

Then, suddenly, they heard a noise. It was a high, whistling noise from somewhere up in the sky, like the noise of a jet plane shooting by. And Mummy and Benjy and Sid and Daddy all looked up together, but they did not see any jet plane. They did not see anything special at all: just a few clouds, and the bright, shining, midday sun.

But the noise grew louder and louder, and suddenly, while they were all still looking up, they saw what seemed to be a dark speck in the sky, coming over the top of the mountain. It was coming towards them, and it was coming very very fast. It was coming so fast that even before they could blink their eyes to make sure that the speck was really there, it had become ten times bigger and darker, and was now a long black streak, shooting down across the face of the sun and making a big shadow on the ground!

"Oh oh!" cried Daddy, for he had wonderful eyes, even for a television repairman, and saw what it was before any of the others did. "It's the big bird! Wow!"

And indeed it was a big bird! It was an enormous black bird with even blacker wings which flapped up and down very slowly, but which drove it forward at a furious speed! It came nearer and nearer and nearer, and when it was still high in the sky, but directly over the heads of Mummy and Benjy and Sid and Daddy, it seemed to stop still and fold its great wings to its sides, and the loud whistling noise became quiet. There was a second of terrible silence, and then the big bird seemed to tilt slowly forward, and all of a sudden it began a swift, roaring, rushing dive, right down upon them!

And it was now that little Benjy, who was one of the smartest little boys in the whole first grade, began to suspect that something might happen to him.

"Oh Mrs. Mummy Bird!" cried Benjy. "No! No! No! Don't touch little Benjy! Don't give him a bruise! He didn't break the pretty eggie! He didn't even touch it! Honest and true true! Some bad boy did! Don't be cross with little Benjy, Mrs. Mummy Bird! Oh please please PLEASE!"

But it was too late, for Mrs. Mummy Bird, who by now was very close to them, looked very cross indeed! She had a long, dark-red beak which was curved like a Turkish sword, and great red flaming eyes as big as traffic lights and huge red talons which she was lowering slowly from her feathers like a giant landing gear! But she did not land at all! Instead, just as she almost reached the ground, her great wide wings snapped out, her great red talons shot forward, and with a swift WHOOSH she flew by so low that Daddy got a long black feather in his mouth, and she picked little Benjy right off the Picnic Place as neatly as if he were a piece of lint and flew off with him into the sky!

"Oh Mummy Mummy Mummy!" cried Benjy, kicking his fat little legs and struggling to get free. But he could not, for the Mummy bird's great talons were firmly caught in his beautiful suit of fudge-colored velvet which Mummy had bought for him. It was a lovely suit of the nicest, very strongest material, and as it was so strong, it was naturally very good for carrying little boys off in.

"Save me, Mummy, save me!" cried Benjy, his little voice getting fainter and fainter in the distance.

"Mummy's coming, sweet boy!" screamed Mummy. "Mummy's coming!"

And how funny Mummy looked as she stood there on the Picnic Place with her head shooting forward and her feet wide apart and her arms flapping at her side, almost as if she were trying to fly!

"Never fear!" she cried. "Mummy's on her way!" And, strange as it seems, so she was! For, even as little Benjy was being carried off, *another* whistling noise had started overhead, and even though they did not hear it at first, now Daddy and Sid looked up to see *another* bird, bigger and blacker than the first, diving down upon them!

"Oh boy!" shouted Daddy. "Hit the dirt, everybody!" And Daddy hit the dirt, and so did Sid, fast. But Mummy did not. She was too busy flapping her arms, trying to get off the ground. And the big bird, with his great red beak and his great red eyes and his great red talons, came rushing past with another WHOOSH, and as he passed it was clear that he must be the Daddy bird, because of the big tuft of feathers on his head which was shaped like a derby hat! And just as the Mummy bird had picked off little Benjy, so did the Daddy bird pick off Mummy and carry her, struggling and screaming, into the sky!

And up up up they flew, with the Daddy bird flying so fast that he soon caught up with the Mummy bird, and together the Mummy bird, the Daddy bird, little Benjy and Mummy flew into the face of the bright sun, over the top of the mountain, and completely out of sight!

And then everything was very still.

After a while, Daddy got up off the ground, and so did Sid. They stood for a little, looking into the sky, and at the top of the mountain. Then Daddy spoke.

"Wow," he said.

After a minute he lifted his head and began to sniff.

"Cigars," he said.

And it was true: the air was full of the strong smell of old cigars! And of course Daddy did not know, and Sid did not know, what this meant: that Mister Good Fairy was right there with them, and had been for some time, watching little Benjy Boy's wish at last come true!

For, finally, something big and marvelous had happened to Benjy, and surely no one would not agree that it is a big and marvelous thing to be the only little boy in Smiles to be captured by the biggest bird that ever was! And because of his wish, that whatever big and marvelous thing happened to him would happen to his Mummy too, Mummy also had been captured and taken away! And if it had not been for her little boy's beautiful wish, Mummy would never have had this big marvelous thing happen to her, and she would still be standing, flapping her arms, on the Picnic Place!

And the Good Fairy, who was sitting there invisible on a high rock, with his baseball cap tilted down over his eyes to keep out the bright shining midday sun, knew all this and puffed contentedly on his short black cigar with the air of a Good Fairy who has done his work well. Then he pulled the tattered notebook out of his baseball pants pocket and wrote, with his stubby pencil, one last sentence under the name BALLOU, Benjamin Thurlow. Then he put the notebook and pencil away and leaned back comfortably, with his arms behind his head, and sighed.

"Toot finee," he said, and blew a big cloud of smoke.

But Daddy and Sid, who did not know any of this, just stayed around for a few minutes more, and then went home, after first getting away from some of the people who had been at the Picnic Place and who had seen what had happened and who were anxious to ask Daddy questions. But Daddy did not say anything much, and neither did Sid.

And that night, in the living room of the little house, Daddy and Sid sat all alone, watching television. Daddy did not sit inside the television set now. He sat in the big comfortable chair with the footstool in front of it. At his right hand, on a little table, was a big can of beer which he was pouring into a nice cold glass. On the floor, near Daddy's feet, lay Sid. He was all stretched out with his muddy paws making a few marks on the rug every now and then. Under his head was a satin pillow which was one of Mummy's favorite pillows. On it she had lovingly embroidered, A BOY'S BEST FRIEND IS HIS MUMMY!

So Daddy and Sid just stayed there, watching television for a while, because the man on television was a newsman who was talking about Mummy. He was a bald man with a big mouth and sad eyes.

"Yass," he said, "oh yass, dear friends, a tragic story tonight. Mummy Ballou, college graduate, and her little son, Benjy Ballou, birdnapped from a lovely recreation ground in the little town of Smiles, Pennsylvania! Tragic for everyone, but especially tragic for the lone survivor, Daddy Ballou, respected television repairman in that little community! Tonight the hearts of all America go out to that lonely man who, bathed in melancholy most profound, sits alone in his living room, sorrowing, sorrowing, sorrowing. . . ."

And Daddy and Sid watched for a little while more, and then Daddy got up and switched channels and got a Wild West program, the star of which was a hero dog. How Daddy and Sid enjoyed this program! Daddy had a drink from his glass, and then he lit up a very long and quite expensive cigar and started puffing.

"Ah," he said, and sighed a long sigh. Then he said, "Have a beer, Sid?"

Sid shook his head no, but with his paws he thumped the floor in a way which meant, "I like it, but it doesn't like me!"

"Okay," said Daddy, and puffing once more at his cigar, he settled back to enjoy the Western. He spent almost the whole night like this. Every once in a while he had another little drink from his big glass, and then he lit up another cigar, and then he thought, quite often, of Mummy and Benjy. He thought of the strange way in which they had gone away, and he wondered whether they would ever come back. On the whole, he thought, it was very very possible that they would never come back.

And they never did.

The Edge of Sadness

THE EDGE OF SADNESS *is at once a family novel, an urban novel, a novel about growing old, a study of the Irish-American Catholic tradition, and a meditation on man's aloneness, temporal and spiritual. Thanks to the narrator's ironic temper, and to a fine array of comic characters (notably the curate, Father Danowski), the book is often funny as well as melancholy. The narrator is a priest in late middle age, Father Hugh Kennedy, a native of the old red-brick city which is the setting of* THE LAST HURRAH. *At its heart, in the polyglot slum which was once an Irish stronghold, lies Saint Paul's: a parish of dead-beats and transients, whose great church is shabby now and almost vacant.*

Father Hugh has come there as pastor, after a long struggle with alcoholism, into which he fell at the time of his father's death, partly because of his grief, but more because, in his bustling life in a prosperous parish, a spiritual dryness had come on him unawares. His drunkenness and his extended cure have meant a long absence from the scenes and the friends of his youth; and the book opens with a recall from exile: a summons to the eighty-first birthday party of Charlie Carmody.

Charlie is the miserly and tyrannical father of Hugh Kennedy's child-hood friends: Helen Carmody, whom he might have married; John Carmody, who is also a priest; and several others. The novel traces the renewal of their closeness, during which Father Hugh relives his past and theirs, realizing now how old Charlie has stunted or frustrated their lives. Not very much "happens," except that Father John dies; but Father Hugh comes at last to an understanding of Charlie's loneliness, of his friend John's perilous misanthropy, and of his own real duty and destiny as a priest.

The following selections cluster around one theme: Father Hugh Kennedy's pastoral vocation. Taken from three widely spaced points in the book, they begin one-fourth of the way through, when, just returned from Charlie's birthday party, Father Hugh ponders his past, his father's death, and his own sudden downturn into alcoholism.

THIS is not a pretty story, and I have neither the intention nor the desire to go back over all the details — details which even in memory would be humiliating enough to any man, but which are infinitely more so when that man is a priest. For here there is a double betrayal: of the dignity of a man, of the sacredness of a vocation. In any case, it was in these weeks following my father's death that I began to spend most of my time by myself. This was a great departure for me; as I've said, I had always been a gregarious and an active priest. For example, ever since I'd become the pastor of Saint Stephen's, I'd kept up my old ties with Saint Raymond's; there was considerable visiting back and forth. This now stopped. Not all at once, but it stopped. And it stopped because . . . well, because *I* stopped, and when one way of a two-way exchange stops or dries up, the other invariably does, too. So, loyally, they continued to come over now and then, and the visits were always pleasant enough, no one was ever not cordial to the other, but the mutual encouragement, the nourishment that keeps friendship and affection going was lacking, and by-and-by all visits ceased. It was in this way that over a period of time I came to lose all touch with even the Carmodys.

Within the parish the situation was different; the results were the same. Here I was bound by duty as well as friendship, yet without deliberately planning it, without ever waking in the morning and announcing to myself that this day I would remain a little apart, I began to withdraw from my parishioners. There were of course the parish functions — at first I went to them as usual, but now I found myself slipping away at the earliest possible moment, and as the weeks and months passed by, I found myself not going at all. It wasn't that I had turned against the people; it wasn't even that I had now anything so positive as dislike for these gatherings which had once been such a part of my parish life. It was simply that somehow they had stopped mattering, and now it seemed the easiest and indeed the most natural thing in the world to sidestep each one as it came along.

In the rectory I built up further insulation. People came, on any of the multiple errands that can bring the people to their priest, and for a while I continued to see them. Somewhat more briefly than before, however; I managed to discourage the cherished habit of the casual, gossipy, infinitely expanding "chat." Eventually, gradually, I stopped seeing them altogether; for the first time in my life as a priest I now regularly sent down word that I was "out," and passed the problem on to the younger and more willing hands of my curates.

And as for my curates — these two young men who lived with me, who were in my charge, and for whom I was supposed to serve as some sort of example — I'm afraid it was towards them that I behaved worst of all. Not by harshness or severity, but by apathy, neglect. From me they deserved care and respect; they received not even attention. They came to me now with parish problems which I settled perfunctorily and in haste; they no longer talked to me of themselves for the good reason, I suppose, that I no longer asked them about themselves; our rectory small talk grew smaller and smaller, then disappeared entirely; at meals, in the rectory living room, in the sacristy of the church — in short, in all the places where we normally met — my eagerness simply to *get away*, to return to the solitude of my own room, was all too unconcealed. Before their young and puzzled eyes the old, easy harmony of our life together vanished; a chasm cracked open and was never again bridged by either pastor or curates. All this was my fault, and the fault was not a small one. Because there is a sense in which a priest is dependent upon no one quite so much as another priest, for he has no wife, no child, and — in the ordinary meaning of the word — no home. His home is the rectory; his family, his fellow priests. And so while it's true that I was never deliberately unkind or cruel to my curates; it's also true that I was guilty of a graver offense. For what I did was to destroy the spirit of their priestly home. . . .

In this way I came to be alone. I spent most of my time in my bedroom: a pleasant enough room, although this couldn't have mattered less; I wasn't there to bask. Just what I was there for remained an unanswered question. It somehow seemed terribly important that I should be there and that I should be there alone, so that I might do . . . what? Whatever it was that I had to do. An odd restlessness had come over me; I began many things, and finished nothing. I would come into the room, close the door, sit at the table or in the armchair, and begin to read, or to say my office for the day, or to prepare a sermon for the next Sunday. But whatever I began, in no more than a few moments, I would drop the pen and put the book aside, and I would be thinking of my father. And thinking, strangely enough, not of anything big or important that he'd said or done, but of the small things, the little fringe touches: the way his lips formed into a slow, soundless whistle as he went through the careful ritual of filling his pipe; the slight limp in his walk on a damp day (he had broken a bone in his foot as a young man); his habit of courteously saying, "Ah yes, that's a very good point indeed!" — which was his inevitable preliminary to total disagreement. I have an accurate memory, which is not always a blessing, and as these recollections purred soothingly along, they were so fresh and strong in their exactness of detail that I sank into them easily as if they were the only realities that counted, as if they could and would happen over and over again, at any time: now, tonight, tomorrow morning. Then, suddenly, would come the sharp, clearing sweep across the inner eyes, and I would come to, and remember that this was only a memory, an echo of something which was gone and which could never be again. And this would always take me to still one more memory, this one of the memory of my father as I had last seen him: wasted, senseless, unrecognizable. And then . . .

And then I would rise, walk up and down the room — sheer motion, the great therapy of the restless man, pour myself a small drink — which seemed to help, go back to my chair, and begin again the farce of preparing to get down to work. And in a while the whole procedure would be repeated, and then, later, it would be repeated again. The only change was one of emphasis; as time went by, the small drink got no smaller. Slowly it became more important, and over the months the occasional help came to be the steady necessity. At all hours; at night so that I might sleep; the first thing in the morning, to deaden the passage into the long, dull empty ache of the day. . . .

Which is the classic story, of course. It's been told over and over again, especially in recent years; the reformed drunkard is a ready raconteur. It's the familiar story of the trap: does it become much different merely because the narrator is a priest? Probably not — except, of course, that one may wonder why the priest, if caught, stays caught, for surely there must be aids, sources of strength available to him which should be tapped at once. And this is what I tried to do — not at once, but at last. For, strange as it may seem — especially since, in the confessional, I had heard these case histories outlined a hundred times or more — I didn't for the longest time realize just what it was that was happening to me. And then one morning I woke with a clarity rare to me in those blurred days, and suddenly I seemed to see my whole predicament before me, etched in the sharpest, most unsparing detail, complete with every certain consequence. I saw this with a sense of shock, and I remember that, heavy-headed, heavy-eyed, I pushed myself up in bed; I scourged myself

— with words; I shook my head clear and reminded myself that this had become a habit, and that habit could be broken with a strong will; I got to my feet; I made a firm resolve.

This firm resolve lasted for twenty-four hours. It was succeeded, after a while, by another firm resolve, which lasted not quite so long. This was in turn succeeded by another . . . then another . . . and another. . . .

And then, finally, I did what I should have done from the start. Shame, pride, may have held me back; I don't know. But now I remembered that I was God's priest; I went for God's help. I went desperately, because by this time I was badly frightened — but the discovery I now made frightened me even more. For I found that, just when I needed to most, I could no longer pray. I could kneel, I knew the words, I could say the words — and they meant nothing. At night, in the silent room, I could hear myself whispering phrases which I had known from the days when I first knew any words at all, which once had been charged with richness and fervor and love, but which now were empty formulae, dry wisps blown up from the desert of memory. I was praying — and it was nothing more than a child with jackstones in his hand, singsonging his way through the gibberish of games.

And yet — how to explain this? — I never stopped believing: in God, in His goodness, in His justice. I did believe, but prayer is always a kind of talking to God — and now I could not talk at all. I went through the motions, straining to drive into the lifeless words some breath of hope, of devotion. But you can't do this if it isn't there, and now prayer was little more than a succession of distractions, and I seemed to be speaking a language which I had always spoken but whose words no longer had reference to anything I knew, and sometimes it seemed as though a part of me had left me and now stood on the sidelines, observing, a detached and melancholy witness, mourning the vain performance, and whispering back to me, "It's no good, it won't work, you just can't do it any more. . . ."

Then one night, or very early one morning — it must have been three o'clock or so — I awoke in the darkness and, surprisingly, I was neither drowsy nor fuddled. I was wide awake; I had come from dead sleep into an almost preternatural alertness: I was trembling. This passed, but I could not go back to sleep. I tried what had come to be my unfailing remedy; it failed. And so I lay there, forced to think, and finding myself in one of those brief cool spaces of lucidity which now, to tell the truth, I did not particularly welcome. And what I thought about was of course myself: as I was now, nearing fifty, the respected pastor of his parish who was in fact a solitary drinker in his room, dazed most of the time, indifferent to his people, irresponsible in his duties, a spiritually arid priest for whom the wellsprings had dried up, for whom life had been reduced to a problem of concealment and routine. And then the inevitable contrast: the young priest of not too many years ago, zealous, devoted, with fresh and unimpeded hopes, whose parish was his life, whose days were active and busy and full of joy. How had the one become the other? The distance between them was the distance between the poles, yet it had been eclipsed, and in no time at all. How? Why?

Lying there on my bed in the black and silent morning, in this moment of queer lucidity, I found an answer. It was an answer which began back in those early active years, back with the new parish hall, the improved church grounds, the spick-and-span school band, the bridge evenings for the women, the weekly gatherings of men, the outings, the school plays — all those things of which I'd always been so proud, and to which I'd given so much time. And, suddenly, there was the clue before me: the "so much time." So much time that there had been no time for anything else, and I saw now, in a flash of long postponed revelation, and with a sense of shock and dismay, how little by little the unimportant had become important for me, how those things which belonged properly on the edges of my life had in fact become the center. The young priest, without realizing it, had become little more than a recreation director: a cheerleader in a Roman collar.

And it had been so easy, so innocent. There are, after all, certain social duties which a priest has towards his parishioners, and if that priest is as I was — energetic and gregarious, with an aptitude for such occasions — these duties and occasions have a way of multiplying. There's a great attraction to this: he's doing what he likes to do, and he can tell himself that it's all for the honor and glory of God. He believes this, quite sincerely, and he finds ample support for such belief: on all sides he's assured that he is doing the much-needed job of "waking up the parish." Which is not a hard thing for a young priest to hear; he may even see himself as stampeding souls to their salvation. What he may not see is that he stands in some danger of losing himself in the strangely engrossing business of simply "being busy"; gradually he may find that he is rather uncomfortable whenever he is not "being busy." And, gradually too, he may find fewer and fewer moments in which he can absent himself from activity, in which he can be alone, can be silent, can be still — in which he can reflect and pray. And since these are precisely the moments which are necessary for all of us, in which spiritually we grow, in which, so to speak, we maintain and enrich our *connection* with God, then the loss of such moments is grave and perilous. Particularly so for a priest — particularly for a priest who suddenly finds that he can talk more easily to a parish committee than he can to God. Something within him will have atrophied from disuse; something precious, something vital. It will have gone almost without his knowing it, but one day, in a great crisis, say, he will reach for it — and it will not be there. And then . . . then he may find that the distance between the poles is not so great a distance after all. . . .

This was the answer which came to me on that morning. It was not a consoling answer; is it ever consoling to learn that you've been most mistaken in something of which you've been most proud? It brought me closer to desolation than I had ever been before. From that moment on, I grew more desperate and my predicament became more extreme. I did not drink less.

Yet how curious it was that, although this went on for a long time, very few in the parish really knew about it. While I was rarely available to them, I was at least visible: I always managed to say my Mass on Sundays, and while they surely must have sensed the change in me, I've found that towards a priest most people are apt to be either innocent or charitable. Probably a little of both; at any rate, they don't readily suspect the worst. I think they thought I was ill; from time to time I heard reports of their concern. The curates, of course, were another matter. They knew. They could not help knowing. They lived in the same house with me, and in any case priests always know about another priest who drinks. It must have been an intolerable time for them; I must have continually scandalized them. But they said nothing; I'm sure the poor fellows had no idea of what to say or do — nothing in their seminary training had prepared them for the drunken pastor.

Meanwhile, I grew less discreet. I left my room at night now, and wandered about the rectory. Occasionally I was conscious of the guarded creaking of a bedroom door: my progress was being observed. I did not care. Then, one morning, I was found in a stupor on the hall floor, just outside my room; I was helped to bed. I was now becoming more public, and it was only a question of time until what had to happen finally did happen. I was summoned before the Bishop.

At this time the Bishop of our diocese was not the man who had appointed me pastor of Saint Stephen's. This Bishop was new. He had arrived fairly recently to take charge of the diocese; none of the priests knew much about him. He had come here from the West: a large, square-faced, uncommunicative man, as bishops go neither young nor old — roughly the same age as myself. He had come to us preceded by none of the usual tendrils of advance clerical intelligence — for once, the reliable diocesan grapevine appeared to have broken down — and he continued to remain a mystery to most of us. He was certainly a mystery and a stranger to me as, on that morning, I stood before him, in disgrace.

He said only, "Sit down, Father."

His voice was low, and suddenly it occurred to me that I had never heard him speak before except on public occasions. Now, here in the privacy of the room, his voice seemed curiously uninflected, without expression of any kind. I sat facing him across the old Bishop's desk — a great mahogany lake; the wide gray eyes were heavy and as expressionless as the voice. So far, there had been no touch of anger or reproach. Or — less comforting — of sympathy. The low voice said, "How long has this been going on?"

The tone was impersonal: it was like a company physician making a routine inquiry into the history of abdominal pain. I said, "A long time, I'm afraid, Your Excellency."

"Which means . . . what? Weeks? Months? Years?"

I hesitated, and he added, in exactly the same voice, "Since your father died?"

And this was a different kind of question, one which surprised me; clearly, the Bishop was better posted than I had imagined. I nodded, and then, because it seemed important not to use my father's death as any kind of prop, or as the basis of a plea for pity, I said, "Although I don't think it's as simple as that. The cause-and-effect, I mean."

He looked at me, but in an oddly reflective and neutral way, so that I somehow felt that he might really have been studying himself as much as me. He said nothing, and in the silence, I wondered if it was now my move, if he expected me to continue with an explanation, with some attempt at justification. But apparently not. He got to his feet and walked slowly over to the windows, and stood there, looking out at the long broad slope of lawn which stretched away down towards the avenue. It was the middle of a summer morning, and the windows were open: from somewhere outside came the sound of a lawnmower, and there was the smell of freshly cut grass. And the Bishop stood there, looking out, motionless and silent, for what seemed to me a very long time, and then at last, without turning to me, but still looking out the window, he said an astonishing thing. He said, quietly, calmly, simply, "I don't want you to do it again."

And that was all — then there was silence. I said nothing; I was stunned by mildness. All I could do was sit there and stare at him; instead of the thunderbolt, he had delivered a tap on the wrist. Why? He turned now, and once more the wide gray eyes took me in with that curious, reflective stare; he said slowly, "What did you expect me to do, Father? Crucify you?"

I said, truthfully enough, "I don't know, Bishop. I don't think I had the slightest idea." And then, because he had been so fair, so decent, and because surely something more than this inarticulate bafflement was called for, I said, "I'd like to thank you. It's very generous. . . ."

But he did not acknowledge this. Instead, he returned to his desk and sat down; he said, "There was some feeling that you should be removed from your parish. Not so much because of what you had done as because of what you might do in the future. The course of prudence. That doesn't surprise you?"

I shook my head, and he said, "Prudence is all right. Still, it can become the easy way out. And then there are other factors. You have a good record in the diocese. And to take a man's parish from him is bound to be a humiliating affair. I don't want to humiliate you, Father." He was speaking evenly and steadily, in a voice which remained as subdued and unemphatic as before: a soft and private voice in which he seemed to be listening thoughtfully to his own deliberations. Suddenly he said, "You were ordained . . . when?"

I told him, and he nodded. "Yes. I thought so. My year. If I had come from this diocese originally we would have been classmates in the seminary. That's not important. But it is another factor. You're not some young curate who comes in here to be reprimanded and sent back to his pastor. You're a man of my own age. You've been a priest as long as I have. What am I to say to you, Father?" He looked at me, and with the look came another of those long and absolutely still pauses; after a while he said, "That a priest has grave responsibilities? That you haven't lived up to yours? That what you've done is wrong, seriously wrong? You know all that. Almost everything I could say to you now you know as well as I do. To give you a talking-to, a lecture, would simply be empty punishment. Rubbing it in. I'm not much interested in that. What I am interested in is seeing that all this stops. As soon as possible. Right now. That's all I say to you, Father: I want you to stop." And very simply and directly, he said, "Will you? Can you?"

Again, easier said than done — especially since the doing was up to me. But I said, "I think so. I give you my word I'll do my best. . . ."

It seemed inadequate, thin: like a Scout's brave pledge at a troop meeting. But he made no comment; he said only, "This problem of yours: I haven't asked you to tell me about it in any detail. Not because I'm not interested. But because I thought you might find it difficult." He said objectively, "I'm not the easiest man to talk to. Also, there are others who know far more about this sort of thing than I do. Experts. They might be of some help. You might want to talk to them."

I mentioned my confessor; he said, "Yes, obviously. But you might also try it on another level. Establishing certain physical safeguards. A different approach. Do you know Father Luke Leary?"

"No. . . ."

"Alcoholics Anonymous," he said bluntly. There was another of the pauses; he said, "Does that shock you, Father?"

"No." Although this was not quite true; it did, a little. I said tentatively, perhaps defensively, "It's just that I'm not quite sure I fit the category."

"No. I don't say you do. But I think it does no harm to talk to someone who understands drinking. A doctor. Or Father Leary. He's a sensible man. Not brilliant, but sensible, practical. I have the feeling that he knows what he's talking about. He drank heavily himself at one time. A bad situation. But he got out of it and since then he's been helping a few of the priests here in the diocese. You see, you're not unique, Father." The low voice seemed to grow more remote; he said, "These things happen. Why, I don't know. Loneliness, I suspect, as much as anything else. They forget what they . . . Well," he said, coming back to me, "think about it. Your confessor, prayer, yes, of course. But I wouldn't ignore the other. The two go together, I'd say. At least they do in my experience." He stood; the interview was over. "Goodbye, Father. I'll give you my blessing."

I knelt for the blessing, and kissed his ring. When I rose, I said goodbye, and thanked him once more for his kindness.

He said thoughtfully, "I don't know that it's kindness. It's more a matter of balance. I can't let anything happen to any of my parishes. But on the other hand I can't afford to lose a good priest. I think the second is as important as the first." With no change of voice he said, "Good luck, Father. Do well. Keep busy."

I had almost reached the door when he said, "Father?"

"Yes, Bishop?"

"But not too busy," he said. "Too many things go on. Save a little of yourself, Father. For what really counts."

It was a shrewd and unexpected stroke. Once again I was reminded that this strange man, so short a time in our diocese, had informed himself surprisingly well. And now I left him and returned to Saint Stephen's: relieved, even happy in a way, somewhat apprehensive, a little uncertain of what was to come, but above all full of high resolve. The second chance had been given, and given with the greatest generosity; from now on, I would make the most of it. . . .

So much for good intentions.

Two months. Two months in which I had not the slightest trouble with my parishioners (there had never been public scandal; news of what had happened had been kept within the rectory). Two months in which my curates were nervously eager to demonstrate to me that nothing, really, had happened at all. Two months in which I talked to my confessor (a stern and careful old man who sat in his chair, his long old body bent forward, his head supported by a veined, translucent hand, his eyes closed; from time to time he would sigh deeply and murmur "Yes yes," with a kind of discouraged impatience which suggested that he had heard this same dreary tale many times before and knew far in advance of the telling exactly what the next detail would be). Two months in which I did not, despite the Bishop's urging, call on Father Luke Leary (for I had no wish to approach the peculiar apostolate of the confessed alcoholic — mainly, I suppose, because of the obvious implication). Two months in which I prayed and tried to recover some sense of dedication; two months in which I stopped all drinking; two months in which, slowly, optimism grew, and I began to feel a confidence that at last a corner had been turned. In short, two solid months of progress and of hope: the prelude to the quick collapse.

Because it was quick. Quick — and mortifying: I capitulated in an instant. There was, one night, after a good day, a sudden onslaught of depression — why, I don't know. I found myself for the first time in weeks smothered by this unaccountable sadness; it seemed to me that everything I'd done for the past two months was purposeless, foolish: the steady strides forward were in fact the steps of an ant up the side of a mountain. It was a mood of despair I couldn't shake. The more I looked at myself and what I was doing, the more it seemed to me that everything I'd prized most belonged to the past, that my father, my own hopes, my life as a priest, my friends, were all gone or damaged forever, and that my future consisted of an endless succession of days in which I would slog along the treadmill, whistling to support the delusion that I was coming ahead by leaps and bounds, while in reality I was moving nowhere: a gray, pathetic, neutral figure, kidding himself until the end of his time. . . .

Bleak moods assail everyone; most of us have our defenses. That night I had none, and as it grew worse there came a moment when suddenly, automatically, without any sense of arriving at a decision, I walked quickly out of my room, and out of the rectory, and down the dark night streets to the familiar door of a neighborhood package store. And so it was that, within the matter of an hour, the hope, the optimism, the confidence, the accomplishments of the past two months were gone, and I was back where I started.

Or rather, much farther back than that: before, I had always had at least a measure of discretion; now, I seemed to have none. My audience was no longer limited to two appalled and extremely unhappy young curates: I had broadened my field. Now, restless and foggy, I not only left my room at night but I left the rectory as well, and often very late at night — or very early in the morning, long before dawn — I walked and walked — alone, aimless, slightly unsteady — through the streets of the parish. The darkness was some protection, but not much; of course I was seen and of course I was recognized. The rectory secret was now a secret no longer. The whispers began and spread and grew louder: the pastor became the public scandal. I did not even spare myself the authentic comic touch: very early one morning, on the front porch, as I was fumbling for the key, I was discovered by whom? The milkman! The traditional encounter: the pure farce. I did not laugh. . . .

Nor did the Bishop. This time the summons came quickly; within a few weeks I was back in his office. He was as expressionless, as impassive as ever, but he had come to a decision; he said at once, "It was a mistake. And not only on your part, Father. But now we have to do what some would say we should have done immediately. Perhaps they're right. Although I don't know. . . ." He looked at me and said quietly, "I'm appointing Father Molloy administrator of your parish."

And so I had lost Saint Stephen's. But of course by now this was inevitable, so much so that even when I heard it announced in so many words, I felt no new pain. I said, "He's a good priest. They'll like him." There was a pause — an awkward one. Then I said, "I'm sorry, Bishop. Genuinely, sincerely. . . ."

And what I meant was a sorrow, not at having lost my parish, but at having failed it. I'm sure he knew this; his head moved forward in a slow and rather absent nod, as if acknowledging the words. But he said thoughtfully, "I think most people who do something they know is wrong are sorry afterward. And genuinely so. The sinner who rejoices in his sin: that must be fairly rare. Everybody's sorry. I'm not trying to cut you off, Father. Or to minimize the value of your sorrow. But I am suggesting that sorrow by itself doesn't really help much. It's too easily neutralized. It doesn't last long. Something else is needed if anything is to be done." The low voice said unexpectedly, "Do you know The Cenacle, Father?"

Or not so unexpected, because this, too, was inevitable. I knew The Cenacle — or more accurately, I knew about it. Located in the desert country of Arizona, it once had been the home of a national figure wealthy enough to be called eccentric; twenty years ago it had been purchased by the Church and had become . . . what? A retreat? A rest home? A hospital? A recuperative center? At one time or another over the years I had heard it called all these things, but whatever the euphemism, The Cenacle was in fact a way station — and, in some cases, a final home — for the errant priest. To be sent to The Cenacle was . . . well, it was not exactly a boost to one's self-esteem. Was the Bishop at this moment thinking of my self-esteem? I thought it unlikely. I looked a him, and once again I saw the slight nod.

"Yes," he said. "There are alternatives. But I think this is best. All things considered." And then this strange disciplinarian asked, "Does it appeal to you at all?"

And what could I say? That I was overjoyed to join the company of broken clerics like myself? I hesitated, then said, "Not very much, I'm afraid, Your Excellency. Although I wouldn't have thought that was a particular consideration at this point. . . ."

He did not respond to this; he said only, "You may feel differently after you've been there awhile. It's not a penal colony. It's a place where you can be put on a decent program. And work with intelligent people. People who understand what it is you're up against. People who can help you. That's what's essential. Independent effort is all very well, but if you're really in trouble, I think it's seldom good enough. We depend upon each other, Father. All of us. We're meant to. In a way, that's what it's all about."

There was another of those extraordinary pauses, in which he seemed to be communicating with himself. Then he said, "But you know all this. I think most people know it. And I think that a man who does know it and would let his pride, for example, stand in the way of such help would have to be a very short-sighted man. Almost a foolish man."

There had been not the slightest shift in tone before this last remark to suggest the special pointedness — yet there was no mistaking that it was there. It was the closest the Bishop had come to the direct rebuke. He stood now; another of our interviews had ended, this one far less happily than the last. He gave me his blessing again; he wished me good luck again; and as I left his office he said again, "Father?"

I turned; he said simply, "Goodbye. And remember, it's not forever. We'll have you back with us again."

It was on this vague note of promise that I left the diocese and went to The Cenacle. . . .

I was not there forever; I was there for four years: a long time. Yet it was a good time. Not always a happy one — particularly in the first few months — but in the end a deeply rewarding one: far more so than I could ever have expected. Because, for one thing, it worked; it did the trick. Here in what was really, I suppose, a desert reformatory — a queer sprawl of adobe building, stripped of the lunatic splendors of its former owner — among a fellowship I had joined with reluctance, with resentment (for it's quite possible to resent what you admit to be just), and with a sense of shame, I did what I could not have done alone: I came to terms with myself; I came to terms with God.

It's pointless to go into any step-by-step account of what happened — although I remember it all, every bit of it. It's easy enough to say, I think, that from the beginning I was given every help by a few compassionate and knowledgeable men. One was a layman, a doctor who had been out there for some years; one was a priest who, although still fairly young, had in fact started The Cenacle, nearly two decades before; three or four more were priests who had no connection with the staff, but who were there because they had been sent there: like me, they had come to be cured. And so, professionals, or merely those who had been through the mill themselves, these men were there to help. The odd thing is that I don't think any of them were what would ordinarily be considered wise men. I look back on our conversations, and I remember little that was at all remarkable: certainly no one was conspicuous for his piety or learning. Yet they had what I needed: they had their experience, they had a clear, hard, practical view of my problem and position, and with an odd combination of bluntness and delicacy, they managed to point out to me just where I stood and what I was. Moreover, they made themselves available to me at any hour, and for what was I think the first time in my adult life I came to have no hesitation in calling on someone to help me, if only to talk to me, when I was at my lowest, when sometimes it seemed as if I might quite literally go mad. Because the moments of despair still came, but now I was no longer allowed the reliable obliteration. And so there was nothing else to do but face them. They were endless, and they were awful. Even with every kindness and encouragement from those around me, it was a bitter and a desolate business. . . .

And yet this bitterness and desolation did not last. Gradually I began to improve, to respond, to notice and even to take an interest in this new world in which I found myself. It was a world completely new to me; everything about it was different, even the setting. Especially the setting. I woke each morning to the bright heat of the desert day, to the pale high sky without a cloud. The house was cool, protected by its thick adobe walls. I could look from my window across the enormous sweep of silent space and watch the play of the morning light on great and distant mountains; at night the sun went down at once, and from a window in the west I could see the dramatic, shifting rush of amethyst and gold flood the sky before the instant, final drop of darkness. It was all strange and completely fascinating to me. I had grown up in the East and had never left it; I had grown accustomed to the smaller scale, the close horizons, the crowds and the places where crowds live, and the sudden spiteful turns of weather. Out here there was none of that: only a vast, unbroken grandeur, the majestic monotony of the hot and brilliant days. I never got used to it; I never got tired of it. I would sit for hours by the window, motionless, thinking, watching, listening to the immense, sunbaked stillness. I suppose it was all a part of the therapy that was going on every day; in any case, it worked wonders for me.

At this time there were perhaps twenty priests at The Cenacle. In addition to the staff, that is, but including the three or four priests I've already mentioned as being especially helpful. During my stay — which, as I've said, was a long one: I could have left earlier, and in fact the Bishop once suggested it, but this time I wanted to be sure — this number varied: sometimes there were more, sometimes less. They came from dioceses all over the country. Like me, most of them were middle-aged, and had come here for the first time and for the one reason; again like me, they had arrived filled with shame and the desire to keep to themselves. But there was in this house an atmosphere —an atmosphere of help, really — which broke down exclusiveness, and this, plus our common bond of all having failed in the same way, sooner or later brought each one into contact with the rest. I came to know them all and to hear their stories — just as they came to hear mine. We talked freely, even insistently: after all, our Topic was there. As in any institution where all the inmates suffer from the same malady, we compared our notes and our cases: the causes, symptoms, expectations of recovery. And I found to my surprise that there was a great similarity to all these stories; in every one, I saw something of my own. As the Bishop had said, I was hardly unique. The telltale thread wound its way through all: the slow neglect of the nourishment of the spirit, the failure to realize that unless this is daily deepened and enriched, then, when the fervor and the drive of the young priest fade — as they must —there will be no replacement by a living, ever-growing love, and then, when the aging priest going through the years meets the inevitable disappointments, crises, or sometimes just the sudden burden of his loneliness, he may meet them with an emptiness where fullness should be, and the result of that will not be a happy one. Because if a priest has not this continuing current of love, he has nothing. He can turn to no one; his marriage is to God, and if he fails in that, his strength is gone, his very purpose is gone. And so, what then? The Cenacle? The Cenacle — if, that is, he's fortunate. If not, there are other roads and uglier destinations, and the priest, like any other man, is not immune to these. . . .

But the priests who were with me were firm and unanimous in one intention: to return to their dioceses, to pick up their lives as parish priests, never to need The Cenacle again. Most of them succeeded in this; they did not come back. Yet there were the sad exceptions, and I can remember with great affection and sorrow one priest who, even during my stay, left and returned four times. He was a small, pale man with a fragile and strangely gay face; he must have been more than fifty, but there was about him such a persistently youthful air that he might have been in his thirties. Each time he came back he was a washed-out, shaking ruin, but he had an astonishing ability to recover, and in no time at all he would be out walking around the grounds with his springy, chipper step, whistling, joking, looking like a mischievous boy. I talked with him often; never once did he admit to being an alcoholic. He never in fact so much as mentioned drink — and this, in The Cenacle, was an extraordinary reticence. Instead he spoke in the vaguest terms of a mysterious respiratory ailment which attacked him recurrently and left him drained and helpless. It was, he explained, a matter of climate.

"I tell you, Hugh, this place works miracles for me!" he said enthusiastically. "It's the steady heat that does it. The bacilli or the viruses or whatever they call those organisms these days simply perish: it's genocide the moment they hit the Arizona state line. Here is where I flourish, yet there I am, nailed to New England. They say that it's the tropics that destroy health, but have you ever stopped to consider who the 'they' are who say this? They all come from Bangor or Providence. Not one of them ever mentions the simple medical fact that the month of March in the Massachusetts bronchial belt is infinitely more debilitating than malaria time in Panama. It's no accident that all the country's best hospitals are in Boston, you know: they want to be close to the source of supply." We walked along, and he whistled cheerfully; every now and then we paused while he traced in the dust with a stick a quick, deft caricature of some diocesan acquaintance. "John Riordan," he said. "The clumsiest priest in America. For some reason he got interested in Boy Scout work and they appointed him spiritual director. His bishop had to remove him after two months. He'd go to the meetings and insist on being one of the boys. You know: splitting firewood, hacking away with hammers and axes and knives. After every meeting he'd come back to the rectory covered with blood. It was wonderful first-aid practice for the Scouts, but this pastor saw that unless something were done in a hurry this priest who'd formerly been all thumbs would very soon be no thumbs at all. So the bishop removed him. No," he said, returning to an earlier theme, "I'd like nothing better than to get out. Of New England, that is. Wouldn't you, Hugh? Don't you ever get fed up with it back there? Wouldn't you like a transfer? Wouldn't you like to wake up one morning and find yourself the only priest in some impossibly hot, impossibly arid land?"

"An American Desert Father? Or someone like Charles Foucauld? No, I don't think so. Not very much. Not at all, really."

"Wouldn't you? *I* would. Oh, wouldn't I!" We continued to walk, and after a while he said gaily, "I might found a new order: The Congregation of the Little Fugitives of the North Atlantic Seaboard. Do you think that Rome would look with favor on it? You could join, Hugh. We'd all ride camels and every year we'd have a grand celebration on the day the first flake of snow falls in the Berkshires. We'd burn a rubber boot. Or a ski. I'm convinced I'd never know another sick day."

He was wonderful company on these walks: imaginative, witty, lighthearted. He was also extremely plausible, and once, early in my stay, when I first met him, I discussed his case with the priest who was the Director of The Cenacle.

"But isn't it possible that there's something in what he says? I don't mean that he isn't an alcoholic, but in back of all the excuses, couldn't it be true that the climate might have a little to do with it? I know people up there who sniffle and whoop and cough six months of the year; I'd imagine that if he's at all susceptible in that direction it wouldn't help his main problem. Probably some sort of transfer. . . ."

"Transfer," the Director said. "To where? He's been practically everywhere you can be transferred to. He's told you about the terrible attrition of the New England winters? Naturally. Did he also tell you that he hasn't spent a winter in New England for the past ten years? Nominally he's attached to a parish there; at least I think he still is. But he's the greatest traveler I know. They're unbelievably indulgent with him in that diocese. I suppose it's because he's so likable. And he is. He's one of the most agreeable, likable men I've ever met. But he's also most unfortunately a drunk. In New England, in California, in Alabama, in South Bend, Indiana, and in a monastery in the Kentucky hills. No, climate has nothing to do with it. Our friend doesn't discriminate. Hot or cold, wet or dry, he finds his drink. And takes it."

"Then what can be done about him? Nothing?"

"Well, I can only tell you what we can do about him here, and *that's* nothing, all right. We can straighten him out for a few weeks or a couple of months, but that's about it. You see, he just won't play ball. You can't treat a man who refuses to be treated. He won't tell me the truth and with the others he's even worse — especially doctors, psychiatrists. He's very charming with them and tells them these fanciful stories. They're trained men, of course, and naturally they don't believe a word he says: they know right away what they've got on their hands. But he pays no attention to what they tell him. I once told him point-blank that of course he was an alcoholic and that it was high time he stopped his nonsense and faced up to it. You would have thought I'd told him he was twelve feet tall. He professed to be astonished; he cautioned me, in the friendliest possible way, against being ruled by an obsession. He explained that it was a common fault of the specialist to interpret everyone in the light of his specialty. And he said that while he did occasionally take a drink to kill the pain — just what pain he didn't say: that's usually left rather indefinite — that was a far cry from being an alcoholic. Alcoholism, he said to me, was a *disease*. So there you are. He won't admit to a thing, and this stops us before we can even get started."

"Yet he knows what this place is specifically for. And he must know what he's doing and what he is. Do you think it's possible that he could not know? I mean, that he could have talked himself into believing that he's not really a drinker?"

"No, he knows, all right. He may not admit anything, but he knows. He's a very intelligent man."

"And he continues to come back, time after time? Have you ever made any difficulties about taking him back?"

"Oh no," he said. "I can't do anything for him, but I'll always take him in. If I could think of anything better to do with him I would, but I can't. So I'll take him. It's a treadmill, but where else can the poor fellow go? Everybody likes him, but no matter where they ship him it's the same old story. A short, delighted honeymoon, then — bang! No one's going to put up with that; no one can afford to. So his bishop and I have a little arrangement, and whenever he goes off the rails they bring him back from wherever he happens to be — and it's not always easy to find him, by the way — and out he comes for another stay. That's all right with me. As I say, he's a most likable man. And by now a fairly helpless one, in spite of the way he looks and walks around here. I think he may be happier here than he is anywhere else; I wouldn't be surprised if he's come to think of it as his home."

A week or so later, the priest we had been discussing and I were taking one of our usual walks. As always, it was clear and hot, and as we walked, little bright-eyed lizards skittered away in the dust before us, coming to a stop yards away, and freezing into immobility. He said, "I'll miss seeing those lizards. They look like half the people I know."

I wasn't paying the strictest attention; I said drowsily, "There's no need to miss them. They'll be here every day."

"Yes, but *I* won't," he said. "The time has come, Hugh. D day. I'm leaving on Friday."

This woke me completely. "So soon?"

"It *is* soon, isn't it? I take no credit: it's all due to long walks in magnificent sunshine. I don't cough any more and apparently my chest has cleared completely. Of course a return to God's country may fix that, but probably not this time: I hear they're having the best summer they've had in ages. Two consecutive days without rain: all that sort of thing."

I said carefully, "Still, it's unpredictable at best. I should think you'd be better off if you didn't rush back. Why not stay out here a bit longer and give yourself a chance to build up some resistance?"

"Do you know, that's just what the Director said? I thought it was extremely nice of him, especially since I must be all kinds of a nuisance around here. Considering, that is," he explained, "that I have no right here in the first place. This establishment has its own special purpose: it's not at all geared to my kind of trivial complaint. But they've been wonderful with me all the same."

"Then why not stay a while longer. . . ."

"No," he said. "No, I have to get back. I have so many things to do. For one thing, I'm anxious to get working on an idea I have for a diocesan pageant. We have one every year, and of course it's always pure lunacy. You know the sort of thing: your friendly neighborhood dentist suddenly popping out from behind the curtain and announcing that he's Saint John of the Cross. Isn't that terrifying? Of course the Episcopalians go even more hog-wild; they've taken to staging little Biblical dramas in modern dress. There's one rather fancy divine in California who presents the Twelve Apostles in berets and Bermuda shorts. We haven't gone in for that yet; at least I don't think we have. But what I want to do is something quite traditional. You know Claudel's *Le Soulier Satin?* Well . . ."

And, in the highest of spirits, he went on to tell me about his plan, which was, in a way, brilliant, and which, I knew, would reach the same stage of completion as all his other plans. The diocesan pageant could much more safely rely on the friendly neighborhood dentist.

When he left we said goodbye warmly, promising to keep in touch with one another. The railroad station was some twenty miles away; he was to be driven there in The Cenacle's old ranch wagon, and he sat in the front seat beside the driver looking small and sunburned and happy. At the last minute he stuck his head out the window, said goodbye to me again, and then took a slow and last look around the flat, still desert landscape.

"Do you know what I'm doing, Hugh?" he said dramatically. "I'm saying a special goodbye to The Cenacle. It's not like saying goodbye to you, because for one thing in the years to come you and I will probably run into each other a hundred times. But somehow, with The Cenacle, I feel it's *final;* I don't expect I'll ever see it again. In a sense that's a little sad, isn't it? Because it's a very pleasant place, and everyone out here was so good to me. But I have to go home, and when I get there I gather I'm to be given all sorts of new responsibilities: the kind that will keep my nose to the grindstone until even the grindstone is worn out. So I really don't imagine I'll be getting out this way again. Ergo. . . ."

And he waved a great flourishing wave, which included all the premises; then he drove off, still waving, at me and at The Cenacle.

He was back in six months. By the time I left The Cenacle — which was a couple of years later — he had been back three times more. And always — after the first few days, during which he kept to himself — he seemed gay and undismayed, although at times a little older, a little more worn. And never once did he speak of his drinking. Now, today, where he is, or how he is, I don't know. I've written to him several times; the letters were not returned, so I suppose he got them. But I've never received an answer: not even a card. I pray for him regularly, as I'm sure many others — whom he met as casually as he met me, and whom he never saw again — do: he's not a man who's difficult to pray for. I hope he's all right, and that wherever he is or wherever he goes someone will be found to take a little care of him now and then, to occasionally do for this poor, engaging, bright-faced wanderer what another man, not necessarily any better, but maybe just a little more prudent, or even a little more selfish, would by instinct do for himself. . . .

I left The Cenacle. I left it at last, thanks to the help, the kindness, the example of those I've already mentioned, and thanks above all to the grace of God. When I left I had been there — as I've said — four years, which was far longer than I had expected, and was I suppose much longer than was strictly necessary. But I was cautious, I wanted no mistakes this time, and the Bishop, understanding this, allowed me to set my own pace. And so I stayed on, gradually becoming almost a part of the place, occasionally helping out with some of the new arrivals — trying to do for them at least a little of what others had done for me — and then too, helping out with the regular, routine physical chores of the place. The staff was small: there was plenty for everyone to do. Then, as time went by, I was quite often sent out from The Cenacle into the surrounding districts to lend a hand wherever a priest might be needed. In that big country there was a shortage of priests, and The Cenacle had become a convenient supply depot: a kind of clerical replacement pool. I would drive off in the jeep to spend a few days assisting at a parish church in one of the towns, or at an army base, or at one of the little Indian missions (Bucky, apart from his romantic notion of the priest on horseback, had not been far wrong in his suspicions). It was work of a kind I'd never known before, and along with everything else, it helped.

Often, driving back to The Cenacle at night, I found that I could think about things I hadn't really thought about for years. And there were moments when, bumping along on a bucket seat over a freeway of baked mud, passing through the strange quiet and the clear shining darkness of the desert night, I would suddenly become aware of a stillness which was something quite apart from the stillness of the night. It was an interior stillness, a stillness inside me, a stillness in which there was the absence of all distraction and unrest, a stillness in which, quietly and without effort, I seemed to come together, to be focused and attentive, to be really *present*, so to speak, a stillness from which it seemed natural, even inevitable, to reach out, to pray, to adore. . . .

And this is what I mean by saying that slowly, but at last, I came to terms with myself and with God. In the end, this is what The Cenacle meant to me. I left it with gratitude and regret; in a way I didn't want to leave at all. But I did leave. I had been there long enough; it was time to go back to the diocese where I belonged.

I went first to the Bishop. Four years had not changed him; he was as undemonstrative as ever. Yet I knew that he was pleased to see me, and after a brief welcome he said, "We have the problem of where to put you. I could keep you here in the chancery for a while, but I thought you might like to get back to a parish."

"Yes, I would. If there's one available, that is."

"We're limited in choice at the moment," he said. "There aren't many vacancies. A few, in different parts of the diocese. None is as agreeable as your old parish." Then he said, "There is one vacancy in your own city. How do you feel about that? It's a question of whether, immediately, you want to go back."

To the scene of the crime? It was a question indeed: I'd thought about it often. For The Cenacle was one thing; the old home town was quite another. And even though it wasn't Saint Raymond's or Saint Stephen's, still, whatever parish it was, it was in the same city, people moved about and talked: encounters, awkward encounters, were inevitable. But just as inevitable was the fact that one day, sooner or later, I would go back: I knew that; postponement wasn't much of a solution. Besides which, it was, after all, an offer, and I was in no position to go about rejecting parishes. And so I said, "I think it might be well to go back right away, Your Excellency."

What did I expect him to do? Clap me on the shoulder, say firmly, "That's the brave priest?" No. Hardly. Which was fortunate, because all he did say was, "All right. In that case . . . do you know Old Saint Paul's?"

I knew Old Saint Paul's. I think every priest in the diocese knew Old

Saint Paul's — or at least knew about it. Just how many of them knew or even suspected that it still survived as a functioning parish was another matter. For the majority, I imagine, it was merely a part of ancient diocesan history; now, abruptly, it had become a part of my history. I tried to feel enthusiasm. I remembered when I had last seen this church. It was on a day about seven or eight years ago, when I had been driving back across the city to Saint Stephen's. Normally the route I traveled took me nowhere near Saint Paul's, but on this day there was a detour, and as the traffic slowly edged its way around through the slum district, I had every chance to take in the tattered neighborhood and the church itself. And just as I was passing the church, a priest — an elderly priest — came out of the rectory next door. I knew most of the priests in the city, but for some reason I didn't know this one. He was a tired-looking man with a dusty soutane; as he walked up the church steps he paused and with one foot nudged an empty bottle and a tin can off the steps and out into the gutter. Then, slowly, he walked into the church. I remember feeling a sympathy for him, and wondering who he was, and what he had done to warrant this albatross around his neck.

And now the albatross was mine. . . .

"Down at the heels," the Bishop said candidly. "It's no prize. But there it is, and it needs a pastor. You've been inside the church? The rectory?"

I said, "Yes, but many years ago." Did I say this hopefully? For, after all, there was the possibility that improvements had been made. . . .

The Bishop doomed the possibility. "Then you know what to expect," he said. Now, once again, as on my first visit to this office, he rose from his desk and walked over to the window, where he stood in silence, looking out. Today the window was closed; there was no sound of the lawnmower and no smell of cut grass. It was a day in the middle of March, and there was snow on the ground; a few minutes before freezing rain had begun to drive down. A gray day, suitable for gray tidings. . . .

The low, private voice said suddenly, "It's an odd place. Grubby. Unexciting. Out of date. They've been after me to tear it down. On the ground that it's a dead loss. They're right, of course. But I have a feeling for Saint Paul's. It's a church that has meant a lot in its time. It stands for something in the diocese. And it's still needed. People know it; it's familiar in a way that a new church could never be. I can't afford to restore it, but at least I can keep it together." He looked over at me and said, "It's not an additional punishment, Father. I agree it must seem so, but I don't mean it as such. It won't be like anything you've had before, but I think you may find it has its own compensations. We'll see. If it doesn't work out I'll arrange something else. But give it a try."

And so at least I had a promise of reprieve. I left the Bishop's office and came directly to Saint Paul's. There had been no dramatic changes: that much was clear at once. The whole place seemed exactly as I had remembered it. I went into the rectory and established myself in the pastor's bedroom; the priest who had been here on temporary assignment greeted me and shook my hand. He shook both hands. Fervently. I think no man could have been happier to see another; I think his bags must have been packed for days. He would not stay the night but left immediately, repeatedly assuring me that Old Saint Paul's was now "all mine." I'm sure he thought I was about to bolt, leaving him once more in full and unhappy possession. . . .

Alone, I began to walk around the rectory in a slow examination of the premises. It was not a cheering tour. There was dust and dirt and ample evidence of mice; light bulbs had burned out and had not been replaced; from old rooms on the top floor came the smell of damp and mildew. After a while I went downstairs and crossed over into the church. It was too dark by now to see what it was really like, but I had a fair idea. I knelt in the sanctuary for a few moments, then I went back to the rectory and into the kitchen. I was suddenly hungry; I looked for something to eat. Provisions, however, were slim: the priest who had left so abruptly seemed to have lived here as if he were camping out in a haunted house. But there were various items scattered around, and from them I put together my first meal as pastor of Old Saint Paul's: a can of Vienna sausage, a glass of nonfat milk, and an apple. Scenes of clerical gluttony: I thought of my father's notes on the theme. And then, because it had been a long and not a particularly exhilarating day, I went back up to my bedroom and there, in the quiet of the rectory — or what passed for quiet in an old building full of mysterious creaks and snaps and sighs and the whispering scurry of small paws behind the walls — I finished my office for the day and went to bed.

The next morning — for no reason at all I remember that it was a Tuesday — I said my first Mass in the old and virtually empty church; there was not even the usual complement of the curious, eager to inspect the new pastor. Here in Old Saint Paul's, they couldn't have cared less. I saw two or three old ladies and, seated halfway back in the church, a Chinese: it was my first glimpse of Mr. Yee. After Mass, I returned to the sacristy to find a thin, dark man with evasive eyes waiting for me. This was Roy, the janitor; he was making what I was later to discover was one of his infrequent appearances. He introduced himself to me; he apologized profusely for not having been on hand to meet me when I had arrived.

"Only," he said, "when you got here, Father, you know where Roy was?"

I did not know.

"*In jail,*" he said. "With cops around him."

It was all I needed. The parish, the rectory, the church, and now a janitor who had arrived fresh from jail. And, moreover, one who spoke of himself in the third person. He continued, even more alarmingly.

"Roy said to them, 'It ain't right to keep me here. You got no right to coop a man up unless you got charges.' They said, 'Oh, we got charges all right. You know we got the charges. We got all kinds of charges. You're one smart cookie, Roy, but we got you at last. You pushed it too much this time, Roy. Smart as you are, you can't never get away with no *kidnapping!*' What you think of that, Father?" he said. "A man that works in church every day and they finger him for a kidnapper! Roy was burned up, Father! Because why? Because here he is, he should be over at the church to do his work and say hello to his new priest, and where is he? In jail on a frame!"

At some point in this narrative belief had suddenly collapsed under the burden of absurdity; I found myself looking at Roy, who had begun to breathe heavily, slap his sides, and stamp on the floor in order to emphasize this account of jailhouse injustice, and all at once I knew that at the moment when he should have been here to meet me he had in all probability been asleep in his bed. There had been no kidnapping charge, no jail, no cops. Roy was, quite simply, embroidering, although with a somewhat wilder hand than most. I congratulated him on having gained his freedom so quickly; he replied darkly that Roy knew the ropes.

"He knows the ropes," he said, "and he knows his rights. Roy don't need no mouthpiece, Father. Not Roy. Not when the right is on his side. He put them cops right in their place. He said to them, 'Look here, you better let Roy go and be quick about it. You better not keep no man from the Catholic church where he works his fingers to the bone each day. You better not keep him from his new priest or that new priest might get mad and come on over here and blow his stack at you!' That's what Roy told them, Father. So they had to let him go. Only," he said regretfully, "too late for him to be here on time."

"Now that you are here," I said, and began to talk to him about the many things that needed to be done about the church. He seemed delighted.

"Roy's been *waiting* to begin," he said. "Just tell Roy where to start, Father."

I told him; he nodded enthusiastically. "That's a good place," he said. "Just let Roy at that place!" But then, suddenly, he left me, saying that he would return early that afternoon. I did not see him for a week. . . .

In this way I began my new pastorate. It was more or less the way I had expected; life in Old Saint Paul's held few surprises. But it did hold one — and that one was the great surprise of my own contentment here. For in spite of all the obvious drawbacks, in spite of every sad expectation having been met, I was not unhappy in Saint Paul's — not even in those first hours of glum exploration. It's not easy to explain, even to my own satisfaction, but for some reason I seemed to feel that in a peculiar way I fitted the parish, that there was some sort of rough equation between Saint Paul's and myself. I'd never been in a parish remotely like it before, yet I didn't feel at all strange or in the least out of place here. There was a quality which drew me to it, made me oddly comfortable — although this was probably nothing more at first than the sheer *calm* of the place. It had the quiet, the absence of turmoil atmosphere that seldom visited backwaters often have. It was so peaceful, so undemanding a parish that to have moved here from The Cenacle seemed actually a very slight transition. I had my parish duties to perform, of course, but as I've said earlier, these were neither many nor arduous. And because my polyglot parishioners kept pretty much to themselves, I found myself with a great deal of time on my hands; with no curate, I found myself alone for long intervals. But this loneliness no longer bothered me. I read more than I had in years, I thought about what I'd learned in The Cenacle, I began to take the long nightly walks through the district, and I worked regularly around the church and rectory, painting and making a few minor repairs, trying to pick the place up a bit. I was helped in this by the acquisition of Mrs. Addione; the hiring of this silent, efficient woman, just a week after my arrival, was a major move. I even came to some sort of rather equivocal relationship with Roy: I raised his salary. Not much, but all I could afford; no matter how little he did, the poor fellow deserved more than he'd been getting. Now, in gratitude, Roy came irregularly but more frequently, each time with a different excuse, or — failing that — some fanciful tale from his imaginary past. He told stories of having been a chef on a transatlantic liner, a professional dancer, the fire chief of a small town in Connecticut, a rum-runner during Prohibition, a newspaperman, a jockey, a Communist. I found these glamorous fictions ingenious and entertaining, but poor Father Danowski, when he came, found them unendurable. He was baffled by Roy; I think he was even a little afraid of him. Sturdy, even powerful, himself, Father Danowski had the strong man's fear of the suspected lunatic, and Roy's sudden plunging movements and occasionally rolling eye made him uneasy. I remember in particular one encounter between them; it took place shortly after Father Danowski had arrived in the parish. Roy had been painting the back of the rectory; Father Danowski had come out and had been cornered. From my room I could overhear a chilling account of Roy's career as a middleweight boxer. The career had been a short one, for it appeared that Roy, once maddened by blood, was uncontrollable. The knee, the thumb, the elbow, the savage kick were all vital parts of his fighting technique; after nearly destroying an opponent twice his size in a memorable bout in San Diego, he had been barred from the ring for life. It was a preposterous story, but Roy was a vivid raconteur and told it with great conviction. Father Danowski was clearly impressed.

"Well well," he said nervously. "Well well, Roy. That is quite a horrible tale. I trust that is all in the dead past now." Then, apparently feeling that a certain facetiousness might now be useful, he added, "I trust Father Kennedy and I may feel safe from your assaults? Although to be sure you undoubtedly would not commit the sacrilege of striking a priest."

Roy had not been reassuring.

"When the mood is on him," he said, "Roy would strike *anything!*"

"He is a wild person," Father Danowski said, reporting this conversation to me some moments later. "A wild and a violent person, Father. Mark my words, we had better have a care or we will all be murdered in our beds!"

But Roy stayed on, and nothing happened. And indeed, in another and larger sense nothing happened: the phrase might almost have been the motto of the parish. For situated as we were, in the middle of the slum, we had few points of contact with the life of the large and active city; the slum served as an untidy but efficient moat. When I came to the parish all sorts of changes and developments were occurring in the city. The winds of political reform were blowing, there was talk of urban renewal, one transportation crisis was succeeded by another, civic bankruptcy was said to be upon us — yet none of this seemed to penetrate the passive, dusty enclave of Old Saint Paul's. I was in the city in which I had spent most of my life and in whose affairs I had taken a small but always interested part; I might have been a thousand miles away. I soon saw that I need have no fear of old acquaintances running up against me bearing fragments of the past in their hands. Now, I met almost no one I had known in the old days. Sometimes an occasional visitor came to the rectory: someone who'd been one of my parishioners in either Saint Raymond's or Saint Stephen's. We talked pleasantly enough, although not for too long; then they went away and did not return. I wondered at first what was behind these visits. Curiosity? Kindness? A little of both, probably. But in any case such visits were few. No one came casually to this part of the city; no one "dropped in." One had to make a special, deliberate point of visiting Old Saint Paul's, and I think that many of those I had known so well hesitated now to make this point, feeling — quite rightly — that under the circumstances the first move was surely mine. I realized this; I knew that for many of them it was their sensitivity to my feelings, their fear of my embarrassment quite as much as their own, which kept them away; I knew that if any hands were to be extended, it was up to me to reach out first. But this I did not do. For several reasons, I suppose: prudence, a sense of shame, a feeling that to evoke even those few parts of the past which meant the most to me — a handful of people, three or four places — might in the end bring the whole thing sweeping in on me: the old principle of inviting the camel's nose under the tent. And so I did nothing. I told myself that there was plenty of time, that one day, some day, perhaps I might make the move. But meanwhile, secure in Old Saint Paul's, I did what seemed best or at least safest: I simply stayed away.

———

I HADN'T seen John since the night of his father's attack; I hadn't visited
Saint Raymond's since long before I'd left the city. And here I was in
the neighborhood with a little time to spare . . . and suddenly I felt a
great longing to see, once more, this rectory where I had been so happy
for so long. So I agreed that I would come back, and then I left Charlie's
house and drove away down the short distance to Saint Raymond's.

It was unchanged. Or so it seemed to me, anyway, as I walked up the
neat series of flagstones which bisected the front lawn — that lawn
which somehow managed to look trim and precise and well tended, even
in these dead months of winter. It seemed, in this moment of approach,
so unchanged that I might have been coming home, fifteen or twenty
years before. Inside, of course, the changes began. They began with the
housekeeper. She was new; she had not seen me before, she had undoubtedly never heard of me; identification was required. And when she
went to notify John, and I began to poke around a bit while waiting, to
peer into and examine some of the old familiar first-floor rooms, I saw at
once that they were not so familiar any more. The marks of the new
pastor were all around. The old décor was for the most part gone; paint
had been applied; the heavy, cumbersome, comfortable interior had
been made cleaner and brighter and whiter: John had a swift contemporary eye for light and cleanness of line. And yet the curious thing was
that although these changes had been made, and although I don't think
that in this first brief inspection there were really half a dozen objects —
a bench, a *Pietà*, a curving sweep of stairs — at which I could look and
say with satisfaction, "This was here when I was here," still, I had no
feeling of *strangeness*. The new broom had swept clean, yes, but with all
the sweeping somehow this house remained recognizable and the same.
The process had not been one of obliteration; the signature of the old
Monsignor and his regime had mysteriously and in some measure survived; and, suddenly and queerly, I felt a sharp sense of *belonging* in this
place: a sense of belonging so powerful that it stopped me, stock-still,
and I just stood there in the center of a room, like some poor idiot

deprived of the powers of speech or thought or motion, stupefied and blinking — and almost bursting with happiness. And this is the way I must have been when John came down the stairs.

"Ah," he said briskly. "Good. I wondered when you'd finally get over here. Well, how does it look? Different?"

"Different," I agreed. "But not altogether; something of the old place comes through."

"I'm working on that," he said sardonically. "But it takes time." Then he said, "Look, I know you gave me the total tour of your establishment, but do you mind if I don't do the same for you today? I've got workmen all over the house, and there's something going on in the church. What, I don't know; there's always something going on here. We ought to put up a sign: We Never Close. And then there's some sort of bazaar or food sale in the parish hall. Home-baked goodies from the ladies of the parish. Brownies and layer cakes: they buy them from each other. God knows why. So let's just go up to my quarters. It's the only place we'll have any quiet. Besides," he said, "for some reason I'm a little tired today."

It was a most unusual admission for him, and he seemed to make it with reluctance. Yet he didn't look especially tired; he looked exactly as always. I said, "Yes, sure." And then, carefully, because I remembered that on the only previous occasion he had spoken of his health he had been rather prickly, I said, "Occupational fatigue?"

"I've been a bit off my feed," he said shortly. "That's all. It's probably the prospect of another glorious winter to be spent in my beloved homeland. Come on, let's go up."

For all his sharpness towards others, his occasional arrogance, he was in a sense a genuinely humble man. That is, I think he actually did what so many are alleged to do: I think he often took a hard, objective look at himself, and then decided he was not pleased with what he saw. I say "I think," because in this matter I could only observe and guess: he volunteered nothing. Ready enough to parade his annoyances and irritations, he shrank from giving personal revelations even more than from receiving them; about himself and his thoughts he was not a communicative man. He was a very private man — perhaps the most private I've ever known. And, inevitably, as he grew older he became more so: isolation enveloped him as, I suppose, it did me — although for rather different reasons. But even so, there were moments — fairly rare, to be sure — when I suddenly felt that his isolation had been shaken, that the shell had cracked slightly and temporarily, that he was willing, and might even have felt a necessity, to open up, to talk a bit on an extraordinary —

for him — level. Not in order to invite sympathy or understanding, but simply, for a few seconds, to have a little human give-and-take. And it seemed to me that now one of those moments had arrived; I said, "It's still the same, then? No better? No growth of . . . what? *Rapport?*"

He didn't answer immediately. Then he shrugged again and said, "No growth. Of any kind. Unless you mean a growth of discontent, which must be mutual by now. Although I see no sign of it on their part; they keep coming. They won't quit. Every day I get up, I walk across to the church, I say Mass — and that's the end of the day for me. Because then they begin to come in. Good God in heaven, how can people *talk* so much? It's endless, Hugh. Endless, endless, endless. My day is spent in listening to one continuous supplicating whine. I know everything they're going to say before they open their mouths: over and over again, the same troubles I've heard for thirty years, the same complaints, the same banalities, the same gossip, the same trivialities, and if you're foolish enough to respond, to actually offer the advice they claim they need so badly, they almost go crazy with impatience. Because you've interrupted them; they haven't finished complaining: 'Yes yes, Father, that's true, that's very true, but there's one thing more, there's one thing more I've got to tell you. . . .' There's always one thing more. Every day. The same old whimpers and whispers and groans and tears from people who can't manage their own lives and who can hardly wait to bolt down their breakfasts before rushing up to the rectory to tell me they can't. And it's all nonsense; it means nothing. I'm a priest, not a wastebasket. These people who every morning sing to themselves, 'Pack up your troubles in your old kit bag and take them up to Father' — I want them for once, just once, to stay at home. Or at least to stop talking. To *shut up*. That's all. Just for a while. Because I'm tired, Hugh. Dead tired. Worn thin. It can't go on this way."

And again I was bothered by a difference: in the old tirades there was never the slightest doubt that he was fully in command of himself and everything he was saying; now, I wasn't sure. These words, all delivered in this new, almost toneless voice, had a tumbling, desperate quality . . . and moreover, what they were saying was slightly unreal. Most pastors, most priests — as I've said — have their nuisance parishioners, and John — as I've said also — for some reason always seemed to have more than his share. But no priest, not even John in Saint Raymond's, is quite this beleaguered, and the exaggeration, which once would have had its comic side, now, in this context, held no comedy at all. It was an extremely serious and delicate business; I said, picking my way, "I think that Saint Raymond's must have changed a good deal since my time. I never knew any priest over here to be so wildly in demand. Petitioners storming the doors, panting to get at you: is that a fact? Are there really so many of them?"

I wasn't at all sure that this was the right tone: I didn't even know exactly what I was aiming for. Was I trying to "jolly" him out of it — to provoke that traditional sign of the return to Common Sense: the slightly shamedfaced grin? This did not happen. To my great surprise there was an even more complete about-face: he collapsed suddenly into acquiescence. "No," he said quietly. "No, I suppose not. Probably no more than there always were. What's different, Hugh, is that there *seem* to be more. And I mind them more. So that's just as bad as if they were really there, isn't it?" He looked at me soberly and said, "You used to be a man who took a drink now and then. I mention this only for analogy: you know how it is, sometimes, with drinkers. They go along for years and gradually they discover that they can't take as much as they once could. It's a question of tolerance. Well, that's the way it is with me and my parishioners. My tolerance is lower. Not that it ever was high, but now it barely exists. If I'm with them, listening to them, or if I even think I'm going to have to listen to them, I feel as if someone were standing behind me, turning a key in my back, tighter and tighter, and that in one more second, with one more turn, the spring will break — and so will I. And all I want to do is run, to get away from them as fast as I can, to get back to —" He stopped here, cutting himself off sharply, and then he said, "I almost said, 'back to my work.' And then what would you have said, Hugh? That listening to these people *is* my work? Would you have said something like that?"

I nodded. "Something like that, I'm afraid. If I'd said anything at all, that is."

"Well, you'd have been right," he said. "I won't argue with you there. It's all fairly elementary pastoral theology, isn't it? We all know what we're supposed to do: the shepherd-flock relationship. But, Hugh, what if the shepherd knows all this, what if he understands exactly what his duties are, what if he realizes that in a very special way this flock is his responsibility and nobody's but his, and that it is in fact the only reason he's where he is and what he is — what if he knows all this and tells himself all this at half-past seven every morning, just after he's finished saying Mass, just after thirty minutes of proclaiming — quite honestly, he thinks at the time — his own love of God, and what if he comes out of the side door of the church with every good intention in the world and suddenly he meets that flock in person? What if, then and there, he sees some old biddy streaking down the street towards him, her jaws already working, or he sees some poor old slob with his hat in his hand hanging around, waiting, outside the rectory door — what if the shepherd sees this and suddenly his stomach turns and all he can feel for his beloved flock is a total, overwhelming disgust! Not apathy, not indifference, but disgust. Disgust for the whole whispering, confiding, sordid, sniveling lot! That's what the truth is, Hugh! It's not simply, as my father has so pleasantly broadcast to anyone who would listen, that I'm a 'cold proposition'; it's more than coldness now. It's that I can no longer stand the sight of them! They make me *sick!*"

And as he said this he actually shuddered, physically, and his voice rose, and I felt an instant and great alarm — God forgive me, but I wondered at that moment if he were quite sane. But he calmed down immediately and said with a tight smile, "Well. It's quite a spectacle, isn't it? All this bitter grousing about being battered to death by people with their problems — and now I batter you with mine. What for I don't know: I'm sorry."

"No no," I said. "I'm glad you did." Which wasn't true, which wasn't true at all: who could be glad to hear anything like this? I didn't even remotely know what to do, where to begin — for what John was doing was asking for help. John, of all people! And from me. Of all people. I said, "You know, it's possible you may be reading into this something that isn't there. I don't mean that it isn't serious; obviously it's that, no matter what it is. But this disgust for people: is that really it? Or is it just your old dislike of this city, this parish, as places? You don't want to be here; you never did. So that couldn't this disgust for all parishioners really be nothing more than this feeling you have against being here? Wouldn't things look entirely different in another parish? Away from here? Transfers can be arranged, you know. . . ."

But it was a simple explanation which I didn't really believe; we were in darker waters than this. He thought so too; he said, "No. That's no answer. The proof is that pretty much the same thing took place in Deerford. The idyllic Deerford I've told you so much about: where by my own report I was so content. It's not true. I wasn't. It was smaller than this, and I didn't know anybody, but in the end I felt the same . . . distaste. It was better than this; perhaps anything would be better than this. But it's not a matter of location. What we're really talking about here isn't anything like that. What we're really talking about is simply this: misanthropy. Isn't that what it is? Pure and simple? What else could you call it? I wouldn't know; I've run out of euphemisms. So there's a question, Hugh: Can a priest be a misanthrope? Can he? And still function? I'll put the question another way: Can a priest who says he loves God really love God — and still throw man away? How's that for a question, Hugh? And if your answer is the same as mine, then, what does that priest do? What do *I* do?"

There was a long silence then. He had finished talking, and I — I had nothing to say. Or rather, nothing I could say. I don't remember now what I thought, or if I thought anything at all in any rational, consecutive way: even in the silence it seemed to me that his words were still pounding on, each one as shocking, as totally unexpected, as tragic as the one before. And when I finally did speak, it was like some buried, blinded animal clawing aimlessly away, hoping somehow to get through to open air: I said, "I don't know about . . . you say it's misanthropy, but that's . . . very rare, surely. Maybe a change . . . would a change help? Not to another parish; I mean away from parish work entirely for a while. I know it's a little late in the day, but possibly a monastery . . . I mean, that might be an answer. . . ."

He just looked at me. "Good God," he said. "A monastery. Don't you think I thought of that? Months ago?"

"And . . . ?"

"And," he said bitterly, "I went to your friend the Bishop. To get the necessary permission. But I didn't have your good fortune with His Excellency, Hugh. He refused. In that charming stolid way of his, he refused. And so I came back here. Right here."

And suddenly he got to his feet, but when I went to move too, he said, "No. Stay there, Hugh. Please. I just have to leave for a minute. I'll be right back. Stay right there."

He went swiftly into the small bathroom adjoining his bedroom, closing the door behind him, and I wondered again if he were ill. Acutely, that is: physically. It was what I had suspected when I first came in here with him, but that seemed a long time ago — and now I knew that if indeed he *were* ill in this way, it was only one of his troubles, and possibly even the least of them. And so I sat there, just as he'd asked me to, and waited for him to come out. I tried to think carefully, to plan step by step, but the steps collapsed, and all I could see was the image of John, facing me across the room — that terrible side-by-side, before-and-after image: at one moment as strong, confident, driving and unshatterable as always, and then suddenly there he was, strange, stripped, defenseless and — the last word I would ever have dreamed of applying to John Carmody — *pathetic*. More helpless and hopeless and pathetic than I had ever been — or so, in that moment, I felt; because to have it happen to me was one thing, to have it happen to him was . . . unimaginable. And yet it *had* happened, and I sat here, my eyes on the bathroom door, my mind unable to touch the future at all, racing over and over again through a scene not five minutes old, which had ended with that agonizing cry: "What do I do?" And I am no man of strength or resource or ready solution; my story is not that of someone who has helped, but of someone who has *been* helped; and so as I had done for myself so often, I closed my eyes and said a prayer for John. For my dear old friend. . . .

He came out of the bathroom and walked to his chair quickly; I had the impression that he couldn't wait to get to it, that his hands were almost reaching towards it as he walked. He sank down with a long grunting sigh; I said anxiously, "All right? Can I do anything?"

He waved me off impatiently. "No. A little nausea, that's all. I said I've been off my feed. I'll live; it's not important." And then he said, "And neither is all this I've been telling you. I don't know why I . . . good *God*, how I hate this sobbing into other peoples' laps! Anyway, do me a favor and forget it. It doesn't mean a thing."

So then, by now he had had time to think it over, and I could imagine with no trouble at all the appalled look on his face when, suddenly, he realized just how much of himself he had disclosed to someone else — and worse than that, that he had asked for *help*. Poor John: he'd had no experience in this kind of humbling, naked arena which isn't quite so rare to most of us — and now, obviously, he had decided that the way out was to pretend that it had all been a mistake, something not worth bothering about: not a serious problem; in fact, not a problem at all. And this seemed to me most unwise; I said, "No, wait. Don't do this. It does mean something. You know that just as —"

"It means nothing," he said, almost angrily. "Be your age. Because that's what it is: age. Or largely so. It happens to all of us. We're not as resilient, we get tired more easily, we say things. . . . I talked like an imbecile. Is it such an unprecedented spiritual crisis when a middle-aged priest occasionally gets tired of his parish? In God's name, who doesn't now and then? Don't you?"

"Yes. Although I didn't know we were talking about 'now and then. . . .' "

He didn't comment on this; he said, "All those people in Old Saint Paul's: you're their pastor. Don't you ever get tired of *them*? The talk, the nonsense, the sheer *abrasiveness*? Don't you ever look down at their faces and suddenly want to head for the hills? Any hills?"

I said again, "Yes. Of course. But —"

"But," he said swiftly, "they don't *disgust* you: is that what you were going to say? Is that the difference? Well, let me tell you about that difference, Hugh: it may not be so much of a difference after all. It may even be the difference between the boy who said he hated oatmeal and the boy who said he didn't — and then one day it turned out that the second boy had a great advantage: he'd never eaten any. So how highly would you rate his considered opinion, Hugh? Without knowledge, without intimacy, without any of the familiarity which is the well-known breeding ground et cetera? And at least I'm intimate enough, familiar enough with my own people over here. I may not want to be, but I am. I can't help it. I'm with them all the time; I can't get away from them. So I know them. Good God, how I know them! From the ground up. That's the solid base for my feelings about them. I *know* them. I'm *with* them. Whereas. . . ."

Whereas. He let it stop there; completion was hardly necessary. It had become all too clear that he had determined to get farther from himself by driving in on me; it was a shift which I found uncomfortable. I said, "What? Ignorance is bliss? You mean that I don't know mine . . . ?"

"Well, do you?" he said, with a crisp reasonableness. "Do you know them? Are you ever with them? All those Syrians and Greeks and Portuguese and whatever else you've got over there: how much time do you spend with them in the course of the week? I appreciate the fact that in a place like that they don't rush you the way they do over here, but — do you rush them? At all? Ever? Or do you keep away from them except for doing what you absolutely have to? Do you know what goes on in their houses? Do you even know their names? Or do you let that Polish comedian you've got in the house with you take care of that end of it?"

It was a sharp, savage attack: far sharper and more savage than any I'd expected — but then of course I hadn't expected to be attacked at all. Out of the blue he had turned the tables completely, the counsellor had become the victim, and for a moment I don't think I really took in what was happening because, absurdly, I actually opened my mouth to begin a defense of Father Danowski — and then it dawned on me that it wasn't he who needed the defending. As for John, he seemed revived: he was bending forward in his chair, so close to me that we were almost touching, and he was talking with all of his old harsh force. It was a recovery for which I did not now feel grateful. I sat staring at him: wordless, gaping — and hurt. The attack had been more than sharp; it had been shrewd, knowing: he had his father's gift for striking, hard and at once, at the vulnerable spot. And it was not over, for he went on talking now with what seemed to me to be almost a kind of joy, conducting all by himself an exuberant dialogue, anticipating the questions I might ask, supplying the answers, explaining, wrapping it all up. . . .

"We were talking about me, not you, Hugh? Is that it? But it's the same thing; it all ties in. I don't want to be here: all right. But look at yourself in Saint Paul's: do you really want to be there? Come clean, Hugh. Do you? Of course you don't. I spotted that the first day I went over to see you. In five minutes. Is it even a parish to you? I doubt it. You're just there. Like a chaplain in a rest home. Ready to be consulted if the occasion arises. But as far as actually going out on your own into those salami-cured tenements, as far as actually bringing anything *to* them, as far as actually working to make your parish any kind of living, breathing spiritual community — well, how about that, Hugh? Yet isn't that just what we were enjoined to do? Most solemnly? Years ago? All of us? And how many of us are doing it today? Am I? We know the answer to that, don't we? And are *you?* Don't we know the answer to that one, too? Don't we, Hugh? I think we do!"

Two old friends at twilight. . . .

And I think what hurt most at this point was not what he said but the peculiar air of *triumph* with which he said it: as if all this were a demonstration of logic, nothing more, and that the only thing that mattered was the skill of the professor. He seemed entranced by his own performance: each question, each accusation, really, was flung out like a jubilant challenge — an invitation to rebut it if I dared. And I didn't rebut it — any of it. I didn't because I was still too surprised, too stunned, to make any kind of effective response. But more than that, I didn't because . . . well, because I *couldn't.* For how do you in any honesty rebut a charge when you know — and have known, really, for some time, even though you may have tried very hard not to know — that, quite simply, it's true . . . ?

He said, "It's a haven. That's what Saint Paul's is for you. Not a parish but a haven. A nice quiet recovery room. For someone who's licked a Problem. And you've done that all right, Hugh. I don't take that away from you for a minute. But how much does that mean to the faithful flock of Old Saint Paul's? You don't drink any more — but how much good does that do *them?* And how much good do *you* do them? Sitting up in a bedroom reading Newman and being grateful to God that You Have Come Through is all very well, but what's it got to do with running a parish? But then of course you can't run a parish if you don't think of it as being really a parish at all, can you? Isn't that so, Hugh? And what kind of parish have you if your church is shopworn and obsolete and falling apart at the seams, and all you ever see in it is a few hundred strangers who look like extras in an Italian movie and who eat funny food and who plant fig trees in the back yard? That's not a real parish at all, is it? We all know what a real parish is. A real parish is an old-time parish. One with a fine, big, old-fashioned, well-kept church with — and here's the important things — lots of Irish to put inside it! People like ourselves, Hugh. The kind of people you grew up with; the kind of people you like; the kind of people you *understand:* comic, picturesque, a little sharp in the tongue at times, maybe, but decent, God-fearing, generous, and devout. The kind of people who can sing 'Ave

Maria' inside the church, but can give you a chorus of 'There's a Little Devil Dancing in Your Laughing Irish Eyes' on the way home. Those are the people the Church was really meant for, wouldn't you say, Hugh? The kind of people we all remember. Or think we do. Isn't that what a real parish is? And isn't that really," he said, his tone suddenly dropping the heavy irony, and becoming one of somber, straightforward accusation, "isn't that really the one kind of parish you want? Don't answer because I know the answer: I know *you*, Hugh. And I knew what you wanted that day I saw you at my father's birthday party — just as I knew it today when you walked into the rectory. It stands out, it *shines* out, all over you: you want to come back, you're homesick. And homesick for what? I'll tell you for what: a dream, a never-never land. You're a sentimental man, Hugh: a romantic. Whether you know it or not, you live in the past: you feed on memories. You think of the world as it was — or as you think it was — before anything happened to you: before your father died, before you drank. The pre-catastrophic world of Father Hugh Kennedy — the happy time. To which, one day, you hope to return. You do want to come back, don't you, Hugh? It's impossible, but you want to do it anyway. You want to come back here, to Saint Raymond's, to Saint Stephen's, to anywhere — so long as you're with your own. Back to where everybody in the parish says 'Hello there, Father!' and you won't be lonely any more. Back to where they all stop on the street for a friendly word because after all you're one of them, they know you, and they knew your father before you. Back to the old crowd, Hugh: back to the Backbone of the Church. Isn't that what they're called? Or is it only what they call themselves? I've forgotten, and it's no matter anyway. My own feelings towards that famous Backbone are well enough known; there's no need for one more sneer from a disaffected pastor. But disaffected or not, at least I don't see them through a ridiculous puddle of moonbeams, and if I'm all wrong as a priest for wanting to get away from them as fast as I can, is it any less wrong for a priest to want to be with them so much that he dreams his hours away thinking only of The Great Day When? And meanwhile neglecting his present parishioners, not even knowing who they are and not wanting to know? Isn't there an extraordinary snobbism here — and isn't the priest who's guilty of it in some danger of confusing that celebrated Backbone with the whole blessed Church? We were talking a minute ago about the differences between us, Hugh, but I'll tell you what the real difference is. It's that I may have turned my back on my parish, but you've never even turned your face on yours. You don't even know it's there. And so what does it all boil down to? Just this: that you don't do your job, either. Only you don't do yours in a slightly different way. That's all."

And it was all. His eyes dropped from mine, and he looked straight down at the floor, his hands folded, his job done. It was absolutely still in the room: I sat there, looking at the top of his bent head, not really seeing anything at all. Then at last I said, with great bitterness, "Do you want congratulations? On knowing me so well? I think perhaps a medal should be struck off for you, John. In tribute to your special powers. With a little motto reading: 'He saw his friends as they really were — and hastened to make them ashamed!' "

For several seconds he didn't answer, but continued to stare downward. Suddenly he spoke — to the floor, to himself, but certainly not to me, for his voice was too low for me to hear clearly what he was saying: it sounded as if he were whispering, rapidly and over and over again, the single phrase, "Oh God!" Then this stopped, and he shook his head briskly — and then he looked up at me.

"I'll give you a different one, Hugh," he said. "One that might serve as an epitaph. 'Here lies John Carmody, parish priest. All his life he envied happiness — and snapped like a dog at his friends who found it.' Don't you think that sums it up? I do. I think that sums it up just fine." He looked down at the floor again for a moment; then he shrugged and said simply, "I'm sorry. It doesn't do much good to say that, does it? I don't imagine it ever really does: a few soft words tacked on after the kick has been delivered. But anyway, I do say it. I *am* sorry, Hugh. I'm desperately sorry!"

It was true enough. I could tell it, not so much from the words, but from his eyes, because I could see the anguish in them: the rare, real anguish that can sweep across a face and tear it apart. And I knew it was there because of what he had said, or done, to me — and I knew that never in all his life could he have expected to do this, or have wanted to. And yet he had, lashing out from the dark spring of his own desperation: misery screaming for company, and not caring how it got it. And so, still angry and hurt, I looked at him now, looking directly into his eyes, seeing the pain, and watching it swell and deepen until finally there came a moment when it seemed as if the eyes and everything around them had vanished, and I was looking at nothing but the pain. It was a strange sensation: I felt as if another kind of vision entirely had taken over, through which I saw John, not as he had been for a few awful minutes in a rectory room, but as he had been at other times, as he had been, in fact, all the rest of his days to me. And it seemed, then, that whatever had been said in these last minutes, it wasn't so earth-shaking after all, that it even was . . . I almost said that it even was *forgotten*, blotted out, but of course this wasn't quite true, and I don't suppose it ever would be: we have a way of hanging on to our moments of humiliation, as if they were prizes. But at least it no longer filled the horizon, and at least the anger and the bitterness were gone; I reached out and took his hand, just as — incongruously, this now occurred to me — a few days ago I had taken his father's, and said, "No bones broken, John. It's no more than the old story of the truth hurting a bit. . . ."

"Even when it's not the truth," he said. "It was all sleight-of-hand: a little bit of the truth made to look like the whole. You *do* cast that look back on the good green fields, and I don't imagine you're really a driving dynamo in Saint Paul's. But that's just a part of the picture — the part you yourself feel a little guilty about. The complete picture is something very different — naturally I didn't give that to you, because it wouldn't have helped my case at all. What I was trying to do was equate us as parish priests. Unhappily, the equation can't be made. I wish it could. But it can't. And I know it. Because in one of us despite everything, the *goodness* comes through. Whereas in the other. . . ." He rose quickly and began to walk across the room; I thought at first he was returning to the bathroom, but he was only walking — walking and brooding. I was extremely uncomfortable; again, I didn't know what to say. Suddenly he stopped, as though a decision had been made; he said, "You reach a point where more words don't help anything; you stall in them and sink deeper. We've said enough for one day, Hugh — I've said far too much. Maybe we can pick this up again sometime later; it might be a good idea. I don't know. But for now, let's call it a day." He looked at his watch and said decisively, "Besides, I have Benediction in ten minutes."

Back to work. And I knew — or felt — that unsettling as all this had been to me, it had been far more so to him, and now, suddenly, he wanted nothing more than to bring it to a close. So this was how my visit — and this strange, disturbing talk — ended. There was no more to be said. John walked with me down to the rectory door: on this return trip I turned no slow inspecting gaze around the familiar scene. It was a quick walk and a silent one, and between us there was, not a frostiness, but a restraint — the restraint that follows when too much has been said. At the door we said goodbye; he hesitated and said, "Again, I'm . . . sorry. For all the world I wouldn't have. . . ." Then he said, loudly and abruptly, "Anyway: no hard feelings? Really?"

I said, truthfully, that there were none. I added — and here I too was hesitant, "About your own . . . difficulty. It's not insoluble, you know."

Although, certainly, I had no idea what the solution could be. And he wasn't disposed to go into it further; he said quickly, "We'll see. We'll see." There was an awkward interval, as though each of us were waiting for the other to go off first. He said, "Well . . . we'll be in touch."

"Yes . . . I'll give you a ring in the next day or so."

"Do that," he said. "Do that." And then he looked at me with an odd, almost an embarrassed smile, and said, of all things, "Thanks." With that there was a short, hasty movement of his hand which I suppose was a wave, and the rectory door closed.

It was a queer and, to me, an affecting farewell. I got into the car and drove off, back towards Old Saint Paul's, and I must have been halfway there before I remembered that this wasn't what I had intended at all, that I had promised Dan that I would return to Charlie's. But it was late now; I had gone too far to turn back and drive all the way there; in any case they would soon be sitting down to dinner; everybody (including the mournful Julia) would be there; at the end of the day visitors to Charlie might not be encouraged; I was expected back at the rectory — in short, I did not want to go. . . .

And so I continued to Saint Paul's.

I must have been poor company at supper that night; still, I doubt that this was noticed. Father Danowski, seldom silent at the table, was tonight more eloquent than usual. He had had an active day in the parish, making his rounds at the end of the year. He was full of gossip and small scraps of information, and dutifully and happily he passed these on to me. . . .

". . . to my utter astonishment that a small crisis was brewing in, of all places, the Elias family! And he is normally the quietest of men. Perhaps you recall him, Father? In the gasoline station at the corner of Camber Street? A very small person? It is rumored that in days gone by he was a most successful jockey. . . .

". . . little Maria Serafin is recovering quite nicely. You remember, Father, the incident of the tiny turkey bone? Which lodged in her throat on Christmas Day . . . ?

". . . how good it was to learn the news of young Sandy Guglielmo! It appears that at *any moment now* he may receive word of his appointment to the United States Military Academy. At West Point, New York. You of course know Sandy, Father. He is not only the somewhat older brother of one of our altar boys, little Sal Guglielmo, but he is, moreover, related by marriage to our own Mrs. Addione. . . ."

And so on. Tonight I didn't really pay much attention to him, or hear much of what he was saying, but occasional snatches kept leaking through, and gradually — and disquietingly — I became aware of what was a persistent narrative trick of my curate's. His stories were all about Saint Paul's and our parishioners, and yet as he talked to me he took great care to equip each figure with a suitable phrase of identification — as if he were telling the stories to a newcomer, a stranger who could not otherwise hope to follow the plot. I hadn't noticed this in him before, but it now occurred to me that of course he must have been doing it for some time — probably, in fact, since he had first come here and had begun these enthusiastic nightly reports on the people he had encountered during the day, and had found, to his surprise, that the names he assumed would be knowingly received instead drew only blanks: the inquiring look, the murmured "Ah!", the polite uncomprehending nod. And so, little by little, perhaps even unconsciously, he had begun to provide a scorecard so that the pastor of the parish could stay somewhere close to the game. It was only tonight that I realized just what he was doing — and I wouldn't have realized it now except for the severe preliminaries of this afternoon. In all innocence, my curate was confirming what — by now — hardly needed confirmation. It was not the most consoling table talk.

But in any case there was no time now for consolation — or for any such luxury. Tomorrow was New Year's Day, the Feast of the Circumcision of Our Lord, and after supper I went immediately into the church to hear confessions. On this last night of the year the confessionals are always crowded — even here in Saint Paul's. The slate is being wiped clean — and sometimes, for the priest, this is tedious and unusually trivial. One can discern, at this time, the impulse of an office-party New Year's Resolution: so much of it is small, negative, not quite serious, like a child solemnly parroting that it will abandon jelly beans as of Jan. 1. Yet these are adults . . . and they take up so much time. On the other hand, I suppose there is at least this desire for a fresh start — which is by no means contemptible. Then too, there are those others whose problems are not at all trivial, but are severe and complicated and often of long standing. They come also on this last night — they take time, but they *need* time: that's the difference. And of course you don't mind giving it to them: that's what you're there for. All the same, it can be tiring, it can even be exhausting: if you've been a priest as long as I have, you hear nothing new, but the old is quite enough — after a few hours of being buffeted by voices whispering alternately the nonsensical, the sordid, and — more rarely but still there — the genuinely evil, you feel beaten, drained dry. . . .

And on this New Year's Eve it was a few hours: a few hard hours. When I left the confessional, in fact, I had only a short time before preparing for Mass. This year, for the first time, we were to have a midnight Mass — just as we'd had on Christmas Eve. I sang it; Father Danowski assisted; there was our new, determined choir. The people came, perhaps not quite in the same numbers as on Christmas Eve, but still, they came. And since I'd been so busy that I really had had no time to think in any full or undistracted way about myself, it wasn't until I went into the pulpit to deliver my sermon and looked down through the half-light of the gloomy church at those who had come, and saw them looking up at me, that John's words came pouring back, unsparing and all at once — and while I continued to talk now, I did so with the greatest difficulty. It's perhaps some measure of the standard set by my sermons that no one seemed to notice. . . .

After Mass, alone in my room, saying my prayers before going to bed, I prayed for John. Too much had happened too quickly for me to think with any exactness or clarity about him — and I was too closely involved for detachment. But obviously he was in a most serious predicament, one in which no priest would want to find himself: the kind of predicament from which escape would seem to depend upon either a great change in himself or great help from the outside. The first was unlikely: unlikely enough for anyone in middle age, and much more so for anyone of John's rigidity; the second . . . well, this was unlikely, too. For from whom could such help come? From the Bishop? Whom John distrusted in any case — and whose actions in this one were surely hard to understand? From some doctor? Whom — and this had of course occurred to me since our conversation — he might indeed need to see, but almost certainly would not? From his family? Obviously not — he had respect only for Helen, and she had no influence over him. From his friends? But these were few now; he had been a lone wolf too long; the only one left, I suppose, was me. And I was someone who was willing enough, heaven knows, but who had neither knowledge nor technique to offer. Who had, in fact, only his sympathy and affection and — his prayers. And so, tonight, I prayed for John. . . .

I didn't pray well. I meant to, I tried to, but my platform was too shaky: my prayers were meant for John, but I kept crowding in. John had said this afternoon that I was a man who lived in the past, and I suppose that this was true: in any case it was the past which bubbled up now, exploding softly through the stream of prayer. My attention fluttered; my old habit of going back in review took over. Yet tonight there was a difference: the past that now came up before me was not the old past, the past of my boyhood, of my father, of the seminary and Saint Raymond's and Saint Stephen's and The Cenacle. It was the recent past, the past of Old Saint Paul's, the past that I hadn't thought of as a past at all — or as a present or a future either, if it comes to that. John had been mortifyingly right: Saint Paul's for me had never really been considered a part of my working life as a priest at all. I lived here in a kind of suspension: I *did* look upon it as a place to which I had come after a crisis; it *was* a recovery room. In which I had been recovering now for more than a year and a half, and doing nothing more than that. Nothing, that is, beyond the absolute minimum required of me as a priest. I don't think I intended this, or that I did it deliberately, but somehow, easily and lazily, I'd slipped into regarding Saint Paul's as being something of an *interval:* a way-station for me, in which my function was to mark time — and wait. Wait for what? Again John had been right. I suppose that in the back of my mind was always the idea that this was a period of probation which would one day end, and that then I would go back and finish my life as a priest in some parish very like the one in which I began. Even if I didn't acknowledge it, this was really what I wanted: to go back to the place I loved, to the people among whom I belonged. And what's wrong with this — except everything? Because, if you're a priest, to speak of *belonging* in this way makes no sense at all: it's as if, having been formally consecrated to God, you confront Him with a condition of employment: "I love You and will serve You to the best of my ability — provided, of course, that You don't take me out of my yard. . . ."

It makes no sense — but the fact was that I had been taken out of my yard, I wanted to go back, and meanwhile — was I doing more than merely marking time? In my own favor, I could at least say this: that towards the people of Saint Paul's I'd always behaved well, I'd never hurt them or scandalized them, I'd always treated them with decency and kindness. So then, this was something — although not much. For decency and kindness can be overrated: many an ante-bellum plantation owner gave that to his slaves — his one small fault was that he didn't regard them as human beings like himself. Or in other words, his one fault was that he failed to give them what they deserved, and never once saw them for what they were — and that being so, did all the rest matter at all . . . ?

So with me in Saint Paul's. I haven't given them what they deserve, and have never once seen them for what they are — John's way of saying the same thing was that I'd never turned my face on my parish. I had been looking ahead to . . . what? To the time when — to use a worn campaign phrase — I'd be back with the first-class citizens again? So John had said, and even though he'd hurried to cushion his indictment in the end, the truth of it remained. It was a truth I should have faced up to long ago, but I'd smothered it, hadn't admitted it, and drifted along lazily, on the whole pleasantly, with a whole part of my being numbed and no longer in use: a semi-pastor, a half-priest. And half a priest is better than none? I'm not so sure. . . .

APRIL passed, then May, and then, in the middle of June, the Bishop came to call. It was not an official visit; he came without notice, and he came, I remember, on a day when the heat and humidity of the summer had begun to make itself felt. He came at a time when Father Danowski was out, Roy was somewhere in the basement of the church, and Mrs. Addione had left for the day. So that I was alone in the rectory, and suddenly the Bishop appeared at the door. He nodded and said simply, "You're not busy, Father?"

I was not busy. We went into the house, and as we crossed into the office he stopped and said, "It's cool in here. The thick walls. . . . When I was a young priest I spent a year or so in the desert country. It was blazing every day. For weeks on end. But we lived in an old adobe structure and we were reasonably comfortable. The same principle, I would imagine . . . you find this bearable right through the summer?"

I said that we did; it was one of the virtues of the building. I wondered, irrelevantly, what he had been doing in the desert country, why he had gone out there as a young priest: the missions? And then I remembered that of course he *was* a Westerner — and I remembered too the outside heat; I said, "Can I get you anything, Bishop?"

He shook his head and sat down. "I came up here this morning for a funeral," he said. "A man named McCartney died. I didn't know him. I don't think many people did. He was a man who kept to himself. He lived alone; apparently he'd made some money in textiles. The first Christmas I was here he sent me a check for ten thousand dollars, with a note asking me to use it for the blind children. And every Christmas since I've had a check for the same amount. For the same purpose. I've never heard from him at any other time, and he's never asked me for anything." He paused now, and in that curious way he had of seeming to speak really to himself, he said, "It's not unprecedented, of course. There's a great fundamental generosity. . . ."

It called for no comment; I made none. After a moment the heavy face seemed to turn out to me again; he said, "Your parish: what's it like these days, Father?"

I said, "About the same, I'd say. We don't change much. There's been no falling off, at least. And I think there's been some improvement. More of them seem to be coming to church, and we've been able to get around and see them a little more often." Then, because he deserved mention, certainly, if anyone ever did, I said, "My curate's been of great help. He's a hard worker. And a good priest."

The Bishop said, "The Polish boy. Yes. He's very young, isn't he? Still, that's not a crime. And there's plenty of time. . . ." Then he said abruptly, "And you, Father?"

"I'm doing well. Saint Paul's has been good for me — and good to me. I have no complaints, Bishop."

The Bishop said simply, "Nor have I." It was the closest he had ever come to a positive compliment; I felt suddenly and childishly pleased. There was another of the long pauses which, as much as any of the words he used, seemed to form a part of his conversation. Then he said, "After the funeral I stopped for a short time at Saint Raymond's. You were a close friend of Father Carmody's?"

And I remembered now what of course I should have remembered at once: that the last time I had seen him had been on the day of John's burial. I said, "Yes. He was my closest friend."

"These deaths," he said slowly. "Here in the diocese we've lost three priests in the last six months. None of them old men. All your age and mine. I knew Father Walker fairly well. And Father Byrne was with me at the Cathedral." Then he said to me, "Tell me about Father Carmody."

In a few well-chosen words? I said uncomfortably, "It's a rather long story, Your Excellency. . . ."

But he said only, "I have time."

And so I told him about John. It was a John he could never have known, because it was John as he was to me — and, for the most part, John as he was when he was younger. For once the excursion into the past served some good purpose, because I wanted the Bishop to glimpse, at least, a little of the happier side of someone he must have known only as a rather forbidding and difficult subordinate. I said nothing, of course, about the private problem that had harassed him at the end, and I said almost nothing, indeed, about these later days, his time at Saint Raymond's.

The Bishop listened quietly: with a strange absolute physical stillness. When I finished there was a silence; then he said, "I brought him back to Saint Raymond's. It may not have been a wise assignment. I don't know. But it's not always. . . ." He did not complete the sentence; after a moment he said, "Your priest who becomes a recluse for no apparent reason: this happens, sometimes. I don't know why. Disappointment. Boredom. Pride, perhaps. And for some there seems to be a special temptation: one towards loneliness. . . ." He fell silent, looking at the wall opposite him with that familiar, steady, self-communicating gaze which seemed to go with the private voice. "It's always a problem. The parish can become a formula; the priest can become . . . a number of things. To some extent this was happening in Deerford. That was why I brought Father Carmody back here. It was possible that Saint Raymond's was a parish in which, for obvious reasons, he might find it hard to . . . calcify. And he was a gifted priest; I thought the two might help each other." There was silence again for a few seconds before he said, "They didn't. And yet I . . . does this distress you, Father?"

It did, of course . . . oddly, it was the mention of Deerford which struck with sudden pain, because it brought back John's voice bleakly reciting the truth of his failure in that parish which he had so long proclaimed as his ideal. I said, "A little. . . ." And then I asked the question which, I suppose, I had no right to ask, but which had puzzled me ever since that last afternoon with John; I said, "The monastery, Bishop: what was wrong with that as an answer?"

He showed no surprise at my knowing about this. He said, "It was no answer at all. It was an . . . evasion. The monastic life is a specific calling; it's not an escape hatch. Father Carmody knew this. So do you, Father. So do I. You go into a monastery because you want to be nearer to God. Not because you feel a revulsion towards people. It's a question of motive. It was my opinion that Father Carmody didn't really want to go to anything; he wanted to get away from something. It didn't make much sense; it was even slightly . . . frivolous. Like these restless people who suddenly jump on boats or planes: they think that by sailing or flying two thousand miles they'll get away from their troubles. I'm not at all sure about these matters, but I think that Father Carmody wouldn't have gotten away from anything. It was . . . all wrong. And so I refused him, Father. I couldn't do anything else."

I said nothing; I suppose he was right. I thought of poor John with his wall around him, a little more added to it each year, and so really alone that even those who loved him never had a hint of the crisis that threatened him or the sickness that killed him. And all I could say was, "I miss him. And I have great reason to be grateful to him. . . ."

I don't say these things well; it sounded dramatic, a little false —

everything I meant it not to sound. But the Bishop said only. "That helps." And then he added cryptically, "It may even be enough." He got to his feet and said, "I must go."

I walked with him to the door; as I opened it he said, "One thing more, Father. I'm pleased with . . . everything."

So this was good; I thanked him. He said slowly, "And yet . . . I may take you away from here."

He stood by the door, one hand touching it: he seemed to be watching me, listening. And when he said these words I must have stopped dead still. It was one of those moments filled with silence, and then against this backdrop of the absence of noise, the small, distant, irrelevant sounds came swimming by, brushing the silence without disturbing it: the sounds of the street blown in through the partly open door, Roy, who must have left his hideout in the basement, whistling faintly and monotonously from somewhere in the back part of the rectory. In the strange stillness I heard all this, and then I said, "Yes, Bishop. . . ."

"There's a vacancy," he said. "You know what it is. So far I've appointed no successor to Father Carmody. Now I'm going to have to. Soon. The parish needs a permanent pastor. I was thinking of you, Father."

So here it was. After all the months. And the funny thing about it was that as often as I'd imagined this scene — and I think I began to imagine it, really, from the very first day I came to Saint Paul's — rehearsing all possible details with that queer mixture of reluctance and pleasure, conducting long and even rather subtle debates with myself about what I might say and what I might not say, what in all decency and fairness I could do and what in the same decency and fairness I could not do, carefully balancing what was now against what just possibly could be — the funny thing about all this was that now that the scene was actually *here*, it didn't matter at all. I mean, all the rehearsals, the debates, the balancings just didn't count; they were out of date. Because now there was no longer a decision to be made; that decision had been made already, five months ago. On, of all days, New Year's Day. So that despite my superior comments on New Year's Resolutions, I suppose I now had one of my own. . . . But the Bishop was waiting for an answer, and now I knew that Saint Raymond's was mine if I wanted it. And I *did* want it: heaven knows, I wanted it as badly as ever. I think I wanted it even more because . . . well, because now I knew that I couldn't take it. I said, "It's . . . kind of you, Bishop. . . ."

He shook his head "No. It's a good parish, but I think it could be better. I think you might help to make it so." And then he looked at me in exactly the way he had on that day in his office years ago, the day he had told me he was sending me to The Cenacle; in the same courteous, level, uninflected voice, he asked the identical question, "Does it appeal to you, Father?"

I fumbled a bit; I knew what he was offering me and I knew what I had to do, but I didn't want to do it rudely. I said, "I was just thinking . . . have I the choice?"

He nodded. "Yes. I won't transfer you against your wishes. I think you deserve that. But I should tell you this: if you stay in Saint Paul's, you'll stay in a Saint Paul's which won't . . . change. I have no plans for rebuilding or renovating. I can't. It's impractical; it's in fact economically impossible. I'll continue to maintain it. As long as I live it will always be here. It's my guess that it will last a little longer than both of us, but not much longer than that. Meanwhile, it will just . . . be. And that's your future in Saint Paul's, Father."

I said, "I think . . . if I could . . . I might like to stay."

There were no frowns. And no cheers, certainly. The heavy face was as impassive as ever; he said, "All right. I'll decide on Saint Raymond's later. But . . . this is yours, Father."

It was done, then. I thanked him, and then I said, "You're not offended, Bishop?"

He smiled faintly. "No," he said. "I'm not offended, Father. I'm not offended at all." He put out his hand and said, "Goodbye. My blessing."

And so I said goodbye to him at the door. He walked down to the waiting car; the chauffeur sprang out and ushered him in. He looked through the window again; there was just a brief nod; and then he was off, down the hot summer street. . . .

So I was alone again. It was hardly the first time I'd been alone in this rectory — but now there was a difference. This was the first time I'd ever stood, all alone, in the silence of this old building filled with little but the echoes of a past which was over before my own began, and looked around me, and slowly realized, at last, that this was mine and would be mine: that it was my home for the rest of my life. And with this at first I felt a touch of regret, an edge of sadness: I knew that as long as I lived in Old Saint Paul's it would never mean to me what Saint Stephen's and Saint Raymond's had meant — that it could never grip my heart and affections in the same way. And then, out of nowhere, a single question came before me: *Was it ever intended to?* It was a simple question, but one I'd never asked myself before. I had no direct answer, but possibly the question itself was enough, for slowly another feeling came in, rising over regret, a feeling which swelled until it was almost . . . what? Joy? Maybe that's too strong a word at this point, but it grew and grew until I felt it so strongly that I could feel nothing else: an awareness, an *assur-*

ance that while something was over forever, something else had just begun — and that if the new might not seem the equal of the old, that might be because the two were not to be compared. The new was something of another kind, something I had never known before. And at this moment, here in the rectory hallway, I stood aching with excitement, for suddenly it seemed to me that something might be ahead which grew out of the past, yes, but was totally different, with its own labors and rewards, that it might be deeper and fuller and more meaningful than anything in the past, and that as a priest in Old Saint Paul's, working day by day in this parish I had really been shamed into choosing by the scornful words of a dying friend, I might, through the parish and its people, find my way not again to the simple engagement of the heart and affections, but to the Richness, the Mercy, the immeasurable Love of God. . . .

And then the feeling passed, swiftly, leaving me still standing here in the hallway, almost gasping, as if I'd suddenly exhaled some time ago, and hadn't quite been able to catch my breath again. All this could have lasted no more than a moment or two, and what it meant, or if it meant anything at all, I couldn't say. And yet I think it did. . . . I walked into the office and sat down at my desk; I felt, now, a little shaken . . . but strangely hopeful. And strangely happy. . . .

I sat there for some time, thinking. I sat there until Father Danowski came back, some time later. He was excited; a neighbor had told him that the Bishop's car had been parked outside, that the Bishop had been seen on his way inside.

"How I wish I could have been present to see him once again!" he said regretfully. "My admiration for our Bishop, Father, knows no bounds!"

He stood before me, obviously waiting — presumably for news of the visit. But I nodded and said nothing; presently he said, with a great elaborateness, "Might I inquire, Father, if perhaps the Bishop had some special purpose to his visit? I do not wish to pry, of course," he said hastily, "but possibly he had something especial in view? With regard to the parish?"

I said, "No. No, I'm afraid not. Nothing especial at all."

Suddenly he smiled at me, wisely. "Ah ha ha ha, Father," he said. "He may have *said* nothing. But you know and I know, Father, that a busy person such as His Excellency does not make a visit like this with *nothing in mind*. That is not the way bishops are, Father. I am of course not a professional prophet, but I think you will find that one day, before very long, His Excellency will announce *certain plans* relating to Old Saint Paul's. You are too modest to proclaim this, Father, but our parish has of late been moving ahead by leaps and bounds! In my experience, this is not the sort of thing which is ignored in diocesan headquarters. I think that very soon now we may expect to see a vast improvement in our physical surroundings. Oh yes, Father, Old Saint Paul's is quite definitely on the way back up! Mark my words!"

And for just one moment I was tempted to tell him the truth — I thought it might be a kindness. But then I didn't, because it wouldn't have been. For, as the Bishop had said, Father Danowski is still very young. He's a priest who is, in his way, just beginning. And in a few years now he will leave Saint Paul's and will go to another parish. I think he won't like to go, and I think that he'll always remember Saint Paul's — but after a few years he won't remember it with quite the same intensity, and gradually, as he moves along, Saint Paul's will necessarily become less and less a part of his life. Whereas as I move along, it will remain all of mine. So that the situations are hardly the same — and why down a hope or burst a bubble now, when in the end it won't even matter at all? So I said only, "We'll see. We'll see. . . ."

"And *soon*," he said positively. "Unless I am quite wrong, Father, we shall see very soon! And now I must go up to my room and tidy up a bit. I have a few small chores to perform before supper."

He started off up the stairs; when he had nearly reached the top he turned and called down to me.

"Mark my words, Father," he said joyously. "Great things are in store!"

Great things are in store. He bounded happily up the rest of the stairs and disappeared into his bedroom, whistling. I watched him go with amusement, with affection — and with gratitude. And then I left the office and the rectory, and went over into the church to say my prayers. . . .

I Was Dancing

First written as a play (which was produced in 1964, starring Burgess Meredith), I WAS DANCING is about the coldness between generations. "Waltzing Daniel Considine," a retired vaudeville performer in his spry seventies, has established himself comfortably — and, he assumes, permanently — in his son's house. Ever since his sudden appearance on their doorstep, after twenty years' uncommunicative absence, Daniel's son and daughter-in-law have been hospitable to the selfish old man and the eccentric friends who visit him daily; but his presence has become intolerable. His son offers to keep Daniel in an expensive old people's home, and gives him a month in which to pack. The old man has accepted, meekly, but with every intention of overturning his son's plans. In the following selection, Daniel rehearses his showdown scene for his cronies.

IN Daniel's room the two old men had been talking, mostly about Daniel, and not entirely to Daniel's satisfaction. Still, he did not complain. Father Feeley was Father Feeley: he knew that; he told himself that the priest was too old to change, and besides, in a sense it was all just killing time: the real thing was yet to come. Clearly, they were waiting, and it was Father Feeley who at last pulled out his pocket watch, looked at it, and said abruptly, "Where are the others?"

"Billy's never on time," Daniel said. "But Gottlieb should be here by now. He's a very punctual man."

"I like Gottlieb," Father Feeley said. "I've never met a sadder man."

"Oh, he's sad, all right," Daniel said. "They come no sadder than Gottlieb."

"What's the tragedy there?" the priest said. "Domestic?"

"Very domestic. He was a very domestic man. His family meant a hell of a lot to him. He was like me in a way, except that he got along with his wife. Anyways, it was the wife that started it all. She ran off with a band leader."

"Good God in heaven," Father Feeley said. "*Which* band leader?"

"I don't know that you'd remember him. Lester Espinosa."

"Espinosa," Father Feeley said thoughtfully. "Espinosa. Tall, dark, thick-lipped? The face of a degenerate? Played in the pit of the old Orpheum?"

"The very man," Daniel said. "Lester Espinosa."

"Of course I remember him," the priest said. "He's unforgettable. A dreadful man, even for a musician. Virtually an animal. No one could run off with Espinosa."

"Well, Gottlieb's wife did," Daniel said. "And without so much as a word of warning. One night Gottlieb came home for dinner and what did he find but his wife gone and a little note on the bureau saying, 'Goodbye forever, Gottlieb. I've just run off with Lester Espinosa.'"

"Fantastic," Father Feeley said. " 'Goodbye forever, Gottlieb!' What a note. Cheap, vulgar, theatrical: no wonder the man was offended!"

"Oh yes. That, plus the fact she was gone. But that's not the worst. Not by a long shot. After she left he was lonesome, being so much of a family man, so he went out to California to stay with his son. The son lives in Hollywood; he does something in one of the picture studios — I don't know just what. Anyways, Gottlieb went out there to live with him, but in two months he was back. And sadder than before."

"I'm surprised he lasted that long," said Father Feeley. "The place is a swamp. Full of thieves, perverts and crooners. No sane man could stay there overnight."

"Well, it wasn't the place so much as the son," Daniel said. "And the son's new wife. They belong to a crazy bunch out there that had wild parties every night, and Gottlieb likes to go to bed by nine. He never got any sleep; there were always strange women crashing through his bedroom yelling, 'Is this the way to the toilet?' or 'Did I leave my pocketbook in here?' And then the son's new wife was a big redhead about six feet high that dressed in a cowboy suit. She kept on telling Gottlieb to call her 'Tex.' Well, one night —"

And once more he stopped, held up his hand, and listened; he said to the priest, "Did you hear anything?"

"No," Father Feeley said firmly. "I heard nothing. Go on with your story."

Daniel listened for a moment more, then, apparently satisfied, shrugged and went back to the priest. "Well . . . where was I, anyways?"

"Describing a redheaded savage," Father Feeley said.

"Ah. The son's wife. Well, the two of them did a terrible thing to Gottlieb. They made fun of him. They gave a party one night, and told him it was for him. And when he walked into the room it was already full of people, waiting for him to show up. And what was the first thing he saw but a little ape, sitting on a chair at the other side of the room, and dressed exactly like him! They'd got him from a zoo, you see. He was wearing a little suit just like Gottlieb's, and the same color shirt, and even the same kind of glasses. They'd even slipped a special kind of bald wig over his head so he'd be bald like Gottlieb. So all the people laughed when Gottlieb came into the room and saw the ape. But Gottlieb didn't laugh. He turned right around and left, and the next day he came home."

"Yes, of course," the priest said. "You can't remain in a community where you've been successfully impersonated by a monkey."

"So that's why he was sadder than before," Daniel said. "His wife run off with a band leader, his son gone crazy in Hollywood. Oh, I tell you, a thing like that did something to him. It left him sour on show business for good."

"Show business?" Father Feeley said, in some surprise. "I never thought of Gottlieb in that connection."

"Well, that's because you only know him today," Daniel said. "Years ago it was a different story. Years ago Gottlieb was a great man for the theater. There wasn't a vaudeville show came to town he didn't see. He loved vaudeville. And if I played any place within a hundred miles of here, Gottlieb would be right there in the front row. Next to you, he was my biggest fan."

"Well, I was your fan for an entirely different reason," Father Feeley said. "I liked *you:* I never liked vaudeville. By and large it seemed to me a collection of absurd people: middle-aged idiots with dyed hair singing love songs, Chinese laundrymen throwing Indian clubs at each other, malformed women doing indecent gymnastics. Farcical nonentities, all of them. You were an exception, Daniel. It always seemed to me that your performance was a marvelous burlesque of your co-workers. Consciously or unconsciously, you were indicating contempt for the whole imbecilic milieu. It was the kind of performance a sane man could enjoy."

"Well," Daniel said, "I never bothered to figure it out. Like that or any other way. I just did it. I suppose people came to see me for all sorts of reasons. I never gave a damn so long as they came. And when they came, I gave them what they came for: the old dance."

Rising, he broke into just the beginning of his dance. He stopped, and said to the priest, "The funny thing was, I never changed it. The others were always changing their act, but I never did. Oh, sometimes they asked me to, but I always said —"

Suddenly, and once more, he held up his hand; Father Feeley said impatiently, "Now now, Daniel! Enough is enough!"

"Ssshh!" Daniel said. "Be quiet: I heard something!"

And he had, for now there was a knock on the door. It was a soft, apologetic knock; it was also the code knock.

"What the hell did I tell you?" Daniel said triumphantly. "That'll be Gottlieb."

He went quickly to the door and opened it. Standing there, looking at him, was a small, elderly bald man. He was carefully and expensively dressed; he was unmistakably Jewish; there was about him an air of almost radiant dejection. His hands hung down by his sides; as the door opened, he raised his right hand an inch or so in greeting.

Daniel said, "Ah, Gottlieb!"

Still standing at the door, Gottlieb said, in a soft unhappy voice, "I'm not intruding?"

"No no," Daniel said. "Come in, come in. We've been waiting a hell of a while for you."

"I would have been here earlier," Gottlieb said, entering, "but my car: it suffered a breakdown. The radiator cap blew off and almost hit a person." He advanced and shook hands with the priest. "It's a pleasure to see you again, Father."

"You look well, Mr. Gottlieb," Father Feeley said. "Alert. Vigorous. In spite of the heat."

"I'm alive," Gottlieb said, shrugging. "Whether that's good or bad, who's to say?"

"Sit down, Gottlieb," Daniel said. "Sit down and join the party. We're just waiting for Billy."

"To tell you the honest truth," Gottlieb said, seating himself, "aside from being alive, I don't feel so good today. I just came from an old friend. I saw him yesterday afternoon, he was on top of the world. I saw him this afternoon, he was stretched out in a coffin. What happened was this: he died. A clot."

"Tragic," Father Feeley said. "On the brain, I presume?"

"On the brain," Gottlieb said, nodding. "He died from a clot on the brain. Forty-eight hours ago this very minute that man was out on the golf course. Every day of his life he played a game of golf. He would have been a champion player if he didn't have such short arms. And forty-eight hours ago that man played eighteen holes of golf. He shot an eighty-three from the back tees. Now he's dead from a clot. Gentlemen, I tell you this: a thing like that, it makes a man think. Where are we going? What are we doing? Why?"

Daniel said slowly, "Would that be Glickman, I wonder?"

"Nobody else but," Gottlieb said. "It was Glickman. My old friend Artie Glickman."

"I saw in the papers he died," Daniel said, "but it didn't say what he died of."

"A clot," Gottlieb said. "He died from a clot. And if you asked me yesterday afternoon who would be the last man I know to die from a clot, I swear to God I would have said one name. I would have said the name of Artie Glickman."

Daniel said, "You would of been wrong."

Gottlieb said, "I would have been wrong. About that I wouldn't care so much. A man is wrong, so he's wrong. It happened before, it could happen again. But about my old friend Artie Glickman — that I can't get over so easy. And on top of everything else, you know what they're doing on him? A cremation!"

"Ah, that's a bad business," Daniel said disapprovingly.

"Forty-eight hours ago he shoots an eighty-three from the back tees," Gottlieb said, "and tomorrow he's a little pile of ashes you could put in a coffee cup. Gentlemen, that's the story of us all."

"Dust to dust," said Father Feeley. "And so forth."

"But why the cremation I'll never know," Gottlieb said. "Maybe because he wasn't such a religious person. You know what Artie Glickman's religion was? *Golf.* The game of golf was his only religion. I don't shock you by saying that, Father?"

"No no," Father Feeley said. "Not at all. We live in a crazy world. All things are possible."

Gottlieb said mournfully, "So now — ashes. A stranger could walk into that room and say to himself: 'What was here before these ashes? A cigar? A stick of wood? The *New York Times?*' In a million years he couldn't guess they came from a lovely human being by the name of Artie Glickman. And tomorrow morning at eleven o'clock A.M. they put those ashes on a plane — a Piper Cub — and they scatter him down all over the Red Cross. His favorite charity."

"With a little note," Daniel said, "saying, 'He gave for the last time.'"

"Daniel!" Gottlieb said reprovingly. "A deceased person!"

"I know, I know. I'm sorry, Gottlieb," Daniel said. "All the same, it's a hell of a way to go. All burnt up and ready for the ashtray. Still, they do a lot of that stuff in other countries. India's a great place for all that nonsense. One time I played India for a couple of months and I never saw the like of them for burning people up. There's times the whole damn place is a torch. They're little fellers, you know: all skin and bones. I suppose they burn very fast. That may be it. Anyways, a man would hardly dare to lie down and close his eyes for fear someone would put a match to him. It's kind of like a hobby with them. By God, I was never so glad to get out of a place in my life!"

"A strange land," Father Feeley said. "Contradictions of all sorts. Spiritual, yet sensual, the people half mad with drugs. And of course theologically a mess. I wouldn't have thought they could grasp your act at all, Daniel."

"No, well, I don't think they did, much," Daniel said. "I did as well as anyone, but they're not used to high-class entertainment over there. All they've got is snake charmers and double-jointed dancers and fake magicians. When you get a lot of Indians looking at you, you've got a bad audience. They might giggle and titter a little, but on the whole they're a dull crowd. No, I wouldn't go back to play India for love or money!"

"I still can't get over it," Gottlieb said. "My old friend Artie Glickman: here today and gone tomorrow! A nice man who wouldn't harm a dog. All alone in his motel room at night, watching a Wally Beery movie on the television, and — bam! A clot. Ten minutes later it's goodbye Artie."

"That's a queer one," Daniel said. "Dying, I mean, in the middle of a Wally Beery movie. I never heard of that before. I used to know Wally Beery years ago. Not well, you know, but we used to meet and say hello now and then. He was a hell of an actor. No man ever lived that could scratch himself the way Wally Beery could."

"Dead now himself, isn't he?" Father Feeley asked.

"Oh yes, a good while now," Daniel said. "I forget just when it was."

"Nineteen-forty-nine," Gottlieb said. "In April."

"Leave it to Gottlieb," Daniel said admiringly. "If you want to know a fact about show business — names, dates, or places — there's the greatest man in the country for you."

Gottlieb shook his head. "No. No more, Daniel. Nowadays I take no interest. What you're speaking of is Gottlieb years ago. Before my misfortune. Then, maybe what you said is right. But since my misfortune an atom bomb could go off and blow all the theaters in the world sky-high and to sawdust, and you know what I'd do? I'd go right on reading my paper. If I so much as said one word, that word would be 'Good riddance.' I'm not shocking you, Father? You're not looking at me and saying, 'There sits Gottlieb, a beast in human form'?"

"No no," Father Feeley said. "I frequently feel the same way. Most of the time, in fact."

"And yet," Gottlieb said, "years ago, if anybody had come up to me and said I'd feel like this someday, you know what I would have done? I would have looked him right in the eye and said, 'You are a liar, my friend.' It all goes to show you: we never know. What can we be sure of? Nothing. I tell you, gentlemen, it makes a man think. Artie Glickman dying like that, my misfortune: Why? You're a man of the cloth, Father: why should such terrible things happen?"

"God knows," said Father Feeley. "I don't. We see through a glass darkly. And so forth."

"You're acquainted with the nature of my misfortune, Father?" Gottlieb said.

"Yes yes," the priest said. "Daniel told me. The faithless wife, the serpent son. Tragic. Moving. My sympathy."

"Thank you," Gottlieb said. He paused, then said, "You know, I'm

glad Daniel informed you, Father. Because I couldn't do it myself, not
for a million dollars. Eleven years ago my misfortune happened to me,
and to this day I still can't talk about it to another human being. You
understand how that could be, Father?"

"Yes, yes. Scars, I imagine. Plus a natural delicacy."

"You're absolutely right," Gottlieb said. "So you'll excuse me if I
don't talk about it now?"

"Gladly, gladly," Father Feeley said. "I'm all for reticence. The sorrow
borne in silence: we see far too little of that today."

Gottlieb said, "The funny thing is, it's so fresh in my mind it's just
like it was yesterday. When it happened, I mean. Driving back to the
house from my business, you know, the same time as always: five-thirty,
five-forty-five. I parked the car — a Dodge — I opened the front door —
there's a special lock I had put on so my wife wouldn't be afraid: she's a
very nervous woman — and inside everything looked the same. The big
clock in the hall going tick tock, tick tock, a bowl of nice fruit on the
table, a vase of fresh daisies on the stand by the telephone. What a
flower lover she was, Father! Fresh ones every day. So everything looked
the same, everything even *smelled* the same. There was no big voice that
came to me and said, 'Starting tonight, Al Gottlieb, your whole life goes
to smash!, I didn't even get a hint."

"Just a note," Daniel said.

"Just a note," Gottlieb said. "A piece of paper. Thin, like tissue paper.
A piece of paper that said only one thing: Goodbye. My wife was gone.
Sarah Gottlieb, wife of Al, was gone with the wind."

Daniel said, "And a damn bad wind at that. Named Lester Espinosa."

"What does it all mean?" Gottlieb asked, looking imploringly at the
priest. "A middle-aged lady, she's got a nice home, a hard-working husband who loves her, she wants anything, she lifts her finger and she's got
it! And all this she leaves for a . . . for a what? I'll tell you for a what:
for a flashy dope-taker and a bum! Again I ask you, gentlemen: What's
the answer to a thing like that?"

"Concealed from human view," Father Feeley said. "We live surrounded by mysteries. And scoundrels."

"I've met bad people in my time," Daniel said, "but Lester Espinosa
was one of the worst. I'll never forgive that man."

"Loyalty, loyalty," Father Feeley said. "Commendable. Fine."

"You'd come out onto the Orpheum stage, you know," Daniel continued, "and with the first step you could tell something was wrong. The
music sounded all off key and the wrong beat: you could break a leg
dancing to it. And you'd look down into the pit and who'd be there,
leading the band, but that damned idiot, grinning at everybody, and

blowing away on that fake gold clarinet! I'd hate to tell you how many times he nearly ruined my act. After a week in the same theater with him I was lucky I had any act left at all. Oh yes, that's the kind of a man Lester Espinosa was. You couldn't forgive a man like that."

"And my wife, Daniel," Gottlieb said. "What he did to my wife."

"That too, of course," Daniel said. "Yes, yes."

"So she left me, Father," Gottlieb said, turning back to Father Feeley. "My wife for thirty years left me and she didn't come back. Not even once. And not only that, six months later, my own son, Al Gottlieb Junior, my own Sonny Boy — but about him I can't make myself say a single word."

"No no," the priest said. "Don't try, don't try."

"He broke my heart, Father," Gottlieb said. "What was left of my heart to break, that boy broke it. I raised him up to be a real good boy. He went to nice schools, he played baseball with the other kids, I gave him every advantage. He was a real All American boy — a *good* boy. In the war he was almost a hero. He comes home from the war, all of a sudden he decided California, Here I Come, he leaves his old Mom and Dad and goes out to Hollywood. He becomes a picture agent, he becomes a crazy man. He marries one girl; it's no good. He marries another girl, a giant. She thinks she's a cowboy. He changes his name. Al Gottlieb Junior: what's wrong with that for a name? It's a good name, an honest name, a name he should be proud of. But look it up in the phone book out there, you won't find it. He's got a new name now, Father. You know what it is? LaFrance! That's not crazy enough, you know what his first name is? Chips! I said to him, 'What kind of a name is that? Tell me one person in the whole wide world who's called a Chips!' 'I am, Poppa,' he said. 'Out here everybody calls me Chips.' So my boy, my only son, my Al Gottlieb Junior, is now a Chips LaFrance!"

"Absurd," Father Feeley said. "Ludicrous. And yet typical: we live in the midst of a roaring farce."

"What happened to my nice good boy?" asked Gottlieb, throwing out his arms. "He's gone crazy in the head, he thinks he's a big shot. He said to me out there, 'Poppa, I might go to live in England.' I said, 'Why England, in the name of God? What's the matter with the good old U.S.A.?' He said, 'Poppa, you don't understand: for what I'm doing here, in England I could get made a knight. A *Sir!*' I said to him, 'Sonny, go take a cold shower; you're a crazy person. What an ambition you've got in your head! How could they make you a Sir, they wouldn't even know what to call you? Sir Chips LaFrance? Or Sir Al Gottlieb Junior? Don't talk like this to people, Sonny, or they'll come for you with the doctors!' "

"No no, that's perfectly normal conversation out there," Father Feeley said. "Your son's in complete rapport with his environment. They all talk like that in Hollywood. Sanity is the stranger."

"I wouldn't care if he was only crazy," Gottlieb said. "You've got a crazy boy, you can take care of him. But a *cruel* boy: that's something different. He's a cruel son, Father. My Sonny grew up to be a cruel person. He's got no respect any more; he plays bad jokes on his old Dad. What he did to me you wouldn't believe any boy would do to his father. He gave a party and hired a little gorilla to look like me. I never thought my Sonny would do a thing like that to me. So I came away from him. He didn't want me, so I came away."

"There's no getting around it, Gottlieb," Daniel said. "Your family could of been better to you."

"A family: what is it?" asked Gottlieb. "Gentlemen, I'll tell you: a family is something to punch you in the nose. Hard. Twenty years ago you could shoot me dead before I'd say a terrible thing like that. Today, it should be on billboards. In big black letters. Look at my family: my wife, my Sonny. In one small year they took all the joy from my life. You wouldn't believe it, Father, but Al Gottlieb was once a gay person. Always whistling, always a little song, always going to see the shows. Walking along the street, I'd see a boy, a little kid, a total stranger, crying, I'd go up to him and say, 'Cheer up, sonny: whatever you're crying about, believe me, it's not worth it. Here's a dime: go get yourself a chocolate ice cream cone. With jimmies.' Now, today, if I see a little kid like that, I walk right by him. I feel like saying to him, 'You're crying, so cry. All through your whole life you'll get plenty to cry about, so go ahead: get a good head start.' That's what I feel like telling that little kid, Father. And that's what my family did to me. They made of me a sad man. A bad cynic. That's what families do to people."

"Yes, yes," Father Feeley said. "Well, we all change. I don't think it's a question of family entirely. Disappointment, discouragement with humanity at large: that comes with age, experience, wisdom. I myself have a small tendency in that direction."

"And not all families are like yours, Gottlieb," Daniel said. "I don't say anything about the wives; God knows there's loads of people that get a bad shake in that department. But the sons are different. Not all sons turn on their fathers. Not if you know how to handle them right."

"Daniel, we've known each other a long time," Gottlieb said solemnly. "You'll excuse me for saying something to you? Something I wanted to say to you before? Something I want to say to you now, today of all days?"

"What's that?" Daniel said.

"*Watch out.*"

Daniel stared at him. "Watch out? What the hell is that supposed to mean? Watch out for what?"

"Watch out for young people," Gottlieb said. "They're all the same. I speak from experience."

"What young people?" Daniel said. "Are you talking about Tom? My own flesh and blood?"

Gottlieb said, "All I say, Daniel, not naming any names, is your own flesh and blood — believe me, they can be the worst. You love them, you trust them, and one day — boom! And you don't even know what hit you. Believe me, Daniel, I know what I'm talking about!"

"You know what you're talking about for *you*, Gottlieb," Daniel said. "But what the hell has that got to do with *me*? I tell you, if my son ever tried to pull anything like that on me, he'd damn soon —"

But once again he was interrupted, and again by a knock on the door. It was not the code knock but a loud and indiscriminate banging, and Daniel, snapping around to the door, cried angrily, "Leave us alone! Can't a man have any peace and privacy when he's talking to his friends? Go away!"

But the voice which answered was a familiar one. "Open up, Daniel," it said. "Open up, my dear man. It's Billy."

"Good God in heaven!" muttered Daniel, jumping up and going to the door. Opening it, he said, "Why the hell don't you use the knock, Billy? What do you suppose I have one for if nobody uses it?"

"My apologies, my dear man," Billy said, entering the room, his satchel in his hand. "I'm sorry: I was in such a hurry to get here the knock completely slipped my mind. I was out on a last-minute call, you see: a matter of life and death." As casually as he had early that morning, he now threw the satchel onto Daniel's bed. "Life and death," he said. "Oh yes. It's all around us every day. Hello, Father. Hello, Gottlieb, my dear man."

Father Feeley nodded, pleasantly enough, and Gottlieb raised a hand in silent greeting. Daniel, mollified by the medical explanation, pointed to the satchel, and said, "Why the hell don't you get a new bag? That one's all worn out. It's got rips in the corners. Look, you've got something sticking out now!"

Billy looked; he said, "That's nothing, my dear man: just an old sock. I'm taking some things down to the Chinaman to get them washed. I didn't have time to get over there on account of my patient."

"Who is he?" Daniel said. "Anyone I know?"

"I hardly think so, my dear man. He's over in the East End: a poor old devil of an Italian with a bad bladder. Scientifically speaking, it's the classical bladder case. In the language of the layman, he can't do Number One."

"Is he all swelled up?" Daniel said.

"Tight as a drum," Billy said. "You tap that old Italian's abdomen with the tips of your fingers and you get a sound you can hear two blocks away! The Official Doctors are all for the operation, of course: the same old ignorant knife-happy crowd. Fortunately the family called me in on time. I reassured the man. He was in a panic till I got to him. 'Forget the knife, my dear man,' I told him. 'I wouldn't allow that gang to even cut my fingernails. No, we'll treat you medically. Wonder drugs are the answer. New wonder drugs! The very latest thing! The bladder's friend, they call them. Oh yes,' I said to that man, 'calm down and forget your troubles. We'll have you playing leapfrog in a week!' "

"Well, if that's what he wants to do, good luck to him," Daniel said. "Still, the family was damn lucky they got on to you when they did. How did they do that, anyways?"

"Through the milkman," Billy said. "I once cured his sister of an unpleasant nasal disorder: the double snuffles. Ever since then he's spread the word around." He reached into a pants pocket and produced, for general inspection, a handful of large capsules. "Here they are: right off the boat from the Swedes! The newest wonder drugs of all! I'll slip a few of these to our friend the Italian, and in less than forty-eight hours that man will be a human hydrant!"

"Excuse me, Billy," Gottlieb said, peering at the capsules, "but these are what you're giving to that old gentleman? Just like this?"

"Yes, yes, the very latest thing," Billy said. Generously, he held out his open hand. "Have one, my dear man. Help yourself! Just in case! At your age you never know!"

"No, no," Gottlieb said hastily, backing away. "No, thank you just the same. But if you'll forgive me saying so, Billy, is that so sanitary? Right from your pocket like that, I mean? Look: you see what they've got on them? Lint!"

"It couldn't matter less, my dear man," Billy said. "Wonder drugs like these destroy the deadliest germs in a matter of seconds; what chance do you think lint has against them?"

"Farce, farce!" Father Feeley said suddenly. "We live in the midst of a musical comedy!"

Gottlieb turned to the priest, his face polite and slightly puzzled. "What Billy's saying, Father: you don't subscribe?"

"Subscribe!" Father Feeley said. "Good God in heaven! The jungle pharmacist, pure and simple. Pep pills from a pants pocket! And poor warped simpletons actually take them and yowl for more. We're all two steps from the zoo!"

Billy said equably, "Father and I, my dear man, have a few small differences on scientific matters. He once preached a sermon against me."

"It had no effect, of course," Father Feeley said. "Predictable: nobody listened."

"But you're not angry?" Gottlieb said. "I mean, personally it's all right? No hard feelings?"

"No no, my dear man," Billy said. "I've known Father here all my life. I understand his position perfectly. What he says he has to say. The Church is a miracle of organization, but they're a mossback crowd in matters of science. Look what they did to my colleague Galileo!"

"Galileo!" Father Feeley said. "My colleague Galileo! The perfect equation! The whole thing's a madman's paradise!"

"Well, good luck to the Italian and his bladder," Daniel said briefly. This discussion had ceased to please him. Politely, he had asked a simple question; he had provoked a debate. A foolish debate, a debate which had no connection with anything that mattered, with anything he planned to do. It was Billy again; he knew that. He said loudly, "What we were talking about, Billy, was young people, and the way to handle them. Like Gottlieb's boy."

Gottlieb said, "You're acquainted with my misfortune, Billy?"

"Oh yes, my dear man," Billy said. "I know all about that one. A fascinating case, clinically speaking. The genetically twisted offspring. Or, in the language of the layman, the foul-ball son."

"Gottlieb here was trying to tell me all young people are like that," Daniel said. "We got talking about Tom and me."

"Daniel, for all the world I wouldn't say a word against your own son personally," Gottlieb said. "For all I know he's a marvelous young person who loves his old Dad. For all I know he's a good boy who would cut off his right arm at the shoulder before he would make his old Dad feel bad. That could be. All I'm saying, Daniel, speaking generally and from my own experience, is that today young people want to say only one thing to their old folks: Goodbye Charlie!"

"Well, here's one Charlie they won't say goodbye to," Daniel said grimly. "I can promise you that!"

"You'll excuse me for reminding you, Daniel," Gottlieb said apologetically, "but — *they already did*. Four weeks ago tonight, in this very house, what did he say to you, your own boy? 'Be my guest'? No. You know what he said, Daniel. He said one thing. He said to get out. Just like my Sonny."

"No, not just like your Sonny!" Daniel said. "Not by a damn sight. There's a hell of a difference there, Gottlieb, and the difference is this: *I don't let them get away with it.* Listen to me: I don't say you're wrong about what young people will *try* to do. They're a selfish lot, even the best of them. What I say is, you're wrong because you let them do it. And by God, I don't! When it comes to that kind of scrapping, I know a thing or two myself!"

"The very reason we're here, my dear man!" Billy cried. "The very reason we're on tap. To see the preview of the battle plan! A demonstration, we might say, for the privileged few."

"And I'll give you one," Daniel said. "I promised I would, and I will!" He rose now and stood slightly apart from them, the entertainer before the audience. "Billy," he said, "before I start anything, take a look at that door like a good feller, will you? See that no one's hanging around."

"Little pitchers have big ears, is that it, Daniel?" Billy said, walking over to the door.

"They have damn big ears in this house," Daniel said, "and they're flapping all the time, I can tell you that!"

Billy opened the door and stuck his head out into the hall; Daniel called loudly, "Well, what about it, Billy? Is there any spy out there, as usual?"

"No no, my dear man," Billy said, coming back in. "Not a sight, not a sound. No one was there."

"Oh, she's fast on her feet, I'll say that for her," Daniel said.

"Act one, scene one," Father Feeley said. "The stage is set. The feminine spy. Fast and furtive. Still, it's all possible, I imagine. Anything is."

"It's a damn sight more than possible, it's a fact," Daniel said. "You'd find that out if you lived here instead of in that rectory you keep locked and bolted like a fort so no woman like her can get within ten miles of you."

"Normal defenses, nothing more," said Father Feeley.

"Excuse me, Daniel," Gottlieb said suddenly. "For all the world I wouldn't rush you, but inside an hour I'm expected in town. An appointment. Artie Glickman's sister is crying: she needs a shoulder."

"Yes yes, Daniel, let the performance begin," Billy said. "Too much suspense is bad for the valves. We're all eyes and ears."

"Well, I won't go through the whole thing for you," Daniel explained. "I don't want to take the edge off. And I don't want to get all tired out in rehearsal. But I'll give you enough so you'll get the idea, all right." He paused and stood before them, dramatically motionless; he felt the three men fixed on him; he had their attention. "First of all," he said slowly, "you know what's already happened. What the both of them said to me one month ago."

"Background material, my dear man," Billy said, a trifle impatiently. "The ultimatum is familiar to us all."

"All right," Daniel said flatly. "So you all know that. Well, here's what you don't know. Every night since then Tom's been coming to my door, and knocking on it, and asking me how I am. And do you know what I said back to him? In the whole month? *Not a word.* Not a single blessed word!"

"Oh my my!" Billy said. "Marvelous! The touch of a master! Silence is golden! And what does he say to that, my dear man?"

"Nothing. He doesn't talk much anyways, you know. He's quiet. Sometimes you can't get a word out of him. And when I don't say anything to him, there's nothing he can say back to me. Even if he wanted to. So he goes away. But here's the point: *he goes away thinking.* And that's been going on every night for a solid month now. But tonight when he comes to the door and knocks, things are going to be different."

"Tonight, Daniel," Billy cried, "you'll open the door! You'll *ouvrez la porte*, as the French say. It comes to about the same thing."

"Good God in heaven," Father Feeley said. "Continue, Daniel."

"Well, I'll open the door, you know," Daniel said, "and I'll just stand there. But here's the *way* I'll stand." And now, facing them, he seemed to slump, to curve, to collapse partially, and in this way he appeared to be suddenly smaller, defenseless, and even wistful. "Like this, you see. I'll just stand there like this, looking at him. And he'll just stand there, looking at me."

"Moving, my dear man!" Billy said, impressed. "Deeply moving. Standing there face to face."

Father Feeley said, "The common position, of course. When two people meet."

"Just looking," Daniel said again. He gave no sign of having heard Father Feeley. His voice now had a dreamy, private quality, as if he were thinking instead of speaking, addressing himself rather than the other three. "And what'll go through his head right then and there I don't know for sure, but I can make a guess. A damn good guess. Every night for a month I worked on him. Every night for a month I wouldn't speak to him. Every night for a month I wouldn't open the door to him so he could see me. And now he sees me, and sees the way I am, and how will he feel? I think he might damn well feel one way: *ashamed!*"

"Daniel Daniel Daniel!" Gottlieb said despairingly. "What is he, this boy: a Dr. Schweitzer?"

Daniel did not answer; he put up a hand for silence, and continued. "Yes, he'll be ashamed. And he'll say to himself, 'What am I doing? This is my *Dad*. He's my Dad that put me through good schools, that gave me everything I ever wanted, that made me what I am. And now he's an old man and a sick man, and what does he want from me? Not a damn thing in the whole wide world but one little room where he can spend the rest of his days near the only boy he ever had. That's the only thing he ever asked me for, and what did I say to him? I said Out. O-u-t. That's what I said to him! I said it four weeks ago. And now I see him standing here in the doorway, my own Dad, looking at me like this — *can I still say it to him tonight?*' "

This last interrogation was barely whispered; Daniel stopped, and stood before his audience, waiting. There was a respectful silence, broken by Billy.

"Oh, powerful, Daniel!" he said. "Highly powerful! In the language of the layman, a blow to the belly-button!"

"Yes, yes," Father Feeley said. "Rhetoric, of course. Nicely constructed, well-delivered."

Gottlieb looked perplexed; he said, "Excuse me, Daniel, but — *this* is what you're going to do tonight?"

"It's a part of it, yes," Daniel said. "Why?"

"But Daniel," Gottlieb said unhappily. "This boy of yours — a lovely boy and all that, I don't say he isn't — you really think he's going to say, 'Poppa, I'm all wrong, I take it back'? Just because you stand there looking *sad*? Believe me, Daniel, forget it. Take it from an expert: there's nobody that looks sadder than me, and where did it get me? My Sonny stuck a knife in my heart. Young people don't respect sadness, Daniel. They don't know what it is. They've got no experience. You give them a sad look, you waste a sad look, that's all."

"Now, wait a minute," Daniel said. "Hold on —"

"You think I'm a prejudiced person on account of my misfortune?" Gottlieb said. "Ask Father here: a neutral person. By his religion he's not allowed to have a young boy who could do what my Sonny did to me." He turned to the priest and asked, "What about it, Father? What we just saw now from Daniel: you think it's something good?"

"Fascinating," Father Feeley said. "Faultless in its way. Technically superb. Full of bathos, sentimentality: a caricature of dejection."

"But the boy, Father," Gottlieb said. "You think it could change the boy?"

"Oh no no. I wouldn't think it would have the slightest effect on the boy. In my experience," the priest said, "the young are entirely impervious to that sort of appeal."

"You see, Daniel?" Gottlieb said, turning back to Daniel in melancholy triumph. "You see what Father said? Listen to me. You've got a grown boy, he's made up his mind to tell you Goodbye Charlie, he's got a wife behind him giving him little kicks so he should tell you faster. And for this you're going to look *sad?* Excuse me, Daniel, but it's like a man runs up to you on the street yelling, 'Hurry up, hurry up, the whole city's catching scarlet fever! A real epidemic!' And you say to him, 'Who's worried? I already got a handkerchief.' "

Daniel said again, "Will you wait a minute —"

"Daniel, as a medical man I'm forced to agree with our friends here," Billy said. "Your powerful performance was unforgettable, of course, but with a boy like yours it would all go down the sink. Scientifically speaking, we might say that your chances are one in a thousand. But cheer up, Daniel! We never know about a thing like this. Queer things happen every day that even the best of us can't explain. And why? *Because we just don't know.* They're what we might call Beyond the Realm of Science. They're more in Father's department. I'll tell you what, my dear man: I wouldn't be surprised if Father here got down on his knees for an hour or so for you, something might not happen to your boy, maybe at the very moment you were talking to him. Something to sap his resistance. A spasm of the intestines, maybe. That can be highly painful. He could go soft as a grape; he wouldn't have the strength to say no to you! He might even burst into a Niagara of sobbing tears! Oh yes, Daniel, I'm a man of medicine, but I'm a big enough man to say this to you: When Science fails, call on Father Feeley!"

"Here here here!" Father Feeley said sharply. "That's enough of that nonsense!"

"Don't underestimate the power of prayer, Father!" Billy warned. "I've seen too much of it!"

"DAMN IT TO HELL, WILL YOU WAIT A MINUTE!" Daniel shouted. They all stopped, startled; Daniel regarded them grumpily. "Did you come over here to see what I was going to do, or to argue amongst yourselves?" he asked. "Now for the love of God will you be quiet and let me get in a word edgewise. What the hell is all the fuss about, anyway? What I showed you is just a *part* of it. Just a little something I might begin with. I know damn well nothing like that by itself will do the trick! What d'ye think I am, an idiot or something?"

"Ah, that's better, Daniel," Gottlieb said. "You've got something else: that relieves me."

"Reinforcements from the rear, my dear man," said Billy. "The secret of every successful commander. Look at Napoleon! Look at Bismarck!"

"Both defeated, of course," Father Feeley said. "Ultimately. Still, reserve strength: always wise. Ammunition rather than sentiment. The human animal being what it is."

"What I'll do," Daniel explained, "is this. We'll both be at the door, saying nothing, but looking at each other. I'll step to one side, and I'll ask him in." And now, in illustration, he accompanied his words with a pantomime of what was to come: he stepped aside, beckoned slowly with one hand, and pointed to the center of the room; he said, "He'll come in and he'll stand there. Or maybe he'll sit down. But I'll stay right here, not moving. I'll close the door behind me, but I'll stand right here. And we'll start to talk a little. Or *I'll* talk; he says damn little anyways. He's a listener. So I'll talk. And I'll start out nice and easy, you know, agreeing with him, telling him not to worry about me, he's doing the right thing, and all that stuff. I might throw in a few little things to shake him a bit, but nothing big, you know. But then, all of a sudden," he said slowly, "all of a sudden I might start to change. Right there in front of him, I might start to change!"

With this he resumed the pantomime, this time indicating the nature of his change. Already slightly slumped at the doorway, as the old man began to move forward he slumped even further. As he moved he half turned away from his audience; there was no snap to his step, his progress appeared to be as painful as it was slow, and his right foot dragged. As he came closer to them, he twisted around so that when he stopped he confronted them full-face. He looked, suddenly, very old. His body now began to shake and shake badly. This performance was watched by the three men with the greatest attention, and the attention was on the point of mounting into concern when Daniel miraculously stiffened into his normal upright posture and all shaking ceased. He smiled slightly, and stood there expectantly.

"Oh, very good, Daniel!" Billy cried. "Excellent! A truly magnificent case of the trembles!"

Gottlieb exhaled largely. "Believe me, Daniel," he said, "for one minute there I got a little nervous. A boy looks at his Dad doing that, he could get scared to death."

"Yes yes," Father Feeley agreed. "All the marks of deterioration: first class!"

"It's not bad, at that," Daniel said complacently. "I practiced it a bit, you know, in front of the mirror. That's why I didn't want any of them snooping around, getting wise to what I was doing. It's a damn good stunt, but it's got to be a surprise."

"If it's all the same to you, Daniel, I don't need any more surprises like that," Gottlieb said. "My old friend Artie Glickman dying in a second from a clot, you all crumpled over like a cripple: believe me, it makes me very nervous!"

"Well, that's what it's supposed to do," Daniel said. "It's supposed to make anybody that sees it worried as hell. And don't forget this: you were ready for it. I told you something was coming. But say I sprang it on somebody that was just sitting there, not expecting anything! Well then, maybe we might have some fun!"

"The results can't help but be highly dramatic, my dear man," Billy said. "Unless I miss my guess, restoratives may be needed."

Daniel said, "And then, you know, we don't have to stop with that. There's plenty of other things a man could do. Oh yes. I . . . ah . . . ah . . . ahh . . ."

Without warning, his speech broke off into a choking, gurgling sound; as he uttered it Daniel bent double, then snapped back into an unnaturally stiff, erect position. His face moved as if he had no control over its expression; his tongue popped out and, gasping, he staggered, then collapsed into a chair. He lay there, sprawled out awkwardly, his breathing deep and rasping, one leg jerking spasmodically, his arms flopping bonelessly about. It was altogether an alarming performance and unquestionably it alarmed his audience. Prepared for theatrics, this was something more; they looked at each other and then moved a tentative step forward. It was Father Feeley who finally moved briskly to Daniel's side.

"All right, Daniel!" he said peremptorily. "The point is made." There was no answer; the priest said, "Daniel?"

"Oh my God!" Gottlieb cried. "Artie Glickman Number Two!"

In the chair, the harsh breathing and all movement now came to a stop. The three men saw only the slightest rise and fall of the old man's chest; there was no sound. In a moment there was a grunt, a sigh; they watched as slowly Daniel opened his eyes a little and said, very weakly, "Where is he? Where's my personal physician? Why don't I hear from the medical department?" Then his eyes closed again, and as the men looked at one another, suddenly Daniel sat bolt upright in his chair, opened his eyes fully, and spoke to them in his normal voice.

"Well, Billy!" he said. "How about that one? Don't tell me you thought I was a goner, too?"

"My compliments, Daniel," Billy said, recovering rapidly. "My sincere compliments. That was what we might call the performance of a virtuoso! Oh yes! You almost fooled the trained eye with that one, my dear man. You almost fooled *me!*"

"Listen to me, Daniel," Gottlieb said shakily. "With me there was no almost. I admit it: you fooled me. But that kind of fooled I don't want to be. With that kind of fooling you could give a man a condition. So don't show me any more. Whatever you say you can do, all right: I believe it. I'm a convinced person, Daniel!"

"And what about the clergy?" Daniel said, looking at Father Feeley. "By God, you were over here like a shot, I'll say that for you. *Dominus vobiscum* and the big heave-ho to the cemetery lot: was that the idea?"

"More or less, yes yes," Father Feeley said. "The waxen pallor, the ghastly respiration, the twitching: all authentic, extremely so."

"Especially the twitching, my dear man!" Billy said, in full enthusiasm once more. "I don't want to flatter you, Daniel, but those twitches were A-Number-One! You could go to every hospital in the country and you wouldn't find better twitches than those!"

"Well, that's what I told you," Daniel said. "You don't spend fifty years on the stage without picking up a trick or two. Tricks that come in handy every now and again. Like tonight, say. What son could throw his father out when his father's having fits? Hey, Billy? Specially when they're the kind of terrible fits I have? What son could be as cruel as that?"

"What you're talking about there, Daniel, is the proverbial heart of stone," Billy said. "There's no danger of that here. Thanks to what we might call your consummate art."

"A queer business, this mimicry of dying, "Father Feeley said. "Children do it all the time, adults almost never. Understandable, of course. The closer you are to a thing, the less you want to play games with it."

"What you say, Father," Gottlieb said urgently, "it's true. I tell you, Daniel, there's something about it I don't like. What I don't like is an old gentlemen like you, my own age exactly, lying flat on his back, kicking his legs up in the air, going, 'Ah . . . ah . . . ah.' " He shook his head sadly. "I feel like Father. It's not right. It's not *decent*. It could even be dangerous."

"I'd have to disagree with that, my dear man," Billy said. "Speaking as a medical man, I have to disagree with you and Father there. What could be dangerous about it, with a man like Daniel at the controls?"

"Right you are, Billy," Daniel said. "There's damn well nothing dangerous about it at all."

"You've put your finger right on it, my dear man," Billy said. *"There's nothing dangerous at all.* It's just the pessimists, the Gloomy Guses, who always look on the dark side of things. They're always thinking that one day you'll start one of these fake fits and won't be able to pull out of it. They're always thinking of a day you'll be lying there on your back, kicking away and dribbling and turning blue in the face, needing the doctor fast if you're going to last until sunset, but nobody pays a bit of attention to you because they don't know it's the real McCoy caught up with you at last, and not just you having fun! Oh yes, Daniel, they're always thinking about things like that. Good people, yes, but that's the way they think. They're pessimists one and all! They never come around and cheer a man up!"

Daniel gave him a look which was long, exasperated, and baffled. "By God," he said finally, "you've got the damnedest way of cheering people up I ever saw. If you tell a man Happy Birthday he wants to put his head in the oven." He shrugged, and then returned to his main theme. "Anyways, all that's no matter. I don't give a damn about that kind of nonsense. All I want to know is this: do you agree with me? That it'll do the job? With Tom?"

"Put your mind at ease, my dear man," Billy said. "A stunt like that would do the job with a regiment of Toms!"

"Yes, yes, it should be effective, I think," Father Feeley said. "Fairly effective. I don't know the boy well of course. Still, he's probably typical. They're a strange lot. I don't understand them at all. Sometimes they seem scarcely human. Yet we know they're made in the image and likeness of God. There's a mystery for you!"

Daniel said, "But it'll work?"

"Oh yes," Father Feeley said. "I should think so. I should think it might work quite well. And if it doesn't . . . well, there you are. And so forth. In the end, of course, it all means very little."

"Daniel, I'll give you my frank opinion," Gottlieb said. "When I came into this room a while ago, I said something to myself. I said, 'Poor Daniel: he hasn't got a Chinaman's chance. I know young people; they're all like my Sonny.' But now, Daniel, I'll make a confession to you: I changed my mind. Now I say to myself, 'Gottlieb, you spoke too soon. Those fits you saw: they're horrible things. But maybe they'll scare that selfish boy into keeping his good old Dad around!' "

"Good for you, Gottlieb!" Billy said. "It takes a big man to admit he's been wrong. Look at Columbus, Herbert Hoover . . . oh yes, Daniel, I'm all with Gottlieb on that one. I'll go even further than Gottlieb! I'll say you'll not only be around after tonight; you'll be around here for years to come!"

Daniel smiled slightly. "I'll let you in on a little secret, Billy," he said. "I think you're right. I think you're damned right!"

"Yes, yes, you'll be around," Father Feeley said. "For some time to come, perhaps. My private opinion, of course. Anything is possible." He looked around quickly, smoothed his hair back nervously with one hand, and stepped quickly towards Daniel. "I must go," he said. "Goodbye,

Daniel. I enjoyed the performance. Very skillful. It took me back to the old days."

"If you don't mind, Father, I'll go along with you," Gottlieb said. He too crossed over to Daniel and said, "Artie Glickman's sister, Daniel. She gets nervous. But many thanks to you and good wishes. It was a pleasure and a privilege."

"I'll make it unanimous, my dear man," Billy said. He went to the bed and picked up his satchel. "Duty calls: I've got to get back to my bladder case before some Official Doctor gets in there and does the usual irreparable damage. Goodbye, Daniel. It was a grand treat. You could have sold tickets."

"No no, this one was on the house," Daniel said. "This one was on me!" He was in great good humor. He shook hands all around, and then walked with his three old friends to the door. Once there, before opening it, he motioned at them with a cautioning gesture. "One second now," he said. He whipped the door open and quickly stepped into the hall, looking in both directions. "It's all right," he said. "I guess some people were minding their own business for a change."

"And after tomorrow, my dear man," Billy said, "we'll all come around to call as usual."

"Ah!" Daniel exclaimed. "By God, I almost forgot the most important part. I tell you when I want you to come. Not after tomorrow; I want you to come tonight! All of you!"

The three men looked at each other; Billy said, "Tonight, my dear man? You want us to come in on the very night you're having the big act with Tom?"

"That's right," Daniel said. "Only not while I'm doing it, of course. I want you to come in afterwards. About nine, say; it'll be all over then. And it'd mean a lot to me to have you around. My doctor, my priest, and my favorite fan: all together backstage at Waltzing Daniel Considine's farewell performance! Will you do it?"

Again the three men looked at each other, and with no hesitation all nodded. Billy said jubilantly, "Right you are, my dear man! We'll be here with bells on! To celebrate the happy occasion!"

"Yes yes," Father Feeley agreed. "Well, goodbye, Daniel." He left the room with a quick little gesture of farewell; it was a curious gesture which might almost have been taken for a benediction.

Gottlieb followed Father Feeley; on the threshold he said, "Goodbye, Daniel. And stay in good health. That way, no matter what happens, at least you've got your health."

Billy was the last to go; as he left he waved and said, "Until tonight, my dear man. Tonight at nine! A rendezvous with us all!"

"Fine, fine, fair enough," Daniel said, "Goodbye again."

Billy closed the door behind him, and Daniel was once more alone. He was obviously pleased with the result of the session; he smiled and rubbed his hands. He spoke aloud, and with great satisfaction.

"Boys oh boys!" he said. "Well well well. It won't be long now. Oh no. It won't be long at all!"

He was looking forward to the encounter; he felt like a boy. It had been literally years since he had been so excited. He walked quickly to his mirror and stood facing himself, just looking without any particular expression; then he smiled.

"Oh yes!" he said. "Oh yes yes yes yes!"

More soberly, he began to examine himself in detail. He pulled down the lower lid of his left eye and scrutinized the eyeball critically; it was still white, still fine, still clear. He opened his mouth; he stuck out his tongue and regarded it gravely. He took his pulse as he stood there. Then he stepped back, smoothed his hands over his hair, and looked at himself from head to foot, up and down. He was not displeased with what he saw.

Backing a few steps, he took a deep breath, then abruptly went into the pantomime which had so alarmed his friends. He bent, staggered, limped, and looked older than ever; he collapsed into a chair, and once more the deep and desperate breathing began. The twitches which Billy so admired went on full display. This continued for some moments, after which Daniel got slowly to his feet and returned to his mirror to check on his appearance. He smiled and nodded his head.

"Oh yes," he said again. "We'll see about that! We will, we will!"

This finished, he looked about him as if he were not quite sure what came next. His eyes stopped at the record player on the table; he went over to it, picked the record off, looked at it, then replaced it. He turned up the volume and waited; soon, fading in, came the music of his theme song, and as it did, old Daniel, alone in his room, began to dance, singing softly but happily as he did so:

> *I'll tell you who's a friend of mine —*
> *He's Waltzing Daniel Considine!*
> *Dum dee, dum dee, dum dum dee dum*
> *Dum dum dee dum di dum*
> *Dum dum dee di dee, dee dum dum dee di*
> *Dum dum dee di dee, dum dum dee di. . . .*

And as he danced he reflected that it would be three hours, now, before his son came, before his act began. Eager, impatient, he could hardly wait for the moment. He wished that it were *now*. . . .

All in the Family

Two main strands twine through ALL IN THE FAMILY. Only with the last chapter — in which the narrator's lifelong need of a family of his own is serenely fulfilled — does one realize that this quieter theme is dominant over the story of a conspicuous Irish-American family's eruption into politics.

Their name is Kinsella;* it means new and great riches, nationwide connections, and a formidable clannishness. (It was falsely assumed by many readers, even a few reviewers, that the author had in mind the Kennedy family, whom he knew and liked. The author foresaw this interpretation but had to risk it. To have altered his novel out of prudence would have been to spoil a plan of long standing. He wanted to write about a bitter family fight; he wanted to use his knowledge of the small world of money and influence; and he wanted to deal with politics as conducted a generation after THE LAST HURRAH, on a state and national, rather than purely municipal level. This desire was expressed but not satisfied by the lightly sketched congressional candidacy of Charlie Carmody's grandson in THE EDGE OF SADNESS. The author had much more to say.)

The novel poses two tests of family devotion. Jack Kinsella's marriage is hurt by his wife's escapade with another man, then healed by tenderness and tact. But it proves impossible to bridge the rift which opens between the narrator's cousins, Charles Kinsella, his brother Philip, and old Jimmy Kinsella, their loving and irascible father. The conflict pits family loyalty against political honor, and it ends in an appalling scene of moral breakdown.

The first selection is Chapter One of the novel, a flashback to Jack Kinsella's childhood. After the death of his mother and brother, Jack is taken to Ireland, where he meets his Kinsella cousins and becomes deeply attached to them — to Philip in particular. The narration then moves directly to the moment, twenty-eight years later, when Charles Kinsella is elected governor of the state (whose capital is the city of THE LAST HURRAH and THE EDGE OF SADNESS.)

The second selection describes a party given to celebrate Charles's victory.

* Pronounced with the first syllable stressed and the second almost elided: KINS'lla.

ONE year, when I was a boy — eleven, going on twelve — my father
took me to Ireland. We went because of a tragedy, a family tragedy which was really my first experience with sadness of any kind. We
arrived there early in April and stayed the rest of the spring and all of
the summer. It was the first trip we had ever taken together, for although
my father was a great traveler, before this he had always gone off alone
with my mother, leaving me at home with my younger brother Tom, a
housekeeper named Ellen, and a small, neat red-faced man who could
do anything — fix a car, fly a plane, shoot a rifle, build a tree-house,
whistle through his teeth, and walk like an Indian. His name was Arthur,
and he had been with my father for years. He was a man of unusual
appearance: his face, which was the color of a bright cherry the year
round, was also strangely smooth, looking always as if it had been freshly
waxed, and his hands, I remember, were astonishing. They were freckled
and very large — for someone of his size they were enormous. Enormous,
and powerful: one night, one great night, when I was about eight, I had
their power demonstrated for me in the most dramatic way imaginable.
I had been asleep; I was awakened by a series of loud noises coming from
somewhere in the house. I listened, frightened; Tom was in bed beside
me, still asleep, and in any case too small to help. The noises continued,
and finally — and fearfully — I got out of bed, crossed the room, and
opened the door the smallest possible crack. Through this opening
nothing much was visible to either side, but straight ahead I could see
down the stairs leading into the front hall, and there, at the bottom of
the stairs, just at this moment and as if for my exclusive benefit, Arthur
and a man I had never seen before came bursting into view, moving
swiftly but oddly across the dark parqueted floor, and all at once I
realized that they were fighting! It was a thrilling sight, but an alarming
one, too, for the other man was much bigger than Arthur — to me he
seemed at least twice his size. Suddenly, however, Arthur stepped back,
very quickly, and his right foot shot out, kicking the other man savagely
just below the knee. The other man's arms dropped and he doubled over;

at this Arthur moved in and with a forward sweep of one arm brought the flat edge of his huge hand smashing high and hard against the other man's face. From where I crouched I could hear as well as see the blow: the sound was not loud — a thin sharp *splat* — but the man instantly collapsed and fell to the floor, one leg jerking up and turning as he fell, so that his toe caught and was held in the neck of a large Persian vase. For a moment he lay there, motionless and silent on his stomach, one leg up in the air behind him, and then, amazingly, he began to cry! I was terrified, but also astounded: I had never seen a grown man cry before; I had never seen Arthur like this before. The ferocious kick, the slashing smash to the face did not belong to the Arthur I saw every day; moreover, they were not at all like the squared-off stance and the manly closed-fist attack which, I knew, was the only fair way men and boys fought each other.

This troubled me, and later, when Ellen had telephoned the police and they had come and taken away the intruder — whom, to my surprise, they seemed to know quite well: they even laughed and made jokes with him, in which he did not join — I asked Arthur about it. To my relief he agreed with me at once. "Don't you go by what I done, Jackie," he said. "That's no way for nice people to fight. It's more what you could call a shortcut, like. A little joke I play sometimes on people that's bigger than me."

When my father and mother came back a week or so later and learned what had happened, my mother, who had been an actress before she married my father — she was tall and very pretty and smelled like flowers, and she had soft, pale gold hair and extraordinary eyes that sometimes looked gray and sometimes very green — wept and hugged us hard, first Tom, then me. After we were out of the room and, supposedly, out of hearing, she began to talk excitedly of kidnappers and ransom and declared that she would never again go off and leave us without what she called "adequate protection." My father, who had disappointed me by receiving our great news with his usual calm, laughed and said that of course she was right. He added that this was why we were so fortunate in having Arthur.

"He's as good as a regiment," he said, and when my mother protested that this was not at all what she had meant, he simply nodded and said, "I know. But what would you rather have? Two state cops in the living room? Burning holes in the rug and shooting the mailman by mistake? No, we'll stick with Arthur. He's small but he's tidy. And he's very very tough."

The thrill of this night was never repeated. My mother and father continued to travel, just as before, and we continued to be left with

Ellen and Arthur, just as before. There were no more breaks, no more fights, no more summoned police; as my father had predicted, we could not have been safer.

We were very happy. Ellen and Arthur, who must then have been in their early forties, had no children of their own — Ellen was a widow, Arthur had not yet married — and possibly because of this they gave us great affection as well as excellent care. We responded, naturally, inevitably. Tom, who was five years younger than I, and still not much more than a baby, preferred to stay close to Ellen, but I had some time ago begun to slip away from such placid company and now spent every possible moment with Arthur. This kept me busy, for Arthur was never idle. We lived in a large, old-fashioned house, always painted freshly white, with big round pleasant tower rooms and, up above, a steep crowning cupola with a golden rooster weathervane. We had space to spare, inside and out: there were wide lawns and maple trees and, in the back, some distance from the house, a combination stable-garage which also, at one point, had served as a hangar. My father had owned a small, single-engine plane — silver, with a red, jagged streak of lightning painted on each side — but my mother, who had always objected to his flying, had finally persuaded him to sell it a year or so ago, and now the building housed two cars, my father's horse Sinbad — a powerful, inky, restless animal I feared and avoided — and my own version of a horse: a docile and nearly motionless pony named Theodore. All of this was Arthur's territory: he made his rounds every day, walking briskly and sometimes almost running, but always looking all around at everything, his sharp blue eyes searching for soft spots, for the first signs of damage or decay.

"You got to hop on it before it hops on you, Jackie," he said to me one morning. There had been a thunderstorm during the night, and a cellar window had cracked; sprawled out on the warm summer grass I watched him as he worked swiftly and expertly with his glass-cutter and his putty knife. "You let it get a head start on you, and you know what happens? You wind up livin' like them Lynches!"

I grew up with all the Lynches and never saw one. I met them only in Arthur's stories: a large and very dirty family who had only to move into a house — a good house, Arthur emphasized, a *new* house — and that house died, simply crumbling to pieces in no time at all around its awful tenants. Arthur never told me exactly what the Lynches looked like, but I thought I knew: they were huge and smudged and covered with hair; they threw bones on the floor and circled each room slowly all day long, rubbing against the walls like cattle, their massive shoulders slowly *erasing* the house away. The Lynches must have been very much on Arthur's mind, for he talked about them a great deal, and whenever he set out on his daily tour of inspection, with me at his side, I felt satisfaction and pride in knowing that I was helping him to preserve us all from similar disasters.

I followed him everywhere. If he left the house for so much as an hour — to drive in to the center of the city on an errand, say — I was on the front seat beside him, pelting him with questions, listening to every word as he answered in his high and rather solemn voice. It was the same voice he used to everyone, to my father as well as to me, and it was for me — at least in my father's absence — the voice of authority and adventure, everything it said being one more link to the fascinating world which Arthur knew so well and which I was burning to know:

"Arthur, did you ever shoot a tiger?"

"Only the one I told you about, Jackie. When I was with your dad out in India, there."

"Was that the man-eater?"

"The man-eater, that's right, Jackie."

"Did you ever shoot an elephant?"

"Your dad wouldn't shoot elephants, Jackie. Still, there was one he did. On account of it was crazy. What they call a rogue. They're bad actors, them rogues."

"Are they man-eaters, too?"

"No, elephants don't eat anybody. Not even rogues. What they'd do, they'd spear you with the tusks and then jump on you till you was jelly. . . ."

"Arthur, are you rich?"

"I wouldn't say that, Jackie."

"Is Dad rich?"

"Some people of got more money than other people, Jackie. That's what it all comes down to."

"Buster Mahoney says Dad has millions of dollars. He says my Uncle Jimmy is the richest man there is."

"There's people in this town of got nothin' to do but talk about this family. I wouldn't pay them no mind, Jackie. Mostly they don't know what they're talkin' about. You listen to your dad on that one. . . ."

"Arthur, did you fight in the war?"

"That's right, Jackie."

"Did you kill lots of people?"

"Not many, Jackie. Not many at all. And they was Germans, mostly. They call them Huns."

"How did you kill them? With your rifle?"

"Different ways, Jackie. Different ways. . . ."

I had a marvelous time with Arthur. If I wasn't with him all day long
it was only because by now, unlike Tom, I was old enough to go to
school. There was a public school about a mile from our house, and I
went there from the first grade on. I liked this school, I liked the teachers — or most of them — and I made good friends and had a fine time,
but it always seemed to me that I had a far better time when, at the end
of the day, I got home and ran to find Arthur and talk to him and listen
to him and join him in whatever fresh and exciting project he had found
to do that day.

He could make anything, even painting a wall, seem exciting to me,
and the only people I knew who could make all parts of life even more
exciting were my father and mother. When they came home, everything
and everyone else, even Arthur, slipped into the background — not forgotten, but diminished temporarily — for once at home our parents
filled our lives. We never talked or wondered about this; it was simply
taken for granted that when they came back, they came back to us. They
seemed to do nothing without us, and yet, of course, this could not have
been so — they were young, they were popular, they had a great many
friends here in the city. They must have had a thousand things to do
which had no connection with us at all, and I suppose they did them,
but I have no memory of this. All I remember is that they seemed to be
with us, not just at odd hours or in their free moments, but literally all
the time. And they arranged this so easily, so naturally, that each time
they came home we slid without awkwardness or hesitation into the family routine which had been suspended from the moment they went away.

Exactly what we did depended on the time of year. In the summer we
often drove into the country for long, all-day picnics, or else we went to
the ocean — not far away there was a broad, gently sloping beach which
stretched straight as a string for miles in both directions, and which by
some miracle was nearly always deserted — and here we swam and
played in the surf and, when the tide went out, built our moist, doomed
castles in the sand. In the fall and spring — and in the winter, too, if the
weather was clear and the roads were open — we went on weekend
camping trips to a cabin my father owned, only two hours from our
house in the city, but so cleverly isolated in a dark pine woods that
whenever we were there I felt as if we had been dropped mysteriously
into the middle of a distant northern wilderness for which there were no
maps and which no one but ourselves had ever seen.

I loved this cabin. My mother, who always enjoyed herself up here, but probably found life a good deal more comfortable in our house in the city, never called it anything but "your father's log cabin," although actually there were no logs at all. The building was long, low, shingled, and because of the pines all around it rather dark even in the brightest daylight. It had one central room with a huge stone fireplace, and two small bedrooms; it was situated on the end of a point of land which reached out between small twin lakes. These lakes were blue-black and very clear; except for some weeks from late spring to early fall they were too cold for leisurely swimming. A weird, chilling cry sometimes came floating across these lakes at night, and it was my father who told us that this was a loon. And often around sunset we would see two large domed shells appear suddenly and side by side, to ride sedately and heavily on the surface of the water; they belonged to a pair of enormous turtles who apparently always swam together. My father said that they were very old.

"How old?" I asked.

"Older than anybody," he said. "Anybody you know, that is."

"Older than Grampa?" I mentioned my grandfather — who was always being mentioned by other people — not because I thought about him a lot, or because he was a favorite relation, but only because he was certainly the oldest person I had ever met. I barely knew him: he was my father's father, but he was not a great visitor — I had seen him in our house only a very few times — and my mother told me that he was now almost never in the city and lived mostly abroad.

"Older than Grampa, even," my father said. "If that's conceivable, and I guess it is. Although maybe not to him. Look, give me a hand with this rope, will you? I want to rig a hammock for your mother."

Since so few people came up here during the year, the country all around us was pretty much let alone — particularly the lakes, which were said to be bursting with fish. This would have delighted me if I had been more of a fisherman, but I was not. I hated fishing, and I hated it from the first. One spring, when I was still quite small, my father took me out on the east lake in a large flat-bottomed rowboat he had shipped up to the camp for just this purpose. It was ugly and clumsy, but it was also just about untippable, and this was a condition my mother had insisted on. We rowed slowly out to what my father said was a likely-looking spot, near a patch of lily pads; I had with me the shiny black fishing rod which my Uncle Jimmy, of all people, had sent me a birthday or so ago and which until now I had never used. We anchored, and my father showed me how to bait my hook, how to cast, how to reel in after a strike; then, in silence, we began to fish. And I remember that, sitting there, hunched down in the bow of the boat, a bottle of rapidly warming ginger ale beside me, with the smooth blue monotony of the sky doubling itself in the still water, and the faintest drowsy breeze bringing the first smells of summer through the piny air, and the gentle tugging at the line informing me that soon now one more small perch would either be brought into the boat or else would get away — I did not in the least care which — I decided that fishing was the greatest waste of time I had ever known, and I began to fall asleep. I opened my eyes to find my father looking at me; he nodded encouragingly and said, "This is the life."

"It's swell," I said politely. "Really swell."

"I'm glad you like it," he said. "I had an idea you might not, but some of my friends told me I was missing a real bet, having a place like this and not taking my boy out to fish with me. They said that's all a real boy wants: to be taken out in a boat with his dad, with his fishpole in his hand. As I say, I had my doubts, but now that I know you like it so much we shouldn't have any trouble catching ourselves a couple of hours this way every morning. And maybe in the afternoon, too. How about it?"

I said cautiously, "I might not like it all that much."

"No? Well, that's all right. The problem would be if you didn't like it at all. Then we'd really be up a tree. I suppose then we might just have to try the other way."

He paused thoughtfully. After a moment I said, "The other way?"

"The emergency way," he said. "It's what you do if you finds that one of the people in the boat really can't stand fishing. There's only one thing you're allowed to do in that case. You have to row in to shore, bore a few holes in the bottom of the boat — not too big — and then row out again and sit there while it sinks under you. Boat, bait, fishpoles and all. Then you swim back to shore and never bother with anything like it again. But of course that's an extreme measure; you do it only if someone doesn't like fishing at all. I wouldn't think of doing it to you. Why, do you know what it would mean? It would mean *no more fishing for the rest of the summer!*"

I stared at him, not really believing that I had heard what I had heard, and then I saw that he was smiling, and I felt like yelling because I knew that he not only realized how much I hated it, he hated it just as much himself. And later, after we had sunk the boat — in just the way my father had said — and were swimming back to the shore, with my mother standing on the little dock, just looking at us, he said to me, "You never know till you try. Later on, there's a kind of fishing you could enjoy. But this is for sleepy old men with pipes. You might just as well be knitting."

I said, panting as I swam, "I just remembered — the fishpole. It was a present from Uncle Jimmy."

"I've been wondering what to do about Uncle Jimmy's presents for years," my father said. "I guess we've just discovered the ideal solution. Come on, over on your back, float a little. Keep on with that dog paddle and you won't last another ten seconds."

So the fishing stopped for good, and we passed the time in far better ways. We swam whenever we could; we shot across the lakes in a long, dark green canoe which, strangely enough, my mother (who was always worried about boats collapsing or turning over) loved, and handled expertly; we skated in the winter; we trooped after my father on expeditions through the woods, over narrow trails which had been broken long ago, by whom we did not know. Pine needles had been dropping on these trails for years and had not been disturbed; they formed a thick dry cushion on which we could walk in silence, frequently surprising birds, snakes, rabbits, squirrels, and even deer. Once my father stopped abruptly and simply pointed to the sky; there, taking off from the top of a tall dead tree, his wings moving up and down with a powerful lazy majesty, was an eagle! To me it was like seeing a dinosaur or a roc. I had read all about eagles, but I had never seen one before — and I have never seen one since.

There was a cave at the end of one of these trails; we entered it through a small opening in the side of a hill. It was gloomy and damp and just large enough for my father to stand up in it, but people had lived here — maybe, I thought, Indians. The roof had been darkened with smoke, there were rough scratchings on the walls, and when I began to dig around in the dirt floor, I found an arrowhead. We dug some more: we found another arrowhead, a piece of colored glass, and an old and very large bone. We wondered excitedly about this bone. To what had it belonged? Or to whom?

"A bear or a buffalo, I imagine," my mother said. "It's certainly too big for a man."

"Too big for a man, yes," my father said, looking significantly at Tom and me, "but ask yourselves this: *is it too big for a giant?* Think about that for a minute!"

I thought about it for much more than a minute; I thought about it for days. It seemed to me that as usual my father was completely right.

Often, when we came back to the cabin after one of these expeditions, tired, not talking much, and thinking of many things but most of all of supper, it was quite late and sometimes it was dark. Then there was a different, quieter kind of excitement, for after dark the cabin was a mysterious and even a romantic place. We had no electricity up here: the cooking was done on an oilstove, and the only light came from kerosene lamps and the big fireplace. The fire was seldom allowed to go completely out, but every once in a while it died, and then, if we begged him hard enough, my father would restart it Indian style, using no matches, but twirling a bow with a leather thong rapidly back and forth across a wooden spindle, while we watched breathlessly for the first thin curl of smoke from the little pile of shavings he used for tinder.

After supper we usually went right to bed, and as the final treat of the day my father came into our room to tell us a story. He always waited until we had washed up and said our prayers, and then, as we lay in bed waiting, with the blankets pulled up hard around our necks, he would come in, sit on the bed, and begin. He must have had hundreds of stories; I don't remember ever hearing him repeat one. A few were familiar — I had read them in books, or heard them in school — but only a few; the rest he made up himself, and these, for me, were by far the best. My mother always came in with him and sat on the bed, too, and I think he must have told the stories to her as well as to us, for although she did not listen in the same way we did — she might suddenly laugh where I could see nothing funny at all, or else she might ask a question just as he came to the most exciting part — still, most of the time she listened with great attention, and if the story was an especially long one, and if in spite of everything we could do we sometimes fell asleep before it was over, the last thing I always saw was my father looking down at us, still talking, and my mother, seated beside him with her arm around him, still listening.

This was the cabin, with my father in charge. At home, in the city, he was still in charge, but here it was more my mother's world, and here more time was given to the things she really liked. The theater was one of these. Although she had left the stage for good when she married my father, she was still very fond of anything connected with it, and she kept in close touch with all of her old friends. Whenever a new play came to the city, some of the people who were in it were quite likely to come out to our house for dinner, and one who did so very often was an English actor they called Dickie. He was a great friend of both my mother and father. He was small and bald, with large horn-rimmed glasses and funny teeth; when I saw him he usually had a cold, and he ate very little because of what he called the Old Intestine. I liked him because he was always nice to me and brought me a present whenever he came, and also because he could pop his eyes and play the banjo and sing sailor songs.

One night, shortly after one of his visits to us, my mother and father gave me a surprise treat by taking me to the theater with them, and as I sat between them, not really enjoying or very much understanding what was happening on the stage, suddenly, in one corner of that stage, there appeared a tall man in a long black robe that reached to the floor. His face was dark and evil; he had long black hair and a small pointed black beard. As soon as he took a step forward there was an absolute silence in the theater, a silence which was broken only when his voice screamed out: a malignant, paralyzing howl that seemed to shake the building, then dropped away to the thinnest of whispers that was somehow more frightening than the howl. I sank back against my seat, petrified, and it was a moment or so before I realized that my mother was patting my hand and murmuring that it was all right, that this terrifying figure was really only Dickie! I did not believe this simply because I could not believe that such a thing was possible, and it was not until later, in Dickie's dressing room after the performance, that I was at last persuaded. And it was not until many years later that I learned something which would in any case have meant nothing to me as a child: that our friend Dickie, with his popping eyes and his Old Intestine and his sailor songs, was usually spoken of as one of the few really great actors of that day.

But the theater I liked best was the theater we had all to ourselves. My mother enjoyed family theatricals, and we were always rehearsing and presenting special versions of plays she had selected for us. Whatever these plays may have been in the beginning, by the time they reached us they had been considerably changed to fit our talents. There was always an infant and often nonspeaking part for Tom, and always an older and more heroic role for me. My mother and father doubled in brass, each of them always playing at least two parts, and sometimes three or four, and my father, who was very good at doing magic tricks, found that more often than not a magician was an important figure in our plays. Then he, with my mother as his confederate — he in white tie and tails, she in a long white evening gown — would miraculously change one card into another before our eyes, pull colored flags out of the air, make tennis balls appear and disappear, and once produced, from an obviously empty hat, a small white rabbit for me!

If there was music in the play, as there sometimes was, we all took turns at singing, but it was really only my mother who sang well. She had a pretty voice, light and sweet and true, and I loved to listen to her sing. For years, whenever I thought of my mother I thought of her as standing on the small improvised stage in the music room, holding Tom by the hand on one side of her and holding me by the hand on the other, trying

to keep us swaying back and forth together in rhythm while she sang to
my father a song which went, in part:

> . . . *cannot tell you whether*
> *We'll sail off together*
> *To the golden dreaming sands*
> *Of Zanzibar* . . .

The rest of this song, or even the show in which it was sung, I cannot
remember at all.

We were never entirely alone at these family productions. Since my
mother firmly believed that no play should ever be without an audience,
no matter how small that audience might be, Ellen and Arthur were
invariably called in to watch us. They always applauded loudly, and on
several occasions Arthur told me in confidence that I was a very good boy
actor, and that if I ever decided to go on the stage to earn my living, he
would be enormously surprised if I did not get famous and make a huge
fortune.

We had an interesting, a happy, and a wonderful childhood. More
than most children, I think, we had a *family* childhood, and in a way this
was strange because our parents were away so much more than other
parents. But this seemed to me to make no difference. We knew that
whenever they went away they would soon come back; we knew that we
were loved; I think we may have been *surer* of our parents than most
children. And in the meantime, of course, we had Ellen and Arthur. So
that when I look back upon my childhood — or at least upon this part of
it — in spite of school and the good times there and all my friends, I'm
always tempted to think of it as exclusively a family time, a time in
which there were my father and mother and Ellen and Arthur and Tom
and me and no one else, a time in which I was as happy as a boy could
ever be, a time which was so marvelous that day after day I hoped with
all my heart that it would never end.

It did, of course. It came to an end on a morning in March, when I
was eleven years old. It came to an end most sadly and most unexpectedly; it came to an end in an instant.

We had gone up to the cabin for the weekend. March was always
unreliable, and the winter had been bad, but for more than a week there
had been a warm spell, and when we reached the cabin, late on a Friday
afternoon, the ice which had edged the lakes on our last visit was gone,
the sharp wet smell of winter had left the air, the ground was soft, birds
we had not heard in months were chirping away somewhere in the trees,

and out on the water a fish jumped. Spring had not really and firmly begun, but winter was over, and when we woke the next morning the air was very warm and slow and slightly hazy, as though we had skipped a season overnight and were now in mid-July.

After breakfast, wearing only our shorts on this extraordinary March morning, my father and I went outside and began to work around the cabin, doing the little things that always needed to be done at the end of every winter — there were screens to be replaced, shingles had blown off, paint had flaked away in spots, and a squirrel had started a hole in the back wall near the fireplace. My mother, who always cleaned the cabin each time we came up as if no one had been here for years, stayed inside and, with Tom as an unreliable and occasionally disappearing helper, opened windows, aired bedding, and swept dirt that I could not even see off the floor. When she began her cleaning she usually stayed with it until she finished, but this morning she surprised us by suddenly joining us in the yard. More surprising still, she was wearing her bathing suit.

"Ha!" my father said. "Who's rushing the season? Don't let that sun fool you — the last thing in those lakes was an iceberg."

"I'm having spring fever," my mother said, "for the first time in years. It's all so beautiful I'm taking time off. No swimming, just the canoe. The first ride of the year. Want to come?"

"All right," my father said. He began to get up — he had been plugging the squirrel hole — but then he stopped and said, "On second thought, no. I'd better wait for this stuff to dry. Otherwise I'll have to start all over again. Take Jackie with you: he's a good man in a canoe."

But I was my father's helper; loyally I said, "I want to see this stuff dry, too."

"I can go," Tom said. He was now six years old, a round-headed little boy who came up to my shoulder, with blond hair so light it was almost white, and gray-green eyes just like my mother's. For a long time now I had been making bets — sometimes with Arthur, but mostly with myself — that whenever people came to our house and met Tom and me for the first time, they would always say that Tom was the image of my mother, just as they would always say that I was the image of my father. Tom had been wandering in the woods on the other side of the cabin, and when he came walking toward us now he held in his hand a very small box turtle. "Look what I found," he said. "I could take it in the canoe."

He went over to my mother, who put her hand lightly on his head and mussed his hair a bit. "Good for you, Tommy," she said. "That gives me one customer. That's all, is it? Just the one?"

"And a turtle," my father said. "Don't forget that. And look — don't be too long, will you? I'd like to drive in to the village sometime before noon."

My mother had already started for the lake, with Tom at her side. As they went around the corner of the cabin Tom turned and held up his turtle to show me once more, and my mother, with a little wave of her hand, called back, "We may surprise you: we may never come back!"

And as she called this out to us, her voice was light and very gay. It was almost as if she were singing.

We were working away about ten minutes later when my father paused and said, "Wait: listen. Did you hear anything?"

We both listened; we both heard a shout. My father jumped up and ran down to the point; I followed as fast as I could. We looked out on the east lake, which was the one my mother liked best, and there, some distance out and closer to the far shore than to us, we saw the dark green canoe. We could see it very clearly. It was floating upright, and it was empty. Of my mother and Tom there was no sight at all. My father called my mother's name three times, very loudly; there was no answer. There was no sound of any kind: I don't think that at that moment we even heard a bird. We simply stood there in the complete stillness of the beautiful morning: I, not yet realizing just what had happened, and my father, who must have realized it from the very first shout.

Suddenly my father went "*Aaaggghh!*" It wasn't a call, it wasn't a shout to my mother, it wasn't anything: just a loud and terrible sound. Then without even looking at me or asking me to follow him — but I did anyway — he spun around and ran for the little boathouse, about fifty yards away on the shore of the lake. Here there were a small rowboat and a blue canoe, neither of which had been used since last year; my father began to tug at the rowboat and pulled it into the water. Still without looking at me, with his eyes out on the lake, he said, "Hurry up, get in. Take this can: you'll have to bail. This thing can't be tight. Hurry up, hurry up, *come on!*"

So I jumped in, and by now I was frightened. I had never heard my father like this before, I had never seen him look like this before, and now at last I knew what must have happened. My father began to row very fast, and water began to seep into the boat through the seams — not much, but I had to bail. We moved out over the water, the spray from the oars sometimes hitting me in the face, and as I felt the icy drops I knew how cold the water really was. I thought of my mother and Tom in that water, and suddenly I began to cry. At first my father paid no attention to this, merely keeping on with his rowing and looking constantly over his shoulder at our target: the dark green canoe which continued to float and swing gently about, not moving much in the still morning air. I continued to bail and also to cry, and my father continued to pay no attention, but at one point he looked up from his rowing and stared at me with such a strange expression that for a moment I was sure he was terribly angry with me. But he was not, it must have been something else, for he closed his eyes tight, then opened them and said in a quiet voice, "Don't cry, Jackie. Don't cry. It'll be all right. You'll see. We'll both see. It'll be all right." After this he seemed to row faster than before, breathing quite hard now, and still looking back over his shoulder at the canoe as if he were afraid it would go away before we reached it.

I don't know how long it took us to get there: probably no more than a few minutes, but it seemed a very long time. We came alongside, and my father reached over and grabbed the canoe, pulling it right up against us, and there, on its floor, we saw the pale blue kerchief that my mother had worn around her head, and we saw also, carefully crawling its way across the varnished ribs, Tom's turtle. So the canoe had not turned over: we knew that much. My father stood up in the boat; I started to do the same, but he said, quickly and harshly, "Sit down! And stay down! Don't move until I tell you to!" I sat at once and began to look over the side of the boat, more frightened than ever by the thought of what we were looking for and what I might have to see. The water was dark but quite clear, and although we must have been several feet over my head, I could see to the bottom, but I could see nothing except sand and dark patches of leaves and weeds and a couple of large smooth shapes which I knew were rocks.

My father now knelt in the bow, his head bent forward as if he were trying to reach down through the water with his eyes. Straining to see, he was so close to the water that he seemed to be mostly out of the boat, and suddenly I had the terrible feeling that at any moment he might topple overboard and get lost, like my mother and Tom, and in that case what would become of me? It was a thought that filled me with panic, but I didn't dare to say a word, and after no more than a few seconds my father straightened up and, without taking his eyes from the water, reached around behind him and grabbed one of the oars. Using it as a paddle he began to send us forward quickly but not too quickly, dipping the oar each time very carefully so that it made no ripples to interfere with our seeing. We went in straight toward the shore, then came back out; we zigzagged; we swung around in a big circle, then came back to the center in smaller circles. We covered all the nearby water, with my father kneeling in the bow and with me seated on a thwart in the stern; we saw nothing. Once I asked my father a question, but he gave no sign of having heard me. He continued to paddle, never missing a stroke, and as I sat there behind him, seeing only the blank and silent surface of his slim, strong, freshly sunburned back, my own hope died away, I knew at last that my mother and Tom were gone for good, and I began to cry again, but this time to myself.

My father was paddling faster now, taking less care not to disturb the water, but this did not matter much any more, for while we had been looking a wind had come up out of the north. It was a cold wind, the kind of wind that brings clouds, and these were now scattered all over the sky, huge and gray, all rushing together to block out the sun. The still lake was now fairly rough, the boat began to bump along, and while we continued to search, I realized all at once that with the choppy water and the loss of sunlight I could no longer see the bottom — I could barely see to any depth at all. My father could have been no better off, for suddenly he jumped to his feet, threw the oar down on the floor of the boat, and stood looking all around him, out over all the lake, and then back into the boat and right at me, but looking at me in such a different way that I wasn't even sure he saw me. Then, without a word, he dived over the side and disappeared in the cold dark tossing water!

I screamed at him, but I don't think he heard me. I stood up, still screaming and at the same time crying, for I was terrified now, too much had happened that I did not understand, and I had no idea what was going to happen next. Then, just as suddenly as he had gone, my father was back, pulling himself over the side, standing, breathing deeply, and diving over the side again. I looked over after him, saw him swim down and out of sight, and knew now that he was not leaving me or swimming away: he was going down to the bottom himself to try to find my mother and Tom.

This knowledge was of no help, however, because for the first time it had occurred to me that I was going to drown. The wind had become stronger and the water rougher; the boat was rocking badly, and except for my father's frantic reappearances, I was alone: I was certain that within the next few minutes the boat would capsize and I would be dumped into the freezing water and would never come up again. Meanwhile, my father kept on diving from the boat and a minute or so later scrambling back in — clearly not in answer to my screams, for each time he came back he said nothing to me and didn't even seem to know I was there. The pattern was always the same: my father throwing himself over the side, the splash as he entered the water, my screams, my father bobbing up on the other side and then pulling himself in, waving me away, almost *pushing* me away if I tried to help. Each time he climbed in, the boat tipped more dangerously than before, and twice I slipped and fell to the floor, sprawling out on my back in water which had leaked in through the seams or come in over the sides, while my father stood over me, ignoring me, and breathing in and out noisily, filling his lungs before he hurled himself into the water again. It got worse and worse, and I remember screaming and crying and yelling "Dad! Dad!" whenever he came back in the boat, and thinking that at any moment now we would both go over and that would be the end of me. I was so frightened by my own danger that I could think of absolutely nothing else, and from the beginning to the end of this awful interval I completely forgot the reason, the terrible reason, for our being out on the lake in the first place. I did not once think of my mother or of Tom.

Then, at last, my father climbed into the boat once more, but slowly this time, and very carefully, as if it had only now occurred to him that he might tip the boat over. I had slipped and fallen again and was lying on the floor; my arm hurt where I had cracked it against one of the oars, and I was cold. My father stood over me, dripping water on me, just as before, but now he seemed more like himself, and instead of looking all around him in a wild way and breathing in and out in great harsh gasps, he just stood still, breathing deeply but quietly, his shorts soaking wet and torn by something — a nail in an underwater board, maybe, or a branch. All at once he said loudly, but mainly to himself, "Nothing. Nothing nothing nothing."

At this I sniffled, and he looked down at me with a funny expression on his face; he said, "Jackie."

"I'm cold," I sobbed. "I'm freezing."

"You're freezing?" he said. And he said it almost with surprise, as if he didn't even know that it was cold. Yet the wind was very strong now, there was no sun at all, the temperature must have been dropping all the time; like me he had on only his shorts, and he had been in the icy water. When I looked up at him for comfort I saw that he was shaking and that his skin was pinched and blue. I was shaking too, trembling all over: my teeth had started to chatter and I couldn't stop them. My father looked down at me, and all at once he bent over and lifted me up and held me very close to him, hugging me against his cold wet chest. He held me there for a few seconds, and I could feel him shivering. Then, very gently, he put me down in the stern, propping me up against a wet cushion.

"All right, Jackie," he said. "We're going in now."

And so we went in, with my father rowing as hard as he could, and being helped by the wind which was blowing strong behind us. It must have been a fast trip; it seemed very slow. There were little whitecaps on the water now, the sky was completely covered with low thick dull gray clouds, and it had begun to feel like snow. The beautiful March morning

had gone in an hour, and I was so cold I ached. I was still shaking, I kept
rubbing my arms and legs, and every second the cold seemed to get
worse: great layers of it that passed right through me, freezing the inside
of my bones. I could think of nothing but this cold, the warm cabin
seemed a very long distance away, and I wondered miserably if I would
be frozen to death in the boat before we reached the shore.

My father spoke only once, and that was when he stopped rowing for
a moment and looked across at me as if he had just hurt me. "Jackie," he
said. "Jackie, I . . . good God forgive me, I don't know what to say to
you!"

I said, lying bravely, "It's all right. I'm not so cold any more."

But he just looked at me with the same hurt look and said nothing to
this; he went on with his rowing. It didn't dawn on me that he hadn't
been talking about the cold at all.

When we got to the shore my father leaped from the boat, picked me
up, and carried me to the cabin, running all the way. He ripped my
shorts off and, with a heavy, rough bath towel, began to rub me dry. He
rubbed so hard it hurt, and then he dried off too, and we both put on
heavy winter clothes. All this time he was silent; finally he looked at me
and said, "You ought to be in bed, but I can't — come on," and we ran
out and got into the car and drove to the village.

Here, while I sat in the car, warm and safe now, my father hurried
about, gathering people together, pulling them along with him: the
priest, the doctor, the man with no jaw who ran the gas station. I
watched all this, and as I watched, the odd and awful thing was that I
couldn't feel what I should have felt at all. By now I understood everything that had happened, I knew just what my father was doing and
what he was going to do, but it was as if a part of me — an important
part of me — had not been able to catch up with what the rest of me
knew. What I felt was mainly suspense, a kind of excitement: I was like
a spectator at some game which was interesting but with which I had no
great personal connection. As yet I had not begun to feel anything more
than the faintest trembling beginnings of what I was to feel so devastat-
ingly, and for the first time in my life, later in the day.

My father jumped into the car, bringing some of the men with him,
and we drove back to the cabin, more men following us in two trucks
loaded with some kind of equipment. When we reached the cabin my
father took me inside; he built up the fire and told me to stay in front of
it until he came back. Then he went off to the lake with the other men.

I stayed in the cabin all afternoon. Most of the time I was alone, and
most of the time, as my father had directed, I stayed in the main room
near the fireplace. Obedience was easy; there was really no place else to

go. Once I went outside, into the clearing in front of the cabin, but the weather was worse now, a cold drizzle had begun to fall, and when I peered through the mist across the lake all I could see was men in boats over near the far shore where my father and I had been. And inside, beyond the main room, there were only the two bedrooms. I went into mine briefly. It was just as it had been when we had got up that morning: Tom's pajamas were still on the bed, and his lopsided fort, which he had made out of pillows and blankets, was still standing. I left the room quickly and did not go back. Later, reluctantly, but somehow feeling that I ought to, maybe even that I *had* to, I went into the other bedroom. The first thing I saw, directly opposite the door and hanging over the back of a chair in front of my mother's dressing table, was a bathing suit — one she must have taken out, then decided not to wear: in that moment it looked to me exactly like the one she had worn. On the table was a scattering of her things — combs, brushes, little white jars of face creams, a slim gold bottle of the perfume which she liked best and which my father, for some reason, always called One Night in the Alps — and on the edge of the mirror, stuck in under the frame, was the birthday card from me. It was the first card I had ever sent her, long ago, before Tom was born, and I remember that my father had guided my hand while underneath the printed greeting I wrote a message of my own: *Dear Mom I love you and hope you have a very good birthday. Your son Jackie.*

And so I left this room quickly too. I sat by the fireplace and wished my father would come back. I started to read a book, I pushed around the pieces of a huge family jigsaw puzzle called Big Game of North America, I picked up a pack of cards and began to scale them, one by one, across the room. I did all these things halfheartedly, in fact without any interest at all, because by now I had begun to feel quite different: uneasy, very strange. Here by myself in the silent cabin where I had never been alone before, where nothing I touched or even looked at was all mine but was a part of my father and mother and Tom as well, where into my head now came not vague and passing thoughts but a sudden succession of hard and marvelously clear pictures of things we had all done together and could never do again — here, now, I felt as if something had begun a slow incessant twisting inside me, like a key which was winding me up, turning and turning and turning, tightening me more every second, and this was all so real that all at once the tension shot me out of my chair and I sprang to my feet, stiff and trembling a little and waiting apprehensively for the one final twist that would surely be unbearable. But suddenly it stopped, the tautness let go completely, and when it did it seemed that everything that was in me, even my breath, left me in a single great gushing rush, and I stood there boneless and helpless and absolutely empty. And it was in this desperate, desolate, *total* way that the death of my mother and my brother came home to me at last, and in this awful, cataclysmic misery I thought my heart would really break.

Strangely, I did not cry. I sat back in the chair once more, very lonely and full of a great dull swelling ache. After a while — it might have been minutes, it might have been an hour — my father came back. He came into the cabin alone, he came over to me and hugged me hard again, and then, quietly but very quickly, he told me that a few minutes ago they had found my mother and Tom. And when I heard this it was just as if I had been expecting to hear it, and it made no difference: it just landed in the empty ache, and I didn't feel any worse because, I suppose, I couldn't feel at all. Then the priest came in and took my hand and patted it a few times.

"A brave li'l boys like you," he said, "he don' wan' to cry, eh? You know what for? Because dat brave li'l boys, he know his mama and his li'l brudder, dey're wit' de angels now!"

His name was Father LaPlante; he was a French-Canadian priest who sometimes in the pulpit on Sunday talked English, but most often did not. Everybody else came in then, and some of them said things to me and some of them just looked, but in a little while everyone went away, and they took my mother and Tom with them. I asked my father if I could see them before they went, but he said it would be better a little later.

And so my father and I were alone in the cabin again, but not for long. He went into his bedroom and I heard him moving about; when I looked in I saw him putting some of my mother's things into a suitcase. After this he came out and took me by the hand, just as if I were a baby, and led me out to the car. It was dark, and the cold drizzle had changed to a light and lazy snow. We drove off, and as we took the first turn on the dirt road I looked back through the slow flakes at the cabin, and I saw that my father had not even closed the door.

I never saw the cabin again.

We drove toward the city: a long, silent, immensely sad drive. To my surprise we did not go home; instead, about twenty miles from the city, we left the main road and turned into a small seaside town and stopped in front of an old hotel. My father said simply, "We're going to stay here. Just for tonight."

I had never been in a hotel before, but I knew that this was not a very good one. At the desk downstairs a thin, tired-looking man with watery eyes watched my father sign a big book; over his head was a card which said: PEOPLE *may come and* PEOPLE *may go, but the* BULL *in this place goes on forever.* Upstairs, our room was big and dark and smelled of the sea. There was a wide brass bed, everything was old but looked clean, and on the floor, underneath one of the windows and attached to the foot of the radiator, was a coil of thick rope with big knots in it. Above the rope was a sign in big red letters reading: IN CASE OF FIRE.

It was late, I hadn't eaten since morning, but I wasn't hungry at all; my father said it was time to go to bed. I undressed and knelt by the bed and said my prayers, and I think that this was the worst part of all. For the prayers for the dead were familiar to me, I had said them every night since I had begun to pray, but they had never been in any sense *personal* prayers: no one I knew had ever died. Suddenly I was saying them for my own mother and for Tom, and even now I found this impossible to believe, even though I knew it was agonizingly, shatteringly true.

Finally, I got into bed, and after a minute my father got in too. We lay there in the dark and the silence. There were no night noises from the streets of the town; the only outside sound was from the sea: a dull and regular thudding as the surf broke on the hard shore. There was a thud, then silence, then another thud, then more silence, and in between I could hear only the beating of my heart, which seemed to me very loud and very fast. My father said nothing. He was lying on his back, looking straight up at the ceiling. Suddenly I felt his hand touch mine, then take it and hold it, very lightly and tenderly, and when this happened something seemed to turn completely over inside me, and I twisted around in bed and flung myself up against my father, clinging to him desperately, and as he quickly put his arms around me and held me, I cried for the first time since my father had told me that my mother and Tom had been found.

I cried and kept crying: very hard, and for a very long time. My father just held me, not saying anything, not trying to comfort me with words, and when at last I stopped — or at least gave signs of stopping — he still held me, but he began to talk, and to talk only about my mother. He went back to the beginning: he told me about how he had met her, how she had looked on the stage, where they had been married, and who had married them — the bishop had been at the reception, my mother had been thrilled by the telegram of congratulations from the President, my mother had been terrified when my Uncle Jimmy (at the time, my father explained, a drinking man) had first threatened to punch the governor of the state in the nose, and then in fact had done so. My father told me about their life together before I was born and afterward, of their trips and travels, of the wonders they had seen and the love they had shared. He talked and talked about my mother, and he seemed not to be able to stop talking, and I listened, hanging on every word, just as I had always listened to his stories at night in the cabin, and then, imperceptibly, I began to grow drowsy, and finally — again, just as I had done so often in the cabin — I simply collapsed into sleep with his words still sounding in my ears.

At one point during the night I woke and realized with sudden fright that my father was no longer in bed with me. But then I saw him: he was on the far side of the room, but I could see him clearly. The weather must have broken, for there was a moon, and in its pale light I could see that my father had thrown open the window wide and was in front of it, not standing but kneeling, motionless, his hands joined, and looking out into the still, dark, windless night. I watched him for a moment, and then I must have fallen asleep again, for the next time I saw him he was back in bed and it was morning.

We left the hotel and went home. Ellen and Arthur were waiting for us: Ellen was weeping, Arthur was pale and very quiet. Later in the day my mother and Tom were brought home, and I saw them at last. During the next two days, until the morning of the funeral, I saw them often. Sometimes I was by myself with them, sometimes I was with a crowd of people who came to the wake. On the third morning we all went to the church and from there to the cemetery, and at last it was over, and I knew that from now on I would see them only in my memory.

One week later, my father took me to Ireland.

M ORE than a year before he entered his first political campaign, Charles had made a necessary preliminary move: he had established firmly and unmistakably the fact of his legal residence. He had moved from his apartment — which he and Marie and their three children had used as a headquarters whenever they happened to be in the city — and had bought a private house. The apartment had been pleasant but cramped, and also, in a curious way and despite its years of use, somehow impermanent, as if it were a high-rent bivouac; the house, on the other hand, had room to burn and was undoubtedly here to stay. It was the old Burroughs house: an impressive, gloomily handsome Georgian mansion, tree-shadowed and built like a fort. When I was a boy I had often bicycled by this house, and peeping in through the tall hedge, I had sometimes caught a glimpse of Amy Burroughs — who seemed ancient even then — tottering slowly across the lawn, her long purple dress brushing the tops of the grass, her cane poking the earth ahead of her, while behind trailed a vast and spreading retinue of cats. She was the last of her family; they were now popularly believed to have been old-line aristocrats of faultless pedigree, but this was not true. Her grandfather had in fact been a druggist, who after protesting violently had been dragged off to the Civil War, from which he had emerged as a captain, and then had gone on to make a fortune in nose drops of his own invention. It was he who had built the house, which for some time afterward had been known as Catarrh Castle. The name had died with the captain, the house had acquired a somber majesty over the years, and Charles owned it now.

And now, tonight, this old house, where lonely, palsied Amy Burroughs had never entertained, and where Charles and Marie had given only their small and rather elegant dinners — tonight it was breaking with its tradition of seclusion, and it was breaking with a bang. It was wide open, literally, for the night was very warm — Indian summer, the last gasp — and the celebration had reached out onto the deep green lawn where tables had been set up, gay with paper lanterns. It was light and loud and festive, and through the open windows music sprang into the still night air; coming toward the house I had heard it blocks away.

I arrived late, but even so the traffic jam near the house had not broken. The section in which Charles lived was one of wide, pleasantly curving, carefully patrolled streets, and these were now so crowded with people that all cars could do no more than inch along. For a moment I thought that the official party had overflowed into the streets, but then I realized that the crowd out here was entirely different: they were sightseers rather than invited guests, they were mostly young people who were eager for a glimpse of the new young governor at play. Charles had great strength among the students; there were half a dozen colleges in or near the city, and it seemed that they all had representatives here tonight. I drove through them very carefully; the police were on hand but had little to do, for this was a friendly crowd: they had come to cheer. Many of them seemed too young to vote — I'm sure they were. There were boys and girls dancing on the sidewalk to the music of a portable radio; under one of the simulated gas lamps which illuminated this district a well-dressed young man with a guitar was singing the song of a depressed worker; others were cheering and beating rhythmically with their hands and calling for Charles, hoping to coax him into an appearance. There was only one dissident note: a tall elderly tattered man wearing sneakers and a World War I overseas cap stood on the curb, facing Charles's house and waving his arms; he was shouting, "I hope it thunders and lightnings and rains like the hammers of hell, Charles Kinsella, all over you and your damn garden party!" This was greeted with loud mock cheers and hurrahs which seemed to further enrage the old man. The police watched, but did not interfere.

Finally I got through enough of the crowd so that I was opposite the driveway. A state trooper — symbol of Charles's new station — requested identification; I showed my invitation, and while I was not recognized, my last name of course was. The magic "Kinsella" whisked me, with another state trooper as escort, to a preferred parking space at the edge of the lawn.

The state trooper looked as young as some of the students; he jumped down and held my car door open for me. He said, "It's a great night for all of us, sir. Your brother's a wonderful man. He's really wonderful! A great man to travel around with. Very very considerate!"

"My cousin," I said.

"Oh," he said. His interest diminished, but did not disappear.

I walked toward the house across the lawn, stepping among the tables, occasionally stopping to talk as I recognized a face in the lantern light. At last I reached the house and went in. It was crowded and very noisy, for while many of the guests had gone outside, the main body of the party had preferred to remain indoors — near the food, the liquor, the music, and of course, near Charles. They were gathered mostly in the great long room to the right of the front hall. This had been the old ballroom — question: had Amy Burroughs ever danced? — and I had seen it once many years before: it had been formal and forbidding, massive with dark mahogany. Now it was all cream-white and gold: Marie's touch. As I entered, the orchestra was playing and a chunky blonde girl was singing the simple dreadful song that had accompanied Charles everywhere throughout the campaign:

> *Kinsella!*
> *Kinsella!*
> *He's the man for me!*
>
> *Kinsella!*
> *Kinsella!*
> *It's on to victory!*
>
> *He's marching marching marching*
> *   to the governor's chair.*
> *Goodbye corruption: Kinsella's*
> *   on the square. . . .*

I saw Charles; he was surrounded, on the far side of the room. They were laughing, he was smiling. A heavy perspiring man in a very blue tuxedo came up to me, a plate of food in his hand; he said, "Correct me if I'm wrong, but you're the Governor's brother, right?"

"His cousin," I said.

"Good for you!" he said promptly. "You've got a real sweetheart there!" With his free hand he tapped the plate of food. "Lobster!" he said. "That's the way you can always tell a real big leaguer. Hey, Walshie!"

He grabbed the coat of a man who was about to pass without seeing him; the man stopped, turned, and delightedly called "Edso! Whaddaya say?"

He was very small and very thin, with yellowish eyes and an astonishing set of false teeth which were much too large for his little face; he could hardly have looked less like the man who had stopped him, yet somehow there was a resemblance so strong it was remarkable.

"Happy days are here again!" Edso said. "Walshie, say hello to the Governor's cousin, who's a top-notcher in his own right. Let me see now, the first name is Ralph, am I right on that?"

I corrected him; he accepted the correction joyously. "*Jack!*" he cried. "Of course it's Jack! Don't tell me I forgot that! What the hell am I thinking of: it's a name I know as well as I know my own! How goes the battle, Jack?"

Ritual questions, ritual answers; I said, "Fine, fine."

"You're doing a great job there," he said vaguely. For a moment I wondered what would happen if suddenly I asked just what job it was that I was doing so well, but then of course I knew what would happen: nothing. The question would have been resented as being deeply unfair and antisocial. He said, "Jimmy's your uncle then, am I right on that?"

I said that he was right, and Walshie said, "God bless Jimmy. He's a credit to his people and someone the whole country can be proud of. He was always a good friend to me. And God bless the Governor and his lovely wife as well. You can tell him I said that, Jack. You can tell him it came right from the heart!"

"Right from the heart of a man that's looked death in the face and licked it!" Edso said. "Don't forget to mention that to the Governor while you're at it, Jack. Don't forget to mention that one of his very top campaign workers, Leo J. Walsh, got up off his ass and licked the deadliest enemy of modern times: cancer of the bowels!"

"After all the finest doctors at the Mother Cabrini Hospital had given me up for dead," Walshie said. "I fooled them all!"

"I tell you, whenever I hear a story like that," said Edso, speaking with difficulty, for his mouth was now full of food; he had resumed his eating from the plate he was carrying about with him, "I feel like saying a little prayer. Walshie, did you get any of this lobster? It's positively the greatest!"

Walshie said that he had, and that in fact he was now on his way back to the buffet table for seconds. "By God, a man that serves food like this can't help but be a great governor," he said. "I been in politics all my life, and I always say you can tell a man by the food he serves. Nothin' kills a man faster than servin' bum food. Look at Dan Cohalan. D'ye remember him, Edso? Down at the Department of Health?"

"Big Dan," Edso said. "With the cockeye. Retired now on a three-quarter pension."

"That's him," Walshie said. "Well, one time he decided to go for the City Council, so he gave a little party for himself over in the old Shore Gardens Hotel that's now the parkin' lot. Everybody was there, you know, and pretty soon Dan comes edgin' over to me and he says, 'Well, Walshie, how does it look from where you sit?' I says to him, I says, 'Dan, I got to tell you the truth: you're all done. You haven't got a Chinaman's chance. After servin' food like this you couldn't get elected dog-catcher!' Well, he gets right up on his high horse, you know, and he says, 'What the hell's wrong with this food? The trouble with you is you don't know classy food when you see it! You prob'ly think this is creamed chicken! Well, I'll tell you what this is: *it's genuine creamed capon, that's what is is!*' 'It is, is it?' I says. 'Then it's a damn funny kind of capon, that's all I've got to·say. And if you want to know what I think, I think it's the kind of capon they spell s-e-a-g-u-l-l!' "

"Good for you, Walshie!" Edso said. "Right smack on the button: it served him damn well right!"

He now decided to join Walshie in the search for seconds; they left together, with Edso winking a broad farewell at me, and punching me playfully on the arm as they moved away.

"Over the river!" he said jauntily. "And give my very best to His Excellency. Be sure you tell him that Edso Monahan is behind him all the way!"

I watched them go off into the crowd, Edso's blue tuxedo serving as a vivid, inescapable marker. I had never seen either of them before, but I felt as if I had known them forever and had heard this conversation a thousand times before. The time was the present, the scene had changed, but it was obvious that certain great constants in the political life of the city remained. I wondered exactly how Charles fitted Edso and Walshie into his announced program of the New Look in Government.

Looking across the room once more I could see that Charles was still standing on the far side of the room, his position unchanged, and still surrounded. Just at this moment, however, he looked up and over in my direction, and from the quick smile and the slight beckoning movement of his head I knew that he had seen me. I began to move toward him, but progress was slow, for all at once a great many more people seemed to have come into this room, which was already unpleasantly crowded. They must have come in from the lawn: possibly because a night wind had come up, possibly because they sensed that at any moment now the Governor would speak. It was out of the question to move in any straight path; I tacked my way back and forth among swirling groups of people, and as I did so I noticed for the first time the peculiar nature of this gathering. It was not like the old political crowd — not at all. It was noisy, happy, even jubilant, but it was not a *crowd*. It was, instead, a large grouping of independent knots; walking through them, I saw that although the pressure of too many people in too small a space had forced these knots together, each knot had a life of its own and did not mix readily with its neighbor. They were adjacent islands, not a continent — the tie was Charles and that was all. Some of them I knew quite well, others I knew slightly, most I did not know at all. As I edged my way through them and past them I paused at times to exchange a shouted word, but for the most part I just moved along, and as I did so my pace was so slow and the voices were so loud that for moments I would seem stalled in the middle of a conversation in which I had no part, and every word I overheard seemed to emphasize still further the heterogeneousness of Charles's support. . . .

". . . we flew up yesterday morning. Nick stayed behind to come up with Davy, but that didn't matter because he couldn't vote anyway."

"What's the matter with Nick? Not registered?"

"Sweet, he hasn't registered for *ages*. Not since we bought the place on Cat Key. We're there all the time, we never see anyone any more. Of course, it's an absolute dream, but who wants to be stuck there forever? But it's all because of taxes. . . ."

"Poor Polly. Tell Nick when he comes to write to Archie Tolliver. Archie has an arrangement in Switzerland which is practically bombproof as far as the IRS is concerned. It might be just the thing for you."

"I doubt it. Nick *loathes* Switzerland and I'm not mad about it either. I thought I might ask Charles: he's always so clever. And of course now he's in a position to help, isn't he . . . ?"

". . . you're attempting to tell me that alienation wasn't a factor in this election? Is that what you're attempting to tell me?"

"I'm not attempting to tell you anything. Why should I attempt to tell you a single word? You've got your own personal dialectic, anybody who doesn't agree one hundred per cent is automatically a *schmo*. So all right, I'm a *schmo*. Why should a *schmo* attempt to tell *you* anything?"

"You're a very resentful person, Bernie. The pathetic thing is you don't realize how resentful you are. Believe me, you could use some help. You could use a lot of help. . . ."

"Please, *fellas*. We won, right? So stop *arguing*. . . ."

". . . five hundred bucks a plate. A heavy tab, but a sellout from the word go. I'll tell you who the toastmaster was: Father Artie McGuire. You know? From the Hill? He's just back from Rome. Vatican Council. He did a hell of a job. A million laughs, but something you could take home with you, too. Frank Regan got him for us."

"There's the boy that's loaded these days. Frank Regan. He's got nothing but money. Wall-to-wall. They say he's got all Jimmy Kinsella's insurance."

"And the boys' as well. A real shrewdie, Frank. And JoJo's up for the Federal bench. That's not bad, either."

"The only judge in the state who can't spell 'attorney.' But a prat-boy for Jimmy for years. He was damn near indicted on that finder's fee business. Georgetown, isn't he?"

"The Cross. . . ."

"Har har har! *Hey, Guido* . . . !"

". . . a fair student, no more. I remember a long paper he wrote on Charles James Fox. Not good, not really bad — just undistinguished. That was typical of all his work."

"Yes. I always thought the older brother was the brighter of the two."

"Phil, yes. I had them both; I wouldn't have picked either of them to do much of anything. Two more rich boys who did just enough to slide by, and why bother to do anything more? No, Charles is a great surprise to me. And a very welcome one. You see, what no one could have predicted was the *growth*. He's liberal, he's open-minded, he works hard at all the right things. And he has a quick, complete grasp of whatever you tell him: I found him very impressive all through the campaign."

"No reservations? I must say I'm not entirely happy about that Inner Guard."

"The ex-altar boy types, yes. I agree. But I think they're more a concession to the father than anything else. Charles is something else again. He's not an intellectual, despite all the claims. But he has a respect for those who are; I find him extremely sympathetic. I think you'll find that as time goes on a certain amount of jettisoning will be done, and that you'll be much happier with the replacements. I think that's inevitable. . . ."

". . . so I said, 'You fired this waiter. Why?' He said, 'Because he's not a good waiter any more. He mixes thing up, he drops things, he upsets the dining room.' I said, 'Okay. Now: was he ever drunk on duty?' He said, 'No.' I said, 'Okay. Now: did he swear or use bad words to customers? Did he insult them?' He said, 'No, he didn't do that.' So I said, 'Okay. Then I'll tell you what's gonna happen. You're gonna hire this man back as of now, or else I pull him and everybody else out of this hotel by tomorrow morning, and when all your fancy guests wake up there won't be a waiter or a maid or a bellhop in the joint. So make up your mind!' So they hire him back. They had to. What else could they do?"

"Don't tell that to the Governor. He stays in that hotel lots of times."
"Yeah? Well, maybe he should start stayin' in another hotel. . . ."

". . . trust him? That's what I'm asking you right here and now: *what makes you so sure you can trust him?*"
"And once again I answer you: I would rather trust him than the other."
"You think he understands? You think a rich white man with a million dollars in the bank, you think he even *begins* to understand?"
"I think if we supported only those who understood, we would support nobody. This is a practical situation, it is a situation of relatives, it is not a situation of absolutes. If you ask two men, 'Have we here *de facto* segregation?' and the one man says, 'No, we do not have *de facto* segregation,' and the other man says, 'Yes, we do have *de facto* segregation and it is a bad thing which I promise to do something about,' then it is not a question of absolute trust or of absolute anything but of accepting the better of the two. . . ."

And all this was a long long way from those shouting, cheering, unified throngs of only a few years ago, which as much as anything else, I suppose, were in reality clan rallies honoring the chief. But this was a gathering of disparate social, racial, and intellectual forces which would have been unthinkable behind any one candidate then, and while I had suspected something of this, it was not until I saw the victory party in action that I realized how effectively Charles had cut across the old established lines. So that while the old remained, something new had been added; Edso and Walshie were but a part of a far more complicated spectrum.

The orchestra had continued to play without interruption; directly in front of the musicians a space was being used as a dance floor, but this was pure farce; any sort of rhythmic movement was impossible. The curtains at the sides of the long open French windows began to blow in strongly as suddenly and blessedly the cooler air came into the room. I was close to where Charles had been standing, but now he was no longer there; looking around, I couldn't see him anywhere. Congratulations would have to wait. Still, I kept moving forward slowly — it was as good a direction as any — and as I came almost to the point where Charles had been, a hand touched my arm, tapping it twice, and when I turned I saw Marie.

"Charles was looking for you," she said. "I have a message to give you."

It was a gracious and rather formal statement; I knew that it had been meant not for me, but for the women to whom she had been talking. They were together in a clump, rather alike in appearance: in late middle age they were pale and fat-featured and laughed a lot. I knew that they were the wives of heavy contributors; for their part they would have given "at homes" and "bridge benefits" throughout the campaign. "Will you excuse me?" Marie said to them now. "Just for a minute? More family business."

She smiled at them; they laughed back; they laughed at me: I was lucky, I was family. Marie took my hand and led me a short distance across the room. For the first time that evening I could move quickly, for the crowd parted to allow her smiling passage. We got to a small alcove off the main room where, surprisingly, there were only three or four others, and where, even more surprisingly, the sound from the main room was somehow diminished, so that for a moment I had the impression of being in a place of great and sudden silence.

"No message," she said. "I just wanted a breather. How goes life, Jack? Isn't this a great night?"

She was a big woman, but not in the least bulky or buxom: she was just big and smooth and beautifully made. She was very fair, with large smoky-gray eyes and a full attractive mouth; her skin was marvelously clear and fresh and her hair was so blonde that when Jean had first seen it she had declared that it couldn't possibly be natural — and yet I think it was. There was something in her appearance which suggested the outdoor girl, but then there was something else which suggested a much more feminine side, and in fact that was much closer to the truth. She was very much an indoor girl, she was not fond of golf or tennis or riding or long brisk walks in the country. She paid close attention to her appearance and had a great sense of style — she was one of the best-dressed women I had ever seen. Charles was reported to have said, just before the election, that he considered the greatest contribution to his campaign to have been made by Givenchy.

Men found her very attractive and yet, as I've said, women liked her too. I think this may have been because she treated them not with mere politeness, but with a genuine friendliness. She liked people to like her, and while she had her party manner, she had a great naturalness too, and this kept breaking through. I had not known her before her marriage to Charles — indeed, who had? — but I liked her from the first, and I think that she liked me. At any rate, we had always been easy with each other. She said to me now, without waiting for an answer to her other questions, "How about it, Jack? Am I your first First Lady?"

"I met a queen once, but I'm not sure she counts. She'd been deposed for quite a while, and I guess she hadn't been much of a queen anyway. Besides, she was old and limped and had one eye. So I much prefer you. How are you bearing up?"

"Oh, you know me. I love it. Or most of it. It's exciting and wonderful — Jack, nobody ever won by such a margin before: did you know that?"

"Oh, I did indeed. There's not a loose marble left in the state; Charles has them all today."

"He has, hasn't he?" she said happily. "And the great thing is that nobody thought he could do it. Or almost nobody. For instance, you. You didn't think he could, did you?"

I shook my head. "I thought he'd carry the city easily enough, but I was sure Consolo would have too much strength up north. Not to cop a plea, but remember I'd been away."

"Well, when you got back you should have come to me," she said. "I'd have set you straight in a minute." She was a strong partisan of her husband and could be rather chilly with any of his friends or acquaintances who gave him less than all-out support, yet for some reason I had always been saved from this. Maybe it was because I was a relative for whom special rules applied, maybe it was because Charles himself had never seemed to mind in the least that I hadn't worked for him, or maybe it was simply because she knew that I really liked him — at any rate, all she said now was, "Poor Consolo. Or no, *not* poor Consolo, because he's really rather a dirty little man. He spread all kinds of stories about Charles—and about Charles and me. I'm used to that by now, but these were a little nastier than most. And he could have stopped them but he didn't. So I don't care what happens to him. I'm just happy for Charles." She gazed out into the big noisy crowded room and said, "If I lived to be a hundred and ten I don't think I could ever be any prouder!"

She looked it; I said, "You might even be a little proud of yourself, too."

"I am," she said frankly. "I helped a lot, I think. I went on television and that was all right, and I met old biddies and young biddies and old pols and young pols and people who'd known Charles since he was a baby and people who *said* they'd known Charles since he was a baby and I shook hands and I danced the basic box step with every dreadful dancer in the state. And I went to field days and cookouts and ball parks and rallies and reunions of Charles's old Air Force buddies, and some of it was wonderful and some of it was just so plain unbelievably boring that you'd want to shoot yourself that minute. But I did it, all of it, and I wouldn't *not* have done it for the world, and I know that in the end it helped. So in a way it's my night, too." Then she smiled and said, "And

I'll tell you what I did. Tonight: just before I came downstairs. I'd finished dressing, and my maid had gone out, and I was all alone in the
bedroom. And I stood in front of the mirror and just looked at myself
for a long time. I thought I looked pretty." She glanced down at herself
now with satisfaction. "Pretty enough to be the Governor's wife. And
then do you know what I thought? I thought, 'Well, not bad for a little
Pole from West Nowhere!' And it isn't, is it?"

"It's not bad for anyone from West anywhere," I said, and I meant it.
But she meant it, too. She had been a poor girl, her parents had been
born in Poland, and she herself had in a sense come from nowhere — certainly nowhere that my Uncle Jimmy had been willing to recognize.
Charles had met her shortly after getting out of college, and what had
happened then had been a genuinely romantic story. Because, where
Phil had only the year before married Flossie, whom he had known all
his life — a very fancy and glamorous wedding, with guests flown in
from everywhere, and my Uncle Jimmy presiding loudly and proudly
and lavishly—and I had just become engaged to Jean, whom I had
known for most of mine, Charles, usually so much more watchful and
prudent than either of us, fell in love with a complete stranger the very
first time he met her. Love at first sight — and yet with Charles, of all
people, it had happened. And I had been there when it had: at one of
those huge charity balls held for the armed forces during the first year of
the war. I had come home from the Navy and so had Phil — we had
been able to arrange our leaves together — and Charles, as it happened,
was to go into the Air Force the very next day: the ball was his last
civilian fling. We had all gone together; I had danced mostly with Jean,
Phil mostly with Flossie, and Charles — Charles, after the first dance,
very little with the girl he had brought: I even forget now who she was.
He had danced with Marie — and by what route Marie Granowski had
got there, or with whom she had come that night, I never knew. I did
know that she left with Charles, and that he went into the Air Force the
next morning. He came back as often as he could, sometimes for only an
hour or two; in a very short time they were engaged to be married. This
roaring, swift romance was all extremely uncharacteristic of Charles, so
uncharacteristic that it caught everyone by surprise, including my Uncle
Jimmy. Apparently — although this was hard to believe, considering that
shrewd man — he had suspected nothing: it may have been that he was
too preoccupied with his own activities, which during the war involved
enormous amounts of travel and were said by some to be invaluable. He
had of course met Marie, but then he had met many of Charles's girls;
when, suddenly, he had discovered that this was something different, he
had been furious. First there had been the matter of James, to which he

had only recently become reconciled; now there was Charles. He must have felt that his sons, one by one, were slipping away from his wishes, his plans, his control; he had raged at Charles (although as Charles told me, rather wryly, he could not threaten to cut him off entirely, as he had already settled a large sum on him on his twenty-first birthday); he had actually put detectives on Marie.

"And then when that didn't turn up anything juicy," she had said to me, much later, "he sent them out to my home town, to get a line on my pop. I think he was hoping for a blackmailer, or at least a thief. Instead all he got was a sleepy Polish butcher, who liked to drink and didn't like to work. So then all he could fall back on was the old wrong-side-of-the-tracks, but of course that didn't count much with Charles. And I don't think it really counted too much with Jimmy, either. He's pretty good on things like that. He's pretty good on a lot of things."

"He's just an old dear," I had said.

"No, he's not- *that*. But he is pretty good. The only thing was, he didn't want his boy to be trapped by an adventuress. And then when he decided I wasn't one, he didn't make too much trouble. I think he might have liked me a little, even then. Anyway, he likes me now. So every thing's turned out fine."

And it had. Jimmy had given in. Charles had been respectful but firm; unexpectedly he had received support from his mother, my Aunt Mary making one of her rare dissents from her husband. And Jimmy had capitulated, maybe out of sheer disgust; Charles and Marie had been married: a small wedding, a service wedding, but Jimmy had been there. And gradually he had come around. It may or may not have been true — as Marie had suggested — that Jimmy had liked her even then; I always thought that the turning point came sometime after my Aunt Mary's death, when my Uncle Jimmy began to spend more time with Charles and Marie. In any case, it was certain that she was a great favorite now. Charles had married well; Jimmy knew that and loudly gave praise where it was due.

"She's a sweetheart!" he had said to me, about five years ago. "And I had her pegged all wrong at first: I thought she was some kind of Hunky hustler. Well, why not? The woods are full of them. And Charles was a good-looking guy with plenty of dough: a perfect setup for some bimbo sharpshooter. When I first set eyes on this one I said to myself, 'She's got a great pair of legs: I'll bet they can run like hell after a million bucks!' Well, I was all wet. She's been the greatest thing in the world for him. When I think of some of the lemons he could have wound up with!"

For just a moment I had wondered if my Uncle Jimmy might not be turning obliquely to quite a different subject, one he had tried to discuss with me once or twice before — without much success, and with some unpleasantness. But then I had realized that he was not doing this, for he was not a delicate man: if he had decided to go after me again he would have done so head-on, not indirectly or by implication. So I had said nothing more, and neither had he.

Marie said now, "But you haven't even seen Charles yet!"

"I've tried, though. It's not that easy: everybody else has the same idea. But I'll make it."

"We were talking about you one night last week," she said. "Somebody — I guess it must have been your publisher — sent us your new book. We got in the house late one night — I forget where we'd been: campaigning somewhere — and there was your book, waiting for us. Charles picked it up and read it right through that night, all at once. He says it's the best one yet."

"Good for Charles. What did you think of it?"

She laughed. "That's a dirty trick," she said. "You know I haven't read it." Candidly she added, "And you know I won't. I always mean to, but I never do, do I? And everybody says they're wonderful. I always start them all right, but then I can't seem to pay attention to what's going on, and the first thing you know I'm lost. I think you have to have a special kind of mind to read mystery stories; anyway, I've never finished one. Not even yours, Jack. I feel terrible, but that's the way it is."

Ten years ago, I had written a suspense story. I had done this mainly out of uncertainty. I had written two books before this, both of them straight novels. The first had been ignored by all critics and had not sold; the second had been noticed by some, had won a mild respect — and had not sold. My situation had not been desperate, but neither had it been ideal. I was married, the income from the money my father had left me was constant but not large, in order to live comfortably I needed to earn more. There had been no shortage of available jobs, thanks to my Uncle Jimmy's influence, and he had several times urged me in one direction or another. But what I really wanted to do was write. I had no great dreams, I think I can honestly say I never overvalued myself as a writer, but what I did want to do was to write for myself, and to earn a living by that writing. I had discussed this with my publisher after the failure of my second book; he had not been helpful. He had dealt with the crisis in his usual manner: he had taken me to lunch. Here he drank a great deal and talked about his own problems and, toward the end of the lunch, he talked with a kind of mournful hopefulness about the possibility of my next book's achieving a "major breakthrough." I did not believe this, and I could see from his face that neither did he.

It was at this point that I had thought of writing a suspense story. Not a mystery, as Marie called it, not a thriller, not one of the newer *genre* in which the professional spy goes through his dirty business with disgust. I had thought of writing a book in quite another tradition — that of the ordinary unadventurous man accidentally caught up in the sinister world of international intrigue. *The Riddle of the Sands, A Coffin for Dimitrios;* I had often read and thoroughly enjoyed books like these, and now I thought I might try to write one. I did. I wrote it very quickly (for me): in less than four months *No Change for Connemara* was completed.

It was a success. It wasn't a best seller, but people bought it and read it, many more people than had ever bought anything I had written before. There was a fortunate sale to the moving pictures; my publisher began to ask me to lunch more often. I had found my niche at last. Or so he told me; I was not so sure. But when, a year later, I wrote another, and it also did well, then I was ready to believe. It was not the kind of writing I had intended to do in the beginning, but it was a kind of writing which apparently I did well, and — more important — it was a kind of writing I did not in the least look down on. I think they were all good books of their kind: they were honest, decently plotted, with believable characters, and were reasonably well written. I was proud of writing them, in fact; I knew that not everyone could have written them, and indeed that many writers who were better than I could not have written them, either. I was proud, then, of my particular competence. I wrote five more of these books, and by now I had a public: not vast, but steady. They were reliable buyers of my books, and these book sales, coupled with magazine and television rights, gave me an income which, although not handsome — it was miles short of Charles's or Phil's, for instance — still allowed me to live pleasantly and to travel as much as I wanted to.

The latest of these books, *The Zagreb Connection,* was shortly to be published. It was this which Charles had read and Marie, of course, had not.

"You're making a big mistake on this one," I said. "This one is great. It's about a Polish butcher's daughter who's torn between going into politics and becoming a private eye. It's based on real life."

"I'd *read* something like that," she said. "But you —"

She was interrupted suddenly by a roll of drums; we looked out of the alcove in the direction of the music and saw that the leader was standing in the foreground, motioning for silence. I had seen him often before: his name was Shep Nomad, and he was the current "society" orchestra leader, a prominent figure at the more splendid parties and receptions in the city. He was small and sleek and obsequious, and looked always as if he had recently been greased.

"Lovely ladies and your gentlemen!" he shouted. "May I have your kind attention? May I? Please? If you will? Thank you. On this momentous occasion, ladies and gentlemen, I would like to pay my own humble musical tribute, not only to our fine new Governor, but also to his very beautiful and very lovely First Lady. May we now play for your pleasure a song of my own composition, written specially for this great and joyous occasion? I call it 'It's Always Marie!' "

He turned with a great flourish of his baton; immediately the orchestra began to play a melody which sounded very much like several others they had previously played. The chunky blonde girl stepped up to the microphone and once more began to sing:

> *Who's the most beautiful?*
> *It's always Marie!*
> *Who's the most charming?*
> *It's always Marie!*
>
> *If anyone asks me*
> *Who's fairest to see?*
> *I tell them the truth*
> *It's always Marie. . . .*

The song went on for some time, through numberless mindless choruses; when it was over there was tremendous applause. Shep Nomad took the chunky blonde singer by the hand; they bowed together, acknowledging public tribute, and then they looked up and out over the crowd, possibly searching for Marie.

She was standing by my side; she hadn't moved since the beginning of the song. I hadn't looked at her, because I thought she must be dissolving in embarrassment. But now when I did I saw that I had been wrong, because she didn't seem embarrassed at all. The crowd had seen her by now and they were all looking toward us and applauding and shouting her name. She smiled and waved, and when he turned to me I saw that her eyes were truly shining.

"Oh, Jack!" she said. "It's so *cheap*. But isn't it wonderful!"

I suppose it would have been impossible for her to have been any happier than at that moment. She turned back to the crowd again and waved once more, and then, just before she went to meet them, she must have thought of something because she said to me, "Listen: I may not get another chance, but — have you heard from Jean? I mean, lately?"

"No," I said, a little stiffly, and a little untruthfully, too. Because I had heard from her, but this wasn't anything I talked about easily, not even with Marie.

"I wanted to tell you that I saw her a few months ago in Paris. We met on the street one day outside the Meurice. She was alone; I don't know where she was staying. She looked thin but very pretty and terribly chic. She came in for a minute and we had a cup of tea. She talked a lot about you."

"Yes, I know. She does that."

"Oh come on," she said impatiently. "Give her a break. What was so wrong about that? She knew I'd probably seen you and she just wanted to . . . I'll talk to you later," she said hastily, for the others had arrived and were thronging about her, and gradually she went through the crowd, away from me, shaking hands and smiling and accepting congratulations happily; I saw Shep Nomad moving steadily toward her, a sheet of music in his hand: the presentation copy.

For a few minutes after this I paid little attention to Charles's party; Marie's mention of Jean had for some reason troubled me much more than I would have expected. But I didn't think about this for long, because the party simply rode in over all private thoughts: it was too big, there was too much noise. And so once again I began to move around, wedging my way through the moving, shouting, munching surge of tuxedos, looking for Charles, who seemed to have vanished forever. Slowly it all began to seem like a tour of the past for me, because the longer I stayed, and the more I moved about, the more people I saw whom I hadn't seen for a long time, but whom I once had seen very often, some of them every day. One of these, the first I ran into, was a man I had been at school with when we were little boys. I hadn't spoken to him or seen him for thirty years, he was immensely altered — bald and very fat and every feature coarsened — with nothing of the little boy visible today, and I had even forgotten his name, but instantly, the moment I saw him, I knew him, in the way that you somehow do recognize some people who stay forever memorable, not because of themselves, but because of their connection with some early, unprecedented, even calamitous event — and in the case of this man shaking hands with me now, I could remember only that as a boy in the fourth grade he had been sent home to his mother time after time for the simple and appalling reason that he smelled bad.

And now he was greeting me and introducing me to his wife and announcing to me — somewhat disquietingly, in view of my one over-whelming memory of him — that he was my greatest fan. "I read them all," he said, "as soon as they come out. I read them all, and I like them all. They take my mind off myself at the end of a hard day's work. And that's saying something, because I work like a dog, day and night. Still, I can't complain. No man can that's done as well as I have."

"Kinsella," said his wife, looking at me. "Why, that's the Governor's name!"

"His brother," my fan said. "The Governor's his brother."

"His cousin," I said.

"Brother, cousin, what's the difference?" my fan said impatiently. "I'm not related to him at all, but did that stop me from giving him five grand for his campaign? You bet your sweet life it didn't. And there's plenty more where that came from. I may not write books, but I've done all right. I never like to talk about myself, but since you asked I don't mind telling you I've got it made. A good business, my wife here, a lovely home in the country, three wonderful kids, and in the sixty-three per cent tax bracket — how's that for a poor boy who had to make it on his own? And I did, Jack. I've cleaned up. But good!"

In more ways than one, apparently; I wondered if now he sometimes remembered his old humiliations. I thought he probably did; they were usually the hardest to forget.

As I left him, still not able to recall his name, I saw Walshie coming toward me; I shifted course and got away. But the shift brought me smack up against another part of the past, for now I walked directly into a small, jam-packed circle of old acquaintances who were here rejoicing in the victory. I had known them all since college; fifteen years ago nothing could have brought them to a political gathering of any kind, but since that time there had been Adlai, there had been Jack, and now there was Charles. They had felt the touch, they had been spoken to, they had been awakened: for these correct candidates they had worked gener-ously, hard, and sometimes with the arrogance of the freshly converted. In this they were assisted by their wives, who worked even more zeal-ously, inspired by their belief that before the ADA and the League of Women Voters there had been Nothing.

We met, we talked, some of the wives asked me about Jean, but then we went back to politics and the victory which was theirs and the new regime in which it was assumed that they would all play some as-yet-undefined role. They were making their plans, they knew that Charles would call on them, they were very happy.

And still I hadn't done what I had come to do. I continued to walk and to stop and talk and to look around, but at no time did I so much as catch a glimpse of Charles; then, all at once, someone from behind gripped me by the elbow and held on, and when I turned around, there he was.

"Play your cards right," he said to me, "and I can get you an introduction to the Governor."

I hadn't seen him for months, apart from those television appearances; he looked fine. There were a few faint touches of fatigue around the eyes, but except for this he showed no signs of having been through a long and very difficult campaign. He looked the same as always: no sudden gray, no added lines. He seemed as self-contained as ever, he would never have been as openly rejoicing as Marie, yet I could tell that at this moment he was very pleased, and as I shook his hand and gave him my congratulations, I suddenly felt very happy for him and for Marie. And in a peculiar way I felt a satisfaction of my own, for this state, this city, was after all my home: I had had my childhood here, I had grown up here, I had spent most of my life here, and even though in recent years I had gone away often and sometimes stayed away a long time, I was a poor expatriate — I had never really felt at home anywhere else, and it had never occurred to me that this was not where I belonged. So I was bound here, it was a pleasant place to live, and yet it — and those of us who lived here — had been sold down the river time and time again. Politically it was a mess, and close to being a disaster. It had been this way for years, at least ever since I had begun to be interested in such matters. Someone once said of us that corruption here had a shoddy, penny ante quality it did not have in other states, that here everything was up for grabs and nothing was too small to steal. This probably was one of those facile overstatements much easier to make than to prove, but it's true that underneath everything in our politics there seemed to be a depthless cushion of street-corner cronyism, a special kind of tainted, small-time fellowship which sent out a complex of vines and shoots so interconnected that even the sleaziest poolroom bookie managed in some way, however obscure, to be in touch with the mayor's office or the governor's chair. (Three years ago, for instance, there had been an assistant attorney general who had conducted a series of investigations into fraud in the state. These investigations had been slow, expensive, and productive of nothing; they had been on the point of being abandoned when suddenly, through some slipup, it was revealed that two and perhaps three of those being investigated had hidden but firm business links with the assistant attorney general's mother. Further digging had revealed further facts: the governor had been in a quandary. It was a matter of some delicacy: not only was the assistant attorney general involved, but the mother had some time before been voted our state Mother of the

Year. Reluctantly, and speaking feelingly of a mother's misplaced zeal, the governor had at last fired the assistant attorney general, who had then been tried, found guilty, given a suspended sentence, and had then, in penitence, purchased a rather pleasant property in Jamaica. The Mother of the Year, herself mysteriously at liberty, had never forgiven the persecutors of her son. "The bastards were out to get him," she said grimly, "and get him they did! I hope to God they all fry like sausages in hell!")

This was an accepted condition of our political life. It was given periodic official rebuke and constant unofficial encouragement. And now, with Charles in charge — what? Who knew? He was unquestionably honest, he was competent, he came from a different tradition and had inherited none of the usual obligations, so that he was certainly freer than most to make changes. And yet the question remained: could changes — anything other than token changes, that is — really be made? Given, for example, our legislature? Or given, for another example, our state? Or even, come to think of it, given Charles? Because as I stood here looking at him, congratulating him, and taking pleasure in his victory, I suddenly realized how little I knew him. The Charles I really knew was a fat little boy who fell off horses, who was a pest with his questions, who played catch with me on an Irish lawn, who was my junior by a year and who had always been that year behind me in school. And I suppose I still thought of him in that faintly patronizing way you do think of slightly smaller boys who are a year or a step behind, who always seem to be tagging along, when the truth was that he was a grown man, a rich man, and a powerful man, who must have changed no less than all of us change, who had had three children and all kinds of other experiences which I had not, and who, because he had a life of his own which was increasingly removed from mine, now had ideas and abilities and strengths or defects which I couldn't even begin to assess. So that it was probably presumptuous and even meaningless for me to be standing here, calculating his chances of success, especially when all the room was filled with an excitement, a positive hope that something new and good was about to happen. And despite my own pessimism I couldn't help, just at this moment, feeling at least some of that excitement myself, but all I said to him was, "I'll give you a compliment: you're a great improvement on your predecessor."

"Thanks a lot," he said dryly. "Don't say any more: effusiveness embarrasses me. How've you been?"

"Not bad." We stood, just for a second, looking at each other; I said curiously, "Charles, what does it feel like? Being elected Governor?"

"Oh," he said, "a little like being elected mayor. Only more so. You haven't met these two, have you?"

I hadn't. They were two men who had come up with him and were now standing slightly to his rear. They were slender, neat, unremarkable-looking — I could have seen either one of them a hundred times any day in this city — and young: I guess they were perhaps seven or eight years younger than Charles. And oddly, while they were not at all alike in their appearance, there was something about each one that suggested the other: a shared attitude, I think, more than anything else, an air which was pleasant but extremely alert; it was as if they were both enjoying themselves quietly but keeping their eyes peeled, too. When Charles introduced us I recognized the names as those I had heard again and again during the final weeks of the campaign: they were two of the inner circle of professional young politicians who had rallied to Charles from the beginning, who had served him while he was mayor, and who were now said to be closer to him than anyone with the exception of his brothers and my Uncle Jimmy.

"They know all about you," Charles said. "Jerry's read all your books, including the two early ones. Ray doesn't read much of anything but the voting lists, but then of course he went to Loyola, where the curriculum prepares you for that sort of thing."

The two men smiled; the smaller one — Ray — said to me, "We have one connection, though. I think you know my dad: Bill Keegan. He used to be a cop at City Hall; he was always assigned to Frank Skeffington."

I had known his father well: a slim, solemn-faced man fanatically tidy, impeccably honest — in short, a great curiosity in the force. Skeffington had been very fond of him, and I told his son this now.

He nodded. "It worked both ways. Dad always liked him a lot; he'd never hear a word against him." He smiled again and said, "Apparently the old man used to give him these Babe Ruth autographed baseballs to pass around to the kids. As souvenirs of the city. I always wondered who really did that autographing. Skeffington himself?"

It was a simple question which took me in an instant back across twenty years to a hot, dusty afternoon in summer — early summer, before everyone had left on vacation. The overhead fan was circling slowly in the mayor's office, the blinds were partly closed so that the light came in broken by thin slats of shadow, while the courtly old figure — looking, at this time of the year, like a Southern plantation owner in his ice cream suit — rose from behind the vast mahogany desk, slowly fingering a baseball which he had selected from the big box on the floor beside him.

"Magnificent game," he had said thoughtfully. "It has everything. A golden opportunity to throw deadly objects at the heads of all your friends and still claim it's all being done in the spirit of fun. I've always thought that a game like that had to be invented by the Irish. Come on, let's get these things signed. All these admiring youngsters have parents who vote."

I said now, "Sometimes, when he felt like it. But mostly I did."

The three men looked at each other; Charles said, "The good old days. You see how simple it was?"

"I'll tell my dad I saw you," Ray said. "He's retired now."

"Like Jack," Charles said. "Jack retired from politics years ago because of old age. He was twenty-five. He went out with Skeffington. The difference was that he went out voluntarily." He looked at me with amusement in his eyes. "Any time you want to make a comeback," he said.

And quite suddenly, as he was talking, I realized how odd all this was: standing here in Charles's house, talking to Charles about Frank Skeffington, with Charles himself now incredibly in the same position of powerful control that Skeffington once had held — and talking, moreover, as if we were having a private conversation, when I didn't have to look around or even lift my head to be reminded that it was very far from being private. All the while we had been talking we had been ringed by an audience which had kept the minimum respectful distance, and which seemed to be held back by invisible leashes. They were eager, not missing a word; obviously they were just waiting their chance to swoop in on Charles.

Jerry, who had said very little up to now, suddenly stepped forward and said something quietly to Charles, so quietly that I couldn't hear it. Charles frowned slightly, then looked at his watch and said, "All right. If you can stand it I guess I can." To me he said, "Jack, will you be around awhile? I have to see someone."

"I think I might go along. It's a busy night, Charles; I just wanted to come in to say hello."

"No, stay," he urged. "We're all getting together up in the library. Pa's here, Aunt Gert: everybody. They'll want to see you, and I want to talk to you. Go on up to the library in about fifteen minutes; they'll all be there by then. Meanwhile," he said, glancing around, then coming back to me with the same amused look in his eyes, "I have a treat for you. Just to help you pass the time. And to remind you of those good old days."

He beckoned to the crowd and said, "Ben, come on over here a moment." Immediately a thin long-faced man in his late middle age shot out of the crowd and was by our side. Unlike the others in the room, he was not wearing formal clothes. He had on a military uniform, and in his hand he held an overseas cap. He said, in a voice which was like a salute, "Governor, at your service!"

"This is Commander Ben Bannigan, who's in charge of one of the posts of the Veterans of Foreign Wars," Charles said, looking at me now with a complete absence of any kind of expression. "The Commander came to us several times during the campaign with a problem that's been bothering him, and I'm afraid we may have let him down. Knowing your deep interest in the veterans, Jack" — and here, privately, for me, there was just the flick of expression — "I thought you were probably just the man to help him out. Ben," he said, switching to the Commander, "this is my cousin, Jack Kinsella. He writes books, but more to the point, he used to be the confidential secretary of a great friend of yours, Frank Skeffington. So I know that your particular kind of problem is right up his street. Now, if I were you, I'd tell him all about it."

It was a dirty trick; I knew that even before I saw Charles's two aides exchange glances, I knew it as soon as I saw the Commander. He was a familiar type; he was on me even before Charles, with a little nod and just the faintest of smiles, left.

"Thank God you were a personal friend of Frank's!" the Commander said; he had me by the coat, grabbing me with a thick-veined little hand. "There's the man that could of settled all this with both hands tied behind his back. I don't say a word against your cousin the Governor, we're right behind him all the way, but there's a lot of young wise guys around him that tries to keep the veterans away from him. Wise little sons of bitches that never was near a trench. What the hell do they care about men that left their families and got gassed and died and . . . ."

This went on for some time; after a few minutes he turned to a more particular grievance. A rival organization had been poaching on his preserve: on the previous Memorial Day, Legionnaires all over the state had been observed selling poppies. And not just selling poppies, but announcing them to be the genuine *Buddy Poppies*. The Commander was in a rage.

"What the hell right has the Legion got to sell Buddy Poppies? Buddy Poppies belong to the Veterans of Foreign Wars! We always had that name! There's only one veterans' organization in the country that's always had the right to sell Buddy Poppies on Memorial Day and that's the VFW! And this year what happens but all of a sudden those Legion bastards start showing up on street corners all along the whole parade, telling people that don't know any better that they were selling Buddy Poppies! All a damn lie, but who lifts a finger to stop it? Nobody! You might just as well live in Russia when men that gave up their jobs and their arms and their legs to fight for their country can't even come back and sell their own Buddy Poppies without somebody else that's got no right muscling in and . . ."

Charles had disappeared from the room. The Commander was his legacy to me, his little joke, and I couldn't decide whether he was paying me back for having said merely that he was an improvement over his awful predecessor — which was a fairly pale compliment — or whether he was showing me some of the slight contempt he undoubtedly felt for the older kind of politics and the simpler kind of problem which had been so conspicuous a feature of them — and showing me, moreover, by using (or slightly burlesquing?) a favored technique of Skeffington himself. In any case, I was saddled with the Commander, a survival from another day, and as he churned unhappily along, I heard him without really listening to him and without being particularly bothered or even bored. I had time to kill before I went up to the library, there was no one down here I especially wanted to see, and since more people seemed to have come in it would have been harder than ever to move around. So I stayed where I was, and while the Commander continued his aggrieved chatter, I found myself thinking once more of Skeffington, not only because this was his kind of trick, but because it was he who had taught me how to listen to all such sustained complaints.

"The thing to remember is that all pests are talkers," he had said to me one day. "The women are the worst, but the men are bad enough. There's no such thing as a pest who listens. A pest talks, and he talks all the time. Now, if one gets hold of you, there are a couple of ways of handling him. The first way is simply to stare at him while he talks to you. Just stare: don't answer back, don't say a word, don't make a sound: just keep looking right into his eyes. Sooner or later, this will get to him. Silence unnerves pests. They don't really want you to say anything, but they expect you to nod and make certain ritual sounds — 'uh-huh' is highly acceptable — whenever they pause for breath. That proves you're there and listening. If you don't do that it throws them off; they start to stumble, pretty soon they stop talking, and then they go away. The only trouble is that they're apt to go away mad, and if you're in my profession it's necessary to remember that pests vote too. So I've settled for another way: matter of fact, I've become rather good at it. It requires the appearance of sympathetic understanding. It's not necessary to listen to anything they say — you can keep right on going with your private thoughts

— but every once in awhile you have to cluck or shake your head and make little noises of commiseration. They won't pay any attention to *what* you say; it's the sound that counts. Once you get good enough at it you can say anything: you can spout Jabberwocky at them and they won't bat an eye. The secret is in using the proper tone. And then, when they're all done, you simply look at them, take them by the hand, and say, 'I thank you. You've done us all a great service.' Or words to that effect; I don't want to seem too rigid. You'll have to develop your own style. We've got a prize specimen coming in here in a few minutes; I may be able to give you a slight demonstration."

And when the man had come in he had come in talking; even while Skeffington was shaking his hand he was into his subject. A seedy little fanatic, he had come to talk about playgrounds. The city playgrounds were in poor shape; there were swings and dandles, yes, but where were the adult facilities; a cousin of his, an honor student at a well-known college for gymnasts, had been unable to secure summertime employment at any of these playgrounds; what was going to be done about the men's toilets? Skeffington had listened with courtesy, occasionally inclining his large head in grave agreement; whenever his visitor came up for air Skeffington murmured, indistinguishably and soothingly. This went on for a few minutes and then suddenly, during one of the pauses, Skeffington, using the same soothing tone, said very distinctly, "Abracadabra, dum dum dum!"

Startled, I had looked at his visitor, expecting indignation or at least bafflement. Instead the man had nodded vigorously and said, "Right! And another thing . . ." And he had gone on talking. Skeffington had not even glanced at me during this, but later, when the man had left, after first being thanked for being of service to the city, the old man had said to me, "I'm getting old: I'm showing off. Parlor tricks. But I wanted you to see that with people like that you never have to listen to a word because they never listen to you. And if you want to say anything it's perfectly all right, as long as you say it in the right way. The manner is everything. Now go on home and practice on a relative. Or the parish priest. First thing you know you'll be a virtuoso and you'll save yourself all kinds of trouble in later life."

I had not practiced, I had not become a virtuoso, but simply by being around Skeffington I had at least learned to listen the right way, and this is what I did now with the Commander. Finally he finished; at least there were no more sounds; I said that terrible things were on the increase and this was certainly one of them. We shook hands and the Commander left me, presumably to find another listener. Alone, I looked around, the room was as active and noisy as ever, the music was pounding away, Shep Nomad was now himself singing hoarsely a song of someone else's composition, and I looked at my watch and then I started for the front hall and the stairs which led to the library and the family — the more private division of Charles's great victory party.

THE library doors were closed; it was Phil who opened them. "Aha!" he said. "Writer, traveler, total stranger. Come in anyway. We're talking about politics. How's that for a surprise?"

I hadn't seen him since I had come home. Like Charles, he seemed completely unchanged, and for just that moment of meeting I got, once again, that sudden flash of confusion, the sense of jumbled identities. He said shrewdly and at once, "And the funny thing is I knew you right away."

I said, "Cut it out. Did either one of you ever think of wearing a moustache? Or a badge?"

"Speak to the candidate," he said. "Or correction: the Governor. As of yesterday. He's not here at the moment, but everybody else is, as you can see. We're all running away from that Elks picnic downstairs. How about that turkey-trot music, by the way? Isn't that the greatest? Were you moved?"

"Deeply. Every note an experience."

"I thought so," he said. "Especially that song to Marie. I tell you, Jack, the people who go around saying lovely melodies died with Jerry Kern just don't know Shep Nomad."

"Never mind that," Marie said, coming over to us. "Nobody's ever written a song to you, and nobody ever will."

"Positively not Shep Nomad," he said. "Or at least I hope not. Because for one thing he's queen bee in the local fag set. Just in case you've led a sheltered life."

"Who, the band leader?" my Uncle Jimmy said. He had been standing over by the television set talking to my Aunt Gert and Phil's wife, Flossie; they had all waved as I came in, and my Uncle Jimmy had left them and followed Marie over to us. Now sixty-seven or sixty-eight, he seemed to me the one who had changed least of all, because he looked exactly as I remembered him in Ireland thirty years ago and at all the stages in between. It wasn't that he had preserved his youth; it was simply that, to me, he had always looked just about the way he did now: never young, never old, but persistently ageless. He said to me, "Hello, Jack, how's the boy?" He made a fist and delivered a short mock-punch to my side. "What about that bandleader?" he said. "He's a nance, right?"

"The nanciest," Phil said.

"I thought so," my Uncle Jimmy said. "I can spot a nance a mile away. When I saw this chump with his greasy eyes waving his tail up there I said to myself, 'Oh oh: another one.' I'd get rid of him. Fast. I wouldn't have him around the house for five minutes."

"We thought it was safe enough," Marie said. "What can he do: seduce an alderman on the bandstand?"

From the beginning she had never been particularly deferential to my Uncle Jimmy. She had always spoken up to him, and although this had seldom been welcomed at first, in the end it had won her a position of privilege. It was a position not shared by everyone — Flossie, for example, although originally considered to be a far greater catch, had never quite managed to make the grade.

"Listen," my Uncle Jimmy said, taking me by the arm, "how about giving this subject the old heave-ho? Hah? Charles is Governor, here's Jack back again, and we stand around shooting the breeze about some fat-assed nance. Now if you and Charles want him in your house that's okay with me. Just so long as the kids are out of the way and asleep. For all I care he can shuck off his clothes and chase a monsignor around the piano."

"That ought to help out." I said, "with Charles as Governor. I imagine a thing like that could get into the papers."

My Uncle Jimmy gave me a derisive look. "What'll you bet?" he said. "For instance, what paper? Don't make me laugh. I hear you've got a new book."

"Brand-new," I said. "It comes out practically tomorrow."

My Uncle Jimmy nodded. He was greatly interested in my books. Not that he enjoyed reading them — I don't think he ever read one; in fact I never saw him read any fiction, let alone mine: he had little time for such frivolity — but his conception of family loyalty included more than support to his sons. Indirectly I learned that he bought, personally, a thousand copies of every book I wrote as soon as it was published; he distributed these books to friends and acquaintances everywhere. When, once, I had thanked him for this, and told him that it was far beyond ordinary kindness and, moreover, that it was not really necessary, he had denied the whole thing.

"I might buy a copy or so at an airport," he said, "to give to some lunkhead beside me on a plane. I figure it might keep him from getting airsick and heaving all over me. But that's all."

But I think he was really rather proud of having a writer in the family — even a writer of mysteries — and quite often I ran into people who told me that my Uncle Jimmy had been boasting about me. Quite often, too, I got little appreciative notes from people — sometimes people of surprising eminence — who had been on the receiving end of my Uncle Jimmy's largess. So that now when he nodded I knew that he was making a mental note for still another purchase order.

"I've seen it around the house," he said. "Charles has got it. He read it and liked it. Have you seen him yet?"

I said I had, and he said, "There's a sweetheart for you: he'll show them all how to do it before he's through. He ran a campaign that would knock your hat off."

I said, "I hear you helped."

"You're damn right I did," he said. "I hear you didn't."

I often wondered how long my immunity from my Uncle Jimmy's displeasure would continue. Like Charles, like Marie, like the rest of the family, he had always seemed to accept the fact that I just didn't get involved in Charles's campaigns, and this was curious, for although I think he understood the reason, I don't think he had any great sympathy with it, and he had always expressed himself frequently and loudly on the need for solidarity in family matters. Also, it was my guess that he privately thought that any contribution I might make would be negligible. I wasn't sure of this, though: he was a prickly man, and whenever he spoke sharply — as he had just now — I suspected that an explosion might be near. But I had always found directness the best tactic with him, and so I said, "That's right, I didn't. So I guess we both heard right."

Phil said easily, "Pa, are you getting set to wallop Jack?"

But it was all a false alarm; my Uncle Jimmy just laughed. "Listen," he said, in great good humor, "I feel too good tonight to wallop anybody. Anybody. And can't you see an old poop like me trying to wallop this kiddo; he's got a build like a fullback!" It was a pleasant, if absurd, exaggeration: it was my Uncle Jimmy's high spirits. He swung another mock-punch at me and said, "And why should I want to wallop him? Hah? Whose beeswax is it if a sharp young guy with a lot on the ball wants to stay home horsing around with fairy stories when he could be out in the action and helping to run the show? All because he got mixed up with that old chromo twenty years ago and after that he got sour on the whole deal! Right?"

"You know that's the second time tonight somebody brought Skeffington up," I said. "The first time it was Charles, about a half an hour ago. It's interesting the way he seems to stick in your mind."

"Don't try to give me the needle!" my Uncle Jimmy said, not quite so jovially. "He doesn't stick in my mind! I dropped that clown in the dead letter slot thirty years ago! All these mush-mouthed Micks around here thought he was God with that fake voice and the big hello! But I had him pegged from the start: a small-timer from the word go! Strictly a local con man: every time he left town to monkey with the big boys they had to loan him his carfare to get home!"

Even so long after Skeffington's death, my Uncle Jimmy spoke with a kind of growing fury; I never knew just what the quarrel between the two men had been. I had asked my Uncle Jimmy but he had refused to be pinned down to any definition; Skeffington had contented himself with ironic reference, calling him Mister Pazoosas, The Father of the Family, or The Kindly One. My father once told me that in his opinion there had never been any single quarrel, but that Skeffington had enjoyed baiting my Uncle Jimmy and had done so almost continually.

"He couldn't resist," my father said. "A man like your Uncle Jimmy, who was so full of the miracle of his own achievement, and who really had very little humor to go along with it, was a natural for Skeffington. The old man just kept on rolling off these elaborate compliments which always turned out to be rather mortifying taunts, and Jimmy kept on frothing at the mouth. It was foolish of both of them, of course. It was foolish of Skeffington because more than once Jimmy could have been of great help to him — and as it was, more than once he nearly ruined him. And it was downright silly of Jimmy, because by then he was operating nationally, he wasn't interested in purely local politics, and what Skeffington said shouldn't have bothered him at all. But it did. Oh my, how it did!"

And, apparently, still did. But it was a subject we left now, because my Aunt Gert and Flossie joined us — my Aunt Gert looking older now, her hair gray, but still laughing, still very fat, still going on her pilgrimages with her girl friends, and still keeping a very sharp eye on the things that mattered: AT&T, IBM, Standard Oil of New Jersey. She had never remarried; she was very rich. She greeted me now hugely and moistly with a great kiss on the cheek, and I said to her, "Aunt Gert, I've missed you more than I can say. I haven't had a word of sensible advice since I last saw you. Let's get together some day soon for lunch. I have a few questions I'd like to ask you about growth stocks."

"Growth stocks!" she said delightedly. "Listen to the boy, Jimmy: *growth stocks!* You might just as well ask me about Zulu cannibals or what it's like up there on the moon. Growth stocks: Mother of God, what would I know about a thing like that?"

And she gave her great laugh. It was a game she still loved to play: a bewildered woman, helpless in a male world run by skillful rascals. Phil said to me, "Aunt Gert's just back from Lourdes. How is it over there this year, Aunt Gert? They're still in the same line of work, are they?"

"Oh yes, they don't change. Well, they're like most of the rest of us, aren't they? I don't think we change much either. Of course," she said pleasantly, "some of us grow up a little."

"Pow!" Marie said. "Did anyone feel that, I wonder?"

"Hey, Aunt Gert," Phil said admiringly, "who taught you how to throw that right?"

Aunt Gert beamed at him. "God love you, dear," she said. "What right? Aren't we having just a little family chat?"

"Jack," Flossie said, in her clear and rather formal voice, "how long will you be back this time?" She was changing the subject and none too artfully, but she was never quite at her ease in the presence of this family badinage, even though by this time she had been exposed to it for a good many years. She was tall, as tall as Marie, but slimmer, dark-haired, and quite beautiful in a strange way: her eyes were a deep, extraordinary violet, really remarkable, and were long and faintly oblique. This gave her something of an exotic appearance which was entirely misleading, for Flossie was a great conservative: she was a good wife and an excellent mother, she did all the correct things instinctively and well. And yet in this family she remained a little bit of an outsider. She came from old, honored Yankee stock — she was the only non-Catholic in my Uncle Jimmy's family circle — and even her accent set her apart; Jean used to call her Little Girl Lost. This was too strong — in the family she was not a lonely or forlorn presence — but it's true that she failed to fit in as completely as the rest. The key to this was of course my Uncle Jimmy. He was neither cruel nor rude to her, but he was apt to pass her by, to pay her less attention than he paid others, and when, feeling this, she tried, with well-mannered little courtesies and well-intentioned behavior, to work herself into his particular good graces, she sometimes tried too hard.

"She presses," Phil had once said to me. It was the only time he had ever spoken to me about his wife and his father, but I knew that it bothered him. "She presses all the time with him, and you can't press too hard with a bulldozer like Pa: it just makes him worse. I've told her that, and she knows it, but she goes on pressing. She can't help it: she wants to be liked. Well, okay, I'm all for that, because he should like her: she's a great girl. But she doesn't understand Pa, and he sure enough doesn't understand her. He thinks she's la-di-da; as soon as she opens her mouth to offer him a hot dog he starts thinking of Episcopal bishops!"

I liked Flossie and felt a little sorry for her. Whenever I thought of her I thought of a well-tanned girl in a white tennis dress — she was a very good tennis player and had won local championships — walking with a brisk, long-legged stride off the court, to be joined by her four little children, who obediently and affectionately followed Mommy to the pool.

I talked with her now for a moment, and then my Uncle Jimmy came back. He had gone off to fix himself a drink; now he came back saying loudly, "Listen —"

But exactly what we were to listen to was not said, for just then James came into the room. He greeted me and explained that he had been off in one of the bedrooms, changing; he was leaving in a few minutes to catch a plane to Miami and then to South America; on the very next evening he would address some sort of ecumenical conference in Peru.

"Why Peru, for God's sake?" Phil said.

"Why not Peru?" James said. With a swift automatic deftness he folded a long white scarf, slipping it into a black attaché case and snapping the case shut. "The trouble is you can't hold all your meetings in Atlantic City if you claim to be a Universal Church. People eventually get suspicious. Besides, I like Peru. There's nothing I look forward to more than preaching in Cuzco. I'll be doing that next Sunday."

"It's your sense of continuity," I said. "The Incas, the Temple of the Sun, and now you."

"It's a matter of height, not history," he said. "You see, in Cuzco you're eleven thousand feet up. The plaza is packed with people, you begin preaching, and pretty soon they start dropping like flies, one by one. You never can be sure whether it's the altitude or the impact of your message. But it's very gratifying: I never come away from Cuzco without feeling slightly awed by my own powers."

Marie said, "James is right out of the Renaissance. A worldly cleric."

"A much-traveled cleric, anyway," Phil said. "This week Cuzco, next week Nome, then on to Barcelona. Have soutane, will travel. Has anyone ever done a paper on *Pan-Am and the Pastor?* James, whatever happened to all those good old country priests I used to read about?"

"They're right where they always were," James said. "In the country." He looked at me and smiled and said, "Actually."

He was not yet forty-five, but his hair was pure white; as slim and as elegant as ever, he was a handsome man: the best-looking of the three brothers. Twenty-five years ago he had surprised everyone by entering the seminary. Most of all, I remember, he had surprised my Uncle Jimmy, who had been furious: he had not raised his oldest boy to become a humble diocesan priest. He had been mollified, however, when

James had not become one. Instead he had become famous. Or moderately so: he was certainly one of the best-known priests in the country, but owing to the imprecision which occasionally marks newspaper coverage of the clergy, he was not infrequently described as "the brilliant Jesuit preacher." This James had come to accept with an exasperated tolerance.

"The papers are wonderful," he had said. "And the magazines. You see, they have a simple gauge: any priest who can say 'nuclear' instead of 'nucular' is by definition a Jesuit. And any Jesuit is of course a brilliant Jesuit. Therefore . . ."

He was surely bright, probably brilliant; he was a remarkably good preacher; he was not a Jesuit. He was in fact a parish priest who had risen far above the limits of his parish. In this rise he was undoubtedly helped by my Uncle Jimmy, whose network of well-placed connections could hardly have been a handicap, but the greatest help of all had come from another quarter in the form of the winds inspired by Pope John and the *aggiornamento*. Extremely able, temperamentally suited to the new movement, James had ridden these winds; in the interest of Church Unity he traveled everywhere, an immaculate, persuasive apostle of peace, healing old wounds, addressing traditional enemies. His work was now almost entirely with what were called the Separated Brethren; so much so that Phil once said to me, "I saw James doing a funny thing this morning: he was talking to a Catholic!"

And now he was leaving the family, and the new Governor, on his way to Peru; my Uncle Jimmy said, "Watch out for those babies down there, boy. A handful of crooked Spics sticking the shiv into a mob of midget Indians: that's Peru. I know; I had a little business down there a couple of years ago. Everybody was on the take."

James said, "I've got protection: my host is Archbishop Segura."

"Forget it," my Uncle Jimmy said. "I know him, too. He's got a hand like a first baseman's mitt and it's always out. You'd be better off staying at the Y."

James nodded, seemed amused, but said no more. He got ready to leave, then drew my Uncle Jimmy to one side and they held a short private conversation while the rest of us talked together. In a few minutes they rejoined us; James said goodbye to us all, gave us his blessing, and then left to go looking for Charles. But this proved to be unnecessary, for just as he opened the door Charles came in. The two brothers stood there for perhaps thirty seconds, talking; James laughed at something Charles said. Then he turned and waved to us and was off on his way to Peru and still another conference.

Charles greeted us, kissed Marie, then dropped into a chair. "Does anybody here want to be Governor?" he said. "I've just finished a fifteen-minute talk with Dan Cogan."

I had known Cogan years ago, when he had been a young, primitive, and extremely ambitious politician. He had had great success and now ruled the state legislature with a firm and rather brutal hand. My Uncle Jimmy said, "What did that bum want?"

"He said he didn't want anything," Charles said. "Except to wish me well."

"For fifteen minutes?" Phil said.

"There did seem to be one thing more," Charles said. "He said he was eager to cooperate in every way. Jack, back in the golden days, what did it mean when a man like Dan Cogan, in Dan Cogan's position, said that he was eager to cooperate in every way?"

I said, "It meant that he wanted a piece of the action. Usually a rather big piece. And of all the action."

He nodded. "It's nice to know that the old customs still hang on. Because that's what Cogan wanted, of course. He reminded me of the help he'd given me during the past year. Then he talked a bit about legislatures and governors, and how one depended on the other. Nothing very specific: just good, general, reasonably offensive talk."

"He's bad news," my Uncle Jimmy said. "You're going to have trouble with that baby."

"I think we're all agreed on that," Charles said.

"He's horrible," Marie said, with a little shiver. "I mean, really horrible: of all the people in the campaign he's the only one I couldn't stand even being near. He's always *touching* you: even when he shakes hands he can't help hanging on for that extra second."

"He touches everyone," Charles said. "Except perhaps his wife; I don't think he cares much about shaking hands with her. He's had a succession of young secretaries; one of them was a pretty little Puerto Rican girl named Rodriguez. She's back in Puerto Rico now with nothing to remind her of Dan but a small income. And a five-year-old son who doesn't look particularly Puerto Rican."

"Can you tag him with that?" my Uncle Jimmy asked.

"No," Charles said. "That's always a chancy business. And in this case you just can't prove it. He's not a stupid man, you know. He's very clever. At least I think he is." He turned to my Aunt Gert and said, "How about you, Aunt Gert? You know about these things. Don't you think a man is clever who has a house in the country worth a hundred and fifty thousand dollars, an apartment in town which rents for thirteen and a half thousand a year, and tools around in a Cadillac Fleetwood —

all on a declared income of twenty-two thousand seven hundred and fifty?"

"God love you, dear," my Aunt Gert said, "I only hope a clever man like that doesn't have any enemies. Because if he did I imagine one of them might put in a call to Charlie Halloran down at the Internal Revenue office. Charlie's a dreadful man for putting clever people in jail."

"I think those enemies have already called Charlie," Charles said. "He and some of his friends from Washington have had several talks with Cogan. It doesn't seem to have amounted to much."

"What about net worth?" my Uncle Jimmy said. "No soap?"

Charles shook his head. "No soap. He knows what he's doing; it's all covered up. Not a trace so far. By the way, how well do you know George Baxter?"

"Baxter Construction? I know him," my Uncle Jimmy said. "We used to play golf together once in a while at Shady Lawn." He said to me, "There was a hell of a golf course, Jack. Every green like a pool table. Your father used to play out there a lot; there was a dwarf caddie he liked. You ever been out there?"

I said I had, and he said, "I drove out a couple of weeks ago: you wouldn't know the place. All changed; it's not even a golf course any more. Some foundation's grabbed it and turned it into a joint where a mob of spongers live for free and tell each other how swell they are. Mostly writers and actors: your kind of racket. You know what I mean?"

"I know what you mean, Uncle Jimmy."

"I walked around for about half an hour," he said. "As far as I could see everybody out there was either a dope fiend or a dinge. Some foundation!"

"Fine," Charles said. "That's the kind of talk I like to hear. Let's get back to George Baxter: do you suppose you can get him in here to see me one day next week?"

"Why not?" my Uncle Jimmy said. "What for?"

"His company just got the contract on the new veterans' hospital," Charles said. "That's a Cogan project. I thought I'd talk to Baxter about a few of the details: there might just be something there. I doubt it, but you never know."

"You won't find out anything from Baxter," my Uncle Jimmy said, "because he's not running the show. The company's been reorganized; the real muscle there is the new treasurer: A sharp little Canuck called Allaire. From Quebec. Baxter's got nothing upstairs. He's a featherhead and he always was."

Charles said dryly, "That's all right with me. For this kind of talk I don't want Allaire; I want the featherhead. Maybe we'll get lucky. And maybe we won't. Maybe we'll just have to play along with the legislative leader a while longer." He looked across to Phil and said, "You haven't said much. No new thoughts?"

"No," Phil said, "but that's only because I'm pretty crazy about the old ones."

Charles said to me, "A behind-the-scenes glimpse of a crack in the solid Kinsella wall. Phil and I differ on the right way to handle people like Cogan."

Phil shrugged. "You're the Governor; you can handle it your way if you want to. That's obvious. And I'm not saying it won't work because I think it will. I *am* saying that in the long run it's dangerous, and dangerous to you. And you know what I mean because we've —"

And then Phil stopped in mid-sentence. He was now looking forward, talking directly to Charles as though the rest of us weren't here, and although he had started by talking casually, almost indifferently, he had suddenly begun to speak with intensity, even passion — which was startling, because no one in the room was prepared for it. Phil had probably realized this, because as he stopped so abruptly he glanced quickly around at all of us, and then he smiled and went back to Charles. He said in a quieter voice, and again as if only the two of them were talking together, "Just for a change, how would it be if I laid off crabbing tonight? And told you that I'm satisfied, that I'm glad, that I'm proud. And hopeful. Very hopeful. Because all that's true, you know. Believe it or not."

Charles looked back at him and smiled and said in the same personal, almost excluding way, "I think I'd like that."

My Uncle Jimmy broke in on this private conversation, sounding both annoyed and slightly baffled. "Hey hey hey!" he said. "What goes on here, anyway? You two going in business for yourself? Hah? What is all this bushwa?"

And for just a moment, in listening to Phil and Charles talk, I had shared my Uncle Jimmy's bafflement, because it seemed to me that I had caught a note I had not caught before — a somehow disturbing note — and when I looked at their wives I noticed that Marie seemed thoughtful and Flossie definitely apprehensive. My Uncle Jimmy stood facing them, his feet wide apart and his pose one of challenge. He was frowning, he was not fond of mysteries, and now, suddenly, and for the first time since I had known him, I found myself wondering whether my Uncle Jimmy was still on top of the family situation, or whether something might not now be going on which was beyond both his knowledge and control.

But this was a quick thought, a flash, an impression gained from no more than a look and two or three sentences, and it could have been all wrong. Certainly from what Phil now said it seemed to be, for he turned to his father with a quick gaiety and said, "Pa, you're right: it's bushwa all the way. Pure, homogenized, grade-A bushwa. The fact is that I've been nagging the Governor on a few minor points and now I've stopped. Anyway, for tonight. So what do you say, Pa? Do you want to lead us in a little family toast? To Charles, and to the greatest break this state has had for the last hundred years!"

"You're damn right I do!" my Uncle Jimmy said. "Only cut out that hundred years baloney. What happened a hundred years ago that was so hot? Hah? Why stop there? No, we'll all drink to Charles, and never mind any phony time limits. And I'll tell you something else: we're going to have *three* toasts, not just one. The first one is for Charles. My boy Charles," he said, looking fondly, almost burstingly, at his youngest son. "And then, when we've finished with that, we're all going to drink a toast to your Ma. Nobody ever lived for all of her family the way she did, and nobody, not even me, would have been happier here tonight. And last of all is another toast. This one I'm going to drink all by myself, and nobody else is going to join me. Because this one," he said, and his voice, which had trembled ever so slightly when he spoke of my Aunt Mary, now seemed for just an instant to become even more uncertain, "this one is for all my boys. For James, for Phil, for Charles. I wish James could be here right now, but he knows what I'm going to say because I told him just what I'm going to tell you. And that is that I'm a lucky man. The papers and the magazines have been saying that about me for forty years: Lucky Jimmy Kinsella. But they had it all wrong, because they never once put down where I was really lucky: with my family, all growing up and sticking together the way I always hoped it would, each one making it better for all the rest of us. I hear people telling me all the time how big a credit James and Phil and Charles are to me. But I never thought of it that way, and I never gave a damn what anybody else thought. Because I know what I know, and that is that nothing I ever did in all my life, except marry your Ma, gave me the right to have boys like you!"

It was an extraordinary speech — extraordinary because it was so completely unlike him. There had been no salty style, no picturesque touches: it had been straight and simple and towards the end it had shaken with emotion. I think it was this emotion which really took me by surprise, for I had never thought of my Uncle Jimmy as being an emotional man at all. Not only was he extremely hard-boiled — and his reputation for this was not merely familial or local: I can remember my sense of shock when, years ago, in a college lecture hall, I had suddenly realized that the man under discussion as the archetype of the newer, harder economic adventurer was in fact my uncle — but he did not have the weakness common to so many hard-boiled men: he did not have a soggy side. He did not weep cheap tears at sentimental movies; he did not weep at all. So that when he spoke as he had just now it took me completely off guard. I knew of course of his enormous pride in his sons, but this had come from more than pride — this had come from love. It had been a cry from the heart — the rarely observed precinct within my Uncle Jimmy — and I found it unexpectedly moving. Obviously, the others did too. The two boys were looking only at their father now, and their faces were not composed; I saw Marie look at Charles and then just touch the corner of her eye; my Aunt Gert made no bones about it: she was crying freely. It was a rare moment, a silent, almost breathless moment, a moment which I've never forgotten and which I know I never will forget.

And then, very quickly, this moment passed as we all drank our toasts and as my Uncle Jimmy, standing all by himself in the center of the room, looking solemn and proud and small and oddly touching, drank the final toast to his boys, his family. Then, suddenly, the atmosphere lifted, everyone began to talk at once, and slowly the emphasis began to shift away from Charles and the election and today back to my Uncle Jimmy and back to yesterday. It became now my Uncle Jimmy's evening, and it was Charles himself who led the way; assisted by Phil, he encouraged his father to reminisce. When my Uncle Jimmy was in good spirits, as he so clearly was tonight, he could do this very well, and over the years I had several times sat in on and been entertained by his memories of coups and deals and behind-the-scenes stratagems which were apt to embrace everyone from members of the hierarchy to Greek shipping magnates to Presidents. My Uncle Jimmy's view of history was that of the insider: he had been there. On the other hand, if he had *not* been there, he was not much interested; the result was that certain events of our time, normally considered as major or even critical by most observers, were in his personalized surveys severely diminished or simply ignored. So that it was a special kind of history, as fascinating as it was unbalanced, and made even more special by my Uncle Jimmy's unorthodox evaluations of the eminent men and women he had known. He was no respecter of reputations. He had few, perhaps no, heroes; he had worked with many of the great and ultimately he had quarreled with them; this intimacy had not bred awe. In my Uncle Jimmy's history the footprints on the sands of time were mostly made by feet of clay.

Tonight, probably in honor of Charles and the occasion, he talked largely about politics. He had never held elective or appointive office of any kind, but for many years he had contributed heavily to the Democratic party, he had ranged in and out of high Democratic councils, and although I don't suppose he had ever really been a kingmaker, he had undoubtedly had his moments of great influence. He had been called in by more than one President to help with specific financial problems, and when he mentioned this in passing now, Phil said, "I'll tell you what I heard: I heard they used to call you the Irish Baruch."

My Uncle Jimmy accepted this equably enough. "Okay," he said. "I don't get too mad at that. What was so wrong with Baruch? He knew what it was all about."

I said, "I guess he must have. Still, I remember reading somewhere that while everybody always said he gave advice to Presidents, nobody really said whether the Presidents ever took it."

It was an ungenerous comment; also, in view of the comparison that had just been established, it was an unwise one, and it did not go down well with my Uncle Jimmy. "Yeah?" he said belligerently. "Well, I can clear that one up for you right now. They took it. They didn't take all of it and they would have been nuts if they did. He wasn't as hot as he thought he was, not by a long shot. He always thought that after they made him they stopped making brains. All that magnolia bushwa. But he was okay. Mostly. And he had a hell of a lot more on the ball than those little left-wing wisenheimers that sat around picking their noses and making dirty cracks at him. Listen, Baruch gave away more in tips to cab drivers in a week than those babies earned in ten years." He stabbed a finger at Charles and said, "You've got a few of them around you, boy. Big liberals, right? They all bleed like hell for the poor Puerto Ricans and they boo hoo hoo all over the joint about civil liberties, but just say to them sometime you think you'll drop over the Pavillon for chow and then see what happens. They'll kick each other to death trying to be first in line! Watch yourself with that gang or you'll all be out playing Pony Boy in the back yard, and guess who'll be the pony!"

"I'll bear it in mind," Charles said, smiling slightly. I had the feeling that this ground had been covered before; at any rate, he now gently changed the subject. "One question. Pa," he said. "Of them all — and I'm talking now just about the top men — which one did you like best?"

"Truman," my Uncle Jimmy said instantly. "A good little guy. And not a bad President. He did all right with what he had. And if you did him a favor he didn't forget it. He was never a doublecrosser, and that was some switch in the White House in those days, because before Truman they had the world's champ!"

This was perhaps his favorite theme: I had heard him often on the subject of his old special hate. Charles said, "All right. But supposing you left all likes and dislikes to one side. I mean, supposing you had to pick one man of them all to be the President purely on the basis of capacity, of sheer ability — then what? It almost has to be Roosevelt, doesn't it?"

Surprisingly — or at least surprisingly to me — my Uncle Jimmy agreed at once. "Sure," he said. "And by miles. He had more soft spots than a banana, especially later on, but he ran the show. Not because he was smart or a genius or a great leader, but because he had what it took: he was a con man. It takes a con man to handle a country like this, and that's what Roosevelt was all the way. He had those chowderheads down in Washington sitting there with their traps open catching flies while he kept on smiling and blowing smoke at them and telling them to guess which shell the pea was under. I didn't like him for a minute and you could never believe a word he said, but he was good at his job. Pretty good. But don't ever hand me that Great Man malarky. 'My *friends* . . .'" he said, derisively imitating the famous voice. "My friends my ass!"

"God bless us all," my Aunt Gert said. "There are ladies present!" And she laughed her great laugh.

Phil said, possibly maliciously, "We haven't heard about the General. What about him?"

"Don't make me laugh," my Uncle Jimmy said. "Amateur night!" then, suddenly recalling something, he looked at me and said triumphantly, "But he showed all you birds something, right? With that book of his he didn't write? He got a capital gains deal out of it and made himself a bundle. Right after that they smartened up and locked the barn door and nobody else in your racket's made a buffalo nickel that way ever since!"

It was true enough, but since my own books were seldom in that category where any capital gains provision would have meant much, I couldn't feel deeply about it and I don't think I responded suitably. But this made no difference because my Uncle Jimmy, having delivered his thrust, saw no point in waiting for reaction, and simply moved on. His talk now took a different turn, for suddenly he left politics entirely and began to reminisce in a warmer, more personal way: he began to talk about the family, not as it was today, but as it had been when he and my father and my Aunt Gert were children together, growing up in the city and living in one of the many three-tenement houses which his father — unknown to them all — owned. I've said that my Uncle Jimmy was not an emotional man, but now as I listened to him talking about those early days I was not so confident. Because I had been over substantially this same ground before, not with my Uncle Jimmy but with my father, and while my father had been in every way kinder and gentler, an infinitely more appreciative and sympathetic man than his brother, his memories of this early family life had been much harsher, particularly when these memories had centered about his father. Whenever I thought of my grandfather I pictured him either as the tight, tough, essentially tyrannical man of my father's stories, or as the old, curiously mottled, largely silent little wisp of a man I had seen in my Uncle Jimmy's castle in Ireland. It was hard to square the one picture with the other; it was harder to square either with my Uncle Jimmy's present and on the whole rather proud portrayal of the returned sailor who had settled down in the city of his birth to build a home, a fortune, a dynasty.

"A hard nut," he conceded. "But he came around in the end. We all got what was coming to us and a little more besides. He was rough in the clinches, but I learned a hell of a lot from him, and not just about do-re-mi, either. I learned about the family and how important it was. You boys know what I've always said to you about the family: all for one, one for all. Right? Well, I learned it from him: he was the original stick-together guy. And if you didn't want to stick together he beat it into you. Even from the time we were little kids with the ring of the pot still on our seats, if he ever caught you going outside saying anything about the rest of us, he gave it to you good. He wouldn't say a word; he'd just shoot you one of those looks and reach for the razor strap. I had a sore tail for ten years, but I wound up knowing what you could do if you all stuck together!"

My father must have had a sorer tail and for a much longer period of time, but with him the lesson, so fruitful and unforgettable for my Uncle Jimmy, simply had not taken. My Uncle Jimmy made no reference to this now; he went on filling in the picture of my grandfather, not entirely ignoring the warts — every once in a while a peculiarly sharp memory seemed to prod him and then he departed momentarily from benignity — but on the whole touching them up here and there, so that while there were glimpses of harshness and silent violence, what finally emerged was a hard but reasonably picturesque figure, whose stern example had taught his children the value of a dollar, and whose extraordinary concealment of his wealth from his own family for so long a time now seemed in retrospect an antic gesture, more eccentric than anything else, arising no doubt from a basic love of that family, and in any case more than atoned for by the healthy settlements made on each of his children. And as I listened I wondered whether there was any kind of truth in this at all — whether, that is, my Uncle Jimmy, so much closer to my grandfather in his temperament and aims, could have caught qualities that my father had ignored or simply had not seen — or whether perhaps it might not be a matter of age, that as my Uncle Jimmy had grown older his memories had mellowed, and that indeed something of the sort might have happened to my father if he had lived, so that their separate accounts of their father might by now have come closer together. But somehow I didn't really think so, and when I looked over at my Aunt Gert for some possible clue — for she was the only other member of the family who had memories of those early days, and certainly by the end she had come to know my grandfather better than had either of her brothers — she was no help at all. She was listening and seemed to be listening intently, but her large white poker face was set in its perpetual and rather pleasant mask of potential laughter.

And so my Uncle Jimmy went on talking, leaving his father after a while and starting to rove at random through the past, and as he continued to do so with a kind of special gusto, and with smiles and laughter from us all — because, tonight, he seemed in really great form — I found myself unexpectedly feeling faintly regretful and sad, as you sometimes do on joyful occasions when there apparently is no reasonable excuse for sadness at all. I sat there for a few moments, not really knowing why I felt this way, still watching and listening to my Uncle Jimmy, but beginning to drift back over the evening, thinking of all the different and rather surprising things that had happened to me since I had arrived, thinking of Walshie and Edso and the extraordinary coalition of forces which had been brought together to celebrate Charles's triumph in the room below, thinking of old memories of other and quite different political nights that had risen to the surface in me, thinking of Charles and Marie standing hand and hand together as though in the first of a series of official portraits, thinking just of Charles — Charles as *Governor!* — but thinking particularly, and for no special reason, of that one brief instant when Phil and Charles had been talking together, so openly but so privately, too. Once again, as I thought back over this, I had the feeling that something had changed, that something was different, that something was going on I didn't understand — and once again I had the feeling that in this I was not alone, that unlikely as it might seem, especially since this was so obviously a family matter, my Uncle Jimmy was in the dark as well.

Was he? I didn't know, of course, but the feeling persisted, it was unavoidable, and yet at the same time the evidence right before my eyes pointed in just the opposite direction. For if he had even suspected that there were family secrets which were being kept from him, he would have been furious and deeply troubled, but now, certainly, no one seemed freer from troubles of any kind — so free, in fact, that suddenly and unexpectedly he began to dance. Or rather, to go into the beginning of a little clog step — it turned out that he was illustrating a point in a story about a small-time vaudevillian who had lived in the tenement above them more than sixty years before. He went through this performance with a heavy-footed exuberance — although a small man, he was not a natural dancer — and as he danced he sang in a jaunty nasal voice:

> *She's the daughter of Rosie O'Grady*
> *A dear little old-fashioned girl. . . .*

He was not a natural singer, either, but sheer energy carried him through: it was impossible to pull away from this vitality, this challenging bounciness. And so here he was, at the moment of my conviction that the focus was somehow slipping away from him, as happy as I had ever seen him, clogging his way through memories, the undisputed center of family doings. Charles was sitting, completely relaxed now, next to Marie; one hand rested lightly on her knee. Phil was standing, half-smiling, behind Flossie, who seemed to have shed for the moment the faint overlay of distress she always brought with her to these family gatherings; my Aunt Gert was as expressionless as ever, but she was humming and tapping the floor with one fat little foot; I saw Phil and Charles suddenly glance at each other in quick delighted recognition of some gesture or piece of business on the part of their father that I failed to catch. It was a complete, unified, strong family scene, all pulled together and made what it was by the same powerful little presence who had always been able to do this, and under the impact of this cohesiveness, this visible shared enjoyment, my own strange feeling of disquiet began to disappear.

Soon after this Charles and Marie left to return to their party downstairs — it was an indication of the strength of the family atmosphere that for the past few minutes I had forgotten completely the real reason for our being all together tonight. As she was leaving Marie came over to me and said, "Back to the lions. Jack, are we going to see you?"

"I hope so. I'll be around, at least for a while."

"Well, so will we. After the first, that is; we're going off tomorrow for about three weeks. Charles hasn't had a break for ages, so we're going to all the places I love. Paris for a week, then down to Rome for two. This late it'll probably rain every day in Rome, but I couldn't care less. We'll have Bill and Pony Brady's house, and you can't do much better than that. Want to come along?"

"Not this year," I said. "It's not fashionable enough: everybody's going to Greece."

"I know: all that good clear light," she said. "We were there last year, in the islands. It was beautiful, all right, but I don't know, I'm not mad about beautiful places where I can't speak the language and I don't like the food. And of course I fool people: they all think I want to put on a bathing suit and go skin-diving or water-skiing, and I don't. My idea of heaven is to be absolutely comfortable in an elegant apartment in a nice big city. . . . Anyway," she said, "listen, Jack: you wouldn't do yourself a favor, would you? And give Jean a call?"

It was one of her quick blunt shifts to the personal which I'd never handled very well and which, instinctively, I tried to duck; I shook my head slightly and said, "Come on, Marie. . . ."

"MYOB?" she said. "When I was in grade school that was the hot slang for Mind Your Own Business. Come on yourself, Jack: don't be so stuffy. She's a good girl. And don't try to tell me that old one about not knowing where she is, because *I* know where she is, and if I do, you do. . . ."

"If I do you do what?" Charles said, coming up and putting his hands on her smooth shoulders.

"Jack's getting in a stew," she said, "because I'm interfering in his domestic affairs."

"I have a pretty good idea," Charles said. "Why don't you stop interfering in his domestic affairs and start interfering in mine? To the extent of going downstairs and acting like a Radiant First Lady."

"That's what the newspapers call me now," she said, turning to me. "Don't you love it?"

"And while you're radiating," Charles said, "tell them I'll be down in a minute. Also, you might tell Jerry I want to see him in the study before I go down."

She made a face at him, kissed his cheek, and said, "All right." As she left she said to me, "Anyway, think it over. What can you lose by being nice?"

Charles watched her go and said to me, not at all as any kind of an apology, but as a plain statement of fact, "She's always liked Jean. And they keep in touch, I think. She likes to strike a blow for the cause now and then."

I said, "Your wife's a romantic girl."

"I know," he said. "But why not? She's had good luck that way: all the best things that have happened to her have been what I suppose you'd call romantic. Tonight, for example." With one hand he made a large, all-inclusive gesture, taking in the room, the family, the party downstairs, the entire occasion. "This is pretty heady stuff," he said.

I said curiously, "For you, too, Charles?"

He nodded at once. "Sure," he said. "I'm not that blasé." He gave me a quick amused smile and said, "I find it easy to be dazzled by my own achievement. By the way, how did you make out with the Commander? Did you have a pleasant chat?"

"Fascinating. Thanks a lot."

"I thought it might be useful for an old-timer like you to see that even in the new politics some things haven't changed."

"Including techniques," I said, and I told him now what I had suspected at the time: that in diverting the Commander to me he had deliberately been using an old Skeffington ploy.

"Oh," he said, "I'm not above borrowing techniques. Especially if they work. Incidentally, I don't share Pa's feeling about your old boss. I don't buy the legend, either, but he was better than Pa thinks. He knew how to get elected most of the time, and he knew how to maneuver all of the time. I'd say a man who could do that was a pretty fair politician."

I said, "That isn't exactly the same thing as saying that he was a pretty fair governor, is it? Or mayor?"

"I guess it isn't," he said pleasantly, "but then, I guess he wasn't." He looked at me again with the same slightly amused expression and said, "Do you really think he was, Jack?"

I said, "That's the old argument, isn't it? I've heard it ever since the first day I met him. I don't know how good he was. I do know that he's the only one who ever did anything. And I know that if I just look around this city today, about every major improvement I can see — buildings, tunnels, roads, playgrounds — was started or finished or helped along by one man. So I guess that's a kind of answer, isn't it?"

"For someone who quit politics in disgust," he said, "you're surprisingly loyal to old politicians. Or at least to one old politician. Although I wouldn't mind betting that hasn't much to do with politics." He added shrewdly, "It's probably all personal. Anyway, I know those major improvements. Or those of them you can see: half of them have fallen down. Your old friend's contractor pals didn't always use the best materials. By the way, you never happened to look at the city's books for the years all this improving was going on, did you?"

I said defensively, "Crooked books, I imagine?"

"No," he said, "not crooked. You're behind the times, Jack: you believe in the legend. I don't want to strip this picturesque old figure of even a shred of his glamour, but he wasn't the great quixotic crook people still think he was. The awful fact is he wasn't a crook at all. Or not much of a one. By the standards of his time, that is: remember that those were the days of 'honest graft.' But the books weren't crooked. They were worse: they were incredible."

"I'm not too surprised. I don't think bookkeeping was his strongest point."

"I'd agree with that," he said dryly. "You know, when I first went to City Hall I thought I'd better have a look at the records, just to see what had been going on. Well, to begin with, I had to find them. It wasn't easy, as you can imagine, but they finally turned up in some side room as dark as a closet, full of old newspapers and sneakers and underwear and, naturally, the official records of the city. All this was presided over by a little old Irishman who'd been there forever and who — again naturally — couldn't read. I got the books out, I had the city's accountants go over them, and then I put Pa's people to work. It all added up to one thing: Skeffington had no financial sense at all. None. He couldn't have known the first thing about money. Except that you took it in and you paid it out, from anyone and to anyone, and of course it became a matter of policy to pay out more than you took in. That was the way he ran the city, and that was the way he ran the state. And it never hurt him for a minute. Not many people knew about it, and most of those who knew didn't care. That's the way things were then. He was very popular, and that's what elections were around here in those days: popularity contests."

I thought of his own enormous margin of victory; I said, "And you don't think they are today?"

"Sure they are, but there's a difference, isn't there?" he said. "It's not that simple any more. Look at it this way: yesterday I got eighty-five thousand votes more than Skeffington did on his best run. Of course we have more voters now, but there are a few things left you can't blame on the population explosion. My percentage of the total vote was still way ahead of his. And why? Because I'm more popular now than he was then?" He smiled again and said, "Nobody is. We both know that. Nobody's got that kind of popularity any more. It was a personal thing that depended on tribal loyalties, immigrants on the way up, racial spokesmen, Communion Breakfasts — there's some of that still around, of course, but in Skeffington's campaigns it was the big thing. You could do very well for yourself if you could get up and tell a few funny stories, quote Robert Emmet, and shout 'Ireland must be free!' for a finish. Today it's slightly more complicated."

"You need a whole new set of quotations," I said.

"That's right. Among other things."

"Which ones? Who are you quoting these days, Charles?"

"Roosevelt, George Washington Carver, Ben-Gurion," he said imperturbably. "And, just occasionally, Robert Emmet. So as not to slight a minority group. And then on another level, and because I have an ex-

tremely well-read staff — you've heard about my support from the intellectuals — Eliot, Unamuno, Aquinas, and Alexander Pope. We try to
box the compass, you see." He gave me the look he had given me twice
before, and said, "Quotation-wise."

It was to me a curious and a fascinating conversation — curious because although the room was still full of family, Charles and I were
talking in unbroken privacy: none of the others had even come our way.
And yet I had no feeling that we were deliberately being "let alone"; it
was rather as if the general family atmosphere had relaxed with the finish
of my Uncle Jimmy's centralizing performance, and the party had split
up into little groups, each one returning for a moment to its own habitual concerns. Phil and Flossie had gone over by the fireplace where Phil
was talking in a low voice, and Flossie was listening and slowly pulling
on her gloves. Directly above their heads on the rear wall hung a large
painting which I had noticed earlier, but which I looked at more carefully now. I knew that I had seen it somewhere before, that it had some
special significance for me, but just for the moment I couldn't place it,
pin it down. Then, suddenly, I remembered: it was the painting of my
Uncle Jimmy in his Knight of Malta costume that I had last seen so
many years ago in his Irish castle — had it now been permanently transferred to Charles's house? My Uncle Jimmy himself had moved from the
center of the room and had joined my Aunt Gert who, having been
silent for most of the evening, was now talking emphatically to him; I
gathered that this might be business, for she did not at this time seem to
be on the point of any merriment. What she was telling him must have
been of some importance, for he was listening without his customary
impatience, but even so, every once in a while I saw him shift his head
just slightly and flick a fast inquisitive look in our direction. It was not
his habit to be left out of anything, not even for a moment, and while it
was now clear that whatever my Aunt Gert was saying was significant
enough to keep him with her, I knew that he ached to be over here with
us, listening to his son.

He might have been surprised by what he heard — although, come to
think of it, perhaps not. I was. Not by anything Charles had said — for
by now I didn't really care whether Skeffington had been a great governor or a good mayor or even a financial responsible; it was all in the past,
and whatever he had been couldn't modify my affection for someone
who had been unfailingly kind to me, and with whom it had been such
great fun and so exciting for a young man to be, day after day — but by
the authority, the easy confidence with which he said it. The same man
who, twenty years ago, had known nothing about politics and who could
hardly bear to sit through my stories about Skeffington and City Hall

and local politicians, was now calmly setting me straight on the facts of my old scene and of political life in general. It was a queer reversal, more than a little incongruous, and yet as I listened to him talk, so easily, so surely, so peculiarly impressively, I didn't think of this at all. What I did think of was that Charles seemed to have changed far more than I had suspected, and I think it was only now, in these few moments of talk, that I began to realize what I suppose I should have realized long before: that Charles was *in fact* the Governor, and that as Governor, and as the man who had worked to become Governor, he was a different and indeed a far more formidable figure than the Charles I had always known.

But all this came from a manner, an attitude, a presence, for there was certainly nothing formidable in anything he said. He talked on casually, apparently in no hurry at all — although of course he knew very well that everyone downstairs was waiting for his reappearance. Just as, of course, he knew very well that they would continue to wait: in this gathering no one was likely to go home imprudently. He said to me, "It's all changed, in every way. It's a matter of style as much as anything else. Frank Dooley is a good example. Do you remember him?"

"Vaguely. I remember the family, of course." The Dooleys had been a conspicuous political family: Frank Dooley's grandfather had been a ward boss, his father had run the state senate, his uncle had been a Superior Court judge for decades. But Frank himself . . . I said, "He hasn't done well, has he? Wasn't he supposed to be a comer? It seems to me they used to talk about him that way."

"He's old hat," Charles said. "He's actually younger than we are, but people think of him as an old-fashioned pol, and that's the kiss of death these days. He had all sorts of possibilities. He's not bad-looking, he dressed well, he's a good talker, and his father sensed which way the wind was blowing in time to send him to a non-Catholic college. The first Ivy Leaguer in his family. The New Breed. But it didn't work. He got to the City Council and that's as far as he'll ever get. He wants to be attorney general and he wouldn't be a bad one. He's reasonably bright, he's not bad on civil liberties — that's the big thing today, by the way — and he doesn't steal. But the minute he leaves the ward he's done. As soon as he gets in a campaign he starts talking like his father. He starts out on the rights of the Negro to equal employment opportunity and then, before he can stop himself, a bit of a brogue creeps in, a 'God love you!' slips out, and that kills him. He just reminds people of yesterday. Thirty years ago he would have been a shoo-in. Today he's a born loser. In a way it's a pity, because he could be useful to someone."

"But not to you, I gather."

He shook his head. "No, not to me. There's too much going against him. Too many drawbacks. Including the fact that in the primary he nearly killed himself trying to stop me from getting the nomination. I guess I think of that as a drawback."

"No magnanimity, Charles?"

"I know the word," he said. "It's sometimes pronounced 'folly.' " He smiled again and said, "It's too bad you can't talk to your old friend. He could tell you all about that."

"How about Skeffington?" I said. "How does he fit the changing-style theory? You don't think he'd do well if he ran today?"

"You used to be a vaudeville buff," he said. "Remember a thing called *Change Your Act or Go Back to the Woods?* Well, I think he'd have had to change his act. And I don't think he would have, and I don't think he could have. So I think he'd probably have had a very hard time. That's the diplomatic answer. If you want to know what I really think, I think that today he wouldn't last five minutes."

I felt one more surge of old loyalty; I said, "Work it the other way. I mean, let's suppose you'd been running in his day: how long would you have lasted?"

"Oh," he said, "that's a different story. In my case . . . say three minutes." He looked at me and laughed and said, "So it's lucky for both of us we came along when we did, isn't it?" And now for the first time he looked at his watch; the conversation was over. He said, "Feeding time. I've got to see a lot of people. Marie probably told you we're going to Rome for a couple of weeks?"

"Yes. Rest period . . ."

His eyebrows went up just a little. "Is that what Marie said?" he said. "She must have thought you were a spy. Did you ever try to rest in Rome? And at Pony Brady's? That's wild and woolly country, Jack."

I remembered that years ago, in his more hectic days, Charles had not been unknown in that wild and woolly country; I said, "You think you can handle yourself?"

"I'll try," he said dryly. "In fact I can hardly wait to try. I've spent most of the past couple of months in the western part of the state: La Dolce Vita out there is a bean supper at the Epworth League. Have you ever been to a bean supper, Jack? I've been to lots of them lately. I don't know of a better reason for going to Rome. Anyway, we'll be back before long, and when we do let's get together."

"Good, fine." And then, not really meaning anything by it, but just making casual small talk in a half-joking way, I added, "Socially? Or professionally?"

And for some reason this seemed to catch him by surprise, and I saw just a momentary change of expression before he answered. "Any way you want to play it," he said. "Socially by all means. I'll even guarantee to keep Marie out of those domestic affairs. Professionally — well, that's up to you, isn't it? You call it. I'm agreeable. I've told you that before and it still goes. You can come along any time you want to. The trouble is that you don't really want to, do you?"

By now I was embarrassed at my own clumsiness in having brought it up; it was something we had talked about now and then over the years, and never to anyone's satisfaction. I said, "No, I guess I don't. Apart from everything else, I like what I do now, and I couldn't do both. Besides, I don't see where anything like that would be very useful — to use a word of yours — for either of us. Especially for you. I'd always have the out that everything's grist to the mill, new material and so on, but I don't see what you'd have to gain at all."

"Oh," he said, "I'd think you could almost leave that to me. I've been known to think of myself occasionally." And then, although his face didn't change, remaining as quietly pleasant as ever, his voice became more sober, more reflective. "It's a funny job," he said. "No complaints, you know, because I wanted it, and I worked like a dog for it. We talked about popularity. All comparisons aside, I had at least a measure of that in my favor, and I had a lot of other things going for me too. If your name is Kinsella around here, that's not a bad head start in itself. We've both always known that, and Pa still packs enormous weight. And then there's Marie and all the peculiar snobberies of the whole family situation: all those little Irish secretaries daydreaming away. A kind of glamour, I suppose. I got the Catholic vote because everybody knows I am one. I got the non-Catholic vote because the others don't think I'm a very good one. Or, as they'd put it, I'm not 'typical.' "

"That matters still, doesn't it? I keep hearing that it doesn't, that bloc voting is all gone, or mostly gone. I've never believed it."

"James sometimes talks like that," he said. "He's very bright and he knows a lot, but he makes one mistake: he thinks ecumenicism has reached Ward Five. No, it still matters. There's a surface civility, and it's not as obvious as that old magic scream, 'He's one of our own!' but it's there, all right. And it's respected: just look at the careful assortment of trash at the head table of the average interfaith dinner. Jack got to be President, but by a hair: he was almost licked by it. Oddly enough, in this situation, it benefited me. And then of course I was lucky in my opponent. He could have won, but first he got clumsy and then he panicked. And finally, I had another advantage. I know I won't shock you when I tell you that to win cost money. Fortunately I had it. And I used it."

I had heard, from the time I had come back to the city, that this had been the most expensive campaign in the history of the state, and now I couldn't resist going to authority. I said, "How much money, Charles?"

"A lot," he said. "I won't tell you more than that because I really don't want to shock you." Again there was the slight smile and he said, "I want you to preserve your illusions. Anyway, I won — and I know why I won. And having won, I think the idea is that I'm supposed to run the state. I can do that all right, but it won't be easy. I told you earlier tonight that being Governor was a little like being mayor, only more so. It's the 'more so' that counts. I used to deal with the City Council; now I'm going to have to deal with the legislature — which is bigger, tougher, smarter, more complicated, and impossible as it may seem, more corrupt. So it's no cinch. But I have a certain amount of experience, and I'm not exactly unarmed. Although I could use a few helping hands."

"I thought you had plenty of those," I said. "What everyone seems to be talking about is your organization, and how strong it is."

"They're very good," he said. "They're all competent. Some of them are more than that. And a few of them I can even trust. You can't reasonably ask for more than that. What I wouldn't mind having around is someone closer, someone I can not only trust, but whom I've known — and who's known me — for a long time. I have a feeling there are times when that's important. Even indispensable." He smiled again and said, "Maybe I'm getting like Pa: the sense of family."

I said, "You couldn't do better in that department: you've got Phil."

He nodded. "I've got Phil. But Phil is one man, and one man, even if he's as good as Phil, can't be everywhere, and can't do everything. Besides, Phil is . . . my conscience, I suppose. Or so it appears." He hesitated just a bit in the middle of saying this, and after he had said it he hesitated again, as if he were going to say something more along the same line. But he didn't; he said only, "If you ever change your mind, or if you feel like talking about it again, let me know. You can't tell, you might get something out of it at that. Something you could use in a book. If worse came to worst, you could even use me. I understand," he said, the dryness coming into his voice once more, "others are planning something of the sort. The difference is that I might not sue you. Anyway, think it over."

I said I would — although I knew that thinking was unlikely to change anything: probably he knew this, too — and he left, slipping quickly out of the room with just a wave at the others. As he did, my Uncle Jimmy came over beside me and for just a moment didn't say anything but stood looking at the door which Charles had closed behind him. I didn't know when he had left my Aunt Gert — during the last few minutes I had been too interested in what Charles was saying to look around at anyone else — but now I saw that she had joined Flossie underneath the Knight of Malta painting, and that Phil seemed to have disappeared. There was another way out of the library; I wondered if he had left by it, to be with Charles downstairs.

My Uncle Jimmy pointed to the door and said proudly, "Some kiddo, right?"

I agreed, and he said, "It's his night to howl and that's jake with me. He's earned it. He's a great boy. Well, they all are. Every one of them." He seemed to be back in his mood of earlier this evening, when he had spoken so emotionally of his satisfaction in his family. He said, "You talk to James at all?"

"Just long enough to say hello. He was on his way out when I came in."

"A funny kiddo," he said. "He could have been anything. Doctor, lawyer, businessman, politician: you name it. And he double-crossed me and became a priest. Well, who wanted that? Hah? He was my oldest boy and he had a hell of a lot on the ball. You think I wanted to see him planked down on his can in some rectory in the sticks, playing Parcheesi every night and watching the ball games on TV? I tell you, I raised hell when it happened. I went to the bishop and asked him if he thought we were some kind of Shanty Mick family that had to hand over a boy a year to the Church!"

I said, "He must have enjoyed that."

"He got thick," my Uncle Jimmy said. "Well, what could you expect? He's a Shanty Mick himself. And that's the way it happened with him: I know the whole story. I would have belted him right in the puss, bishop or no bishop, but he yanked out that cross he wears and started waving it around. Anyway, it all wound up okay. Look at James: today he's all over the world and everybody knows him. Who else in his racket can do what he does? One minute he's up in Alaska singing 'Holy God, We Praise Thy Name' with a crowd of Eskimos that never did anything but swap reindeer bones until he came along. The next he's in Kansas City glad-handing a convention of Presbyterian chumps. The next he's in Rome listening to the Pope asking him, 'What's new?' I tell you, if those Guineas over there have got anything besides Jello in their heads they'll shoot that baby to the top. And fast!"

First Charles, then James; idly, almost automatically, I said, "And then there's Phil. . . ."

But my Uncle Jimmy snapped this up the instant it was said. "What about Phil?" he said truculently. It was possible that he saw in the question an attempt to hurry him along in a family narrative; more probably, though, he suspected what certainly had not been intended: an implied criticism of one of his boys. For it was Phil with whom my Uncle Jimmy felt least secure — or so it had always seemed to me. He was more complex, less clear of outline, harder to figure out: also, by any popular standard, he had not done as well as the others. This was curious, because I had always thought that of the three boys it was Phil who was the most naturally gifted. Whatever he had done, he had done with the appearance of ease; in school, growing up, he had never seemed to study and he had always done well; teachers — even those who had not been eager to placate my Uncle Jimmy — had praised him and spoken of his extraordinary promise. He had gone through college and law school in the same effortless way; like Charles, who had followed him a year later, he had gone on to practice law, but unlike Charles he had at once made his mark as a remarkably good lawyer. He was at his best in a courtroom, preferably caught up in the midst of some incredibly complicated trial, preferably questioning some hostile, positive, slightly pompous and supposedly unshakable expert: two or three times, years ago, I had gone to court just to watch him in such circumstances. He had given a fine performance on each occasion, with his fresh vivid intelligence vibrating through every sentence he spoke, with his old gift for mimicry now and then flashing out to disconcert the witness and delight the rest, and with a kind of swooping sardonic good humor overriding everything so completely that it seemed to fill the court so that, in watching the trial, you were aware of very little else but Phil. It seemed to me in those days that he went to his work with a special feeling for what he did: not merely pride but a positive *joy*. He was popular and respected; his fellow lawyers, like his early teachers, had predicted the arrival of great things for him. And yet — the great things had not arrived. They had not arrived — I think — mainly because Phil had stopped pursuing them. He had been in great demand, but gradually he had given up responding to this demand: he took fewer and fewer cases. There were those who said that he had grown lazy; there were others who said that, thanks to his father, he was already a rich man and therefore had no need to work; and there was Phil himself who, one day, about a year before Charles decided to try his luck in politics, had given me a somewhat different explanation.

"I got bored," he had said. "It's as simple as that. I got bored with a job that a couple of years ago suddenly began to seem silly and then with the passage of time got even sillier. Who was it who said, 'The law is a ass'? Someone in Dickens, I know, but who? Pumblechook? You ought to know, you're the literary man. Anyway, he was dead right, and it gets assier by the second. You wouldn't, you *couldn't*, believe how absolutely trivial it is unless you were mixed up in it every day. And it's all the same. Take the case I wound up last week, the one I got saddled with thanks to Charlie Murphy's very convenient double hernia. My client turned out to be a Mafia hood: the real article, a doughy little olive-eyed thug, a genuine melt-the-man-down-and-stick-him-in-the-highway type. He'd probably knocked off twenty or so of the usual business competitors on his own. Eventually the government decided to go after him, and on what charge? What else? Income tax evasion. The same old comedy. It's like getting McCarthy for disrespect to the Senate. So off we started, playing charades, with this IBM clown from the Feds licking his chops over missing fifty-dollar vouchers and improperly kept expense accounts, with my client's pleasant associates slipping in every now and then to tell him the good news that in spite of all the hard luck the 'stuff' was still moving, with my little killer himself whining to me that if he got sent up even for a day it would probably kill his little Angela who was making her First Communion at Saint Anthony's next month, and with the presiding justice on the bench nobody else but Breezy Willie Magee: seventy-nine years old, an alcoholic, a party hack all his life, and who in those rare intervals when he's fully awake suspects — God knows why! — that the case has something to do with dirty books!"

I had said, "How'd you make out?"

He had shrugged. "Acquittal. Why, I don't know. I didn't really care. By that time it all seemed so absurd that I wouldn't have been surprised if that old imbecile Magee had stood up and announced that he was going to reach his decision by picking the petals off a daisy. In one way there was a certain beauty to it, though. The hood was grateful: he cried. I was invited to watch little Angela receive. And I imagine from now any time I need a trigger man. . . ." He sighed and said, "No, I think the old Romans played it right: they had no lawyers. It was every man for himself, and not a bad idea."

"Then why not leave the hoods alone? Switch around, go in for something else: civil liberties cases, that sort of thing. . . ."

"I told you, they're all the same," he had said wearily. "I've had a few respectable clients in my time. Including Pa. But the *process* is the same. The ritual, the bogus dignity, the words words words, the appeals: it all adds up to nothing — or almost nothing — and what's more important is that it bores the bejesus out of me. I used to get a charge out of it, but either it's changed or I have. It's probably me. Anyway, now whenever I see two lawyers in a court — and especially when I'm one of them — all I can think of is two little men standing on the seashore, taking turns peeing into the Atlantic. They're having a contest: the judge is an old man somewhere on the coast of Japan who decides the winner by measuring the mean high tides in the Pacific. It's all about as meaningful as that. No, I'll keep my hand in — or I expect I will: it's what I know best, and it's a bit late to break new tracks — but it's not for me. It's not really what I want."

And with something of our old intimacy — for suddenly I had become aware that he had changed very much, that the old merriness was not much in evidence now, and I didn't know why and I was genuinely concerned — I had said, "What is for you, Phil? What do you want?"

"Oh," he said, slowly, "I don't know. Something I haven't got, I guess. And I *have* got a good wife and kids I love, so it has to be something else, doesn't it? Something I can get interested in enough to get lost in occasionally. Not that I want to get lost, particularly, but it would be nice to have something worthwhile losing yourself in, wouldn't it? I expect that's all I want." And then his face had suddenly lightened, there was a return of the old high spirits, and he laughed and said, "In other words, something unreasonable. . . ."

I had known him for most of my life, and for a long time during those years he had been my closest friend, yet he had often puzzled me: there had been those times when I felt that as well as I knew him I had never really, entirely, grasped him. I'm sure that my Uncle Jimmy, while at moments enormously proud of him, must often have found him maddening and all but incomprehensible. Publicly of course he would never have said a word, but I knew that he and Phil had frequently had their explosions, and once he had expressed his baffled exasperation to me.

"What drives me nuts," he had said, "is that he's as good as the best, and better than that if he wanted to be. But who knows what he wants? Hah? What the hell is all this mumbo jumbo about wanting something but he doesn't know what? Who's he trying to kid, anyway? For the love of Pete, he's not some teen-age kid on a bicycle: he's nearly forty years old!" And then he had looked at me and I had seen the anger in his face, but also another expression which was much rarer for him: one of puzzlement, of troubled inquiry; he had said, "You think he *is* kidding?"

From all this I gathered that for some reason of his own Phil had told his father approximately what he had told me, although why he had done this was a mystery — perhaps he had been tired or irritated or caught off guard. For no one understood my Uncle Jimmy more completely than Phil, and of course no one knew better how unlikely he was to sympathize with hesitations or self-questioning. My Uncle Jimmy had stood there, waiting impatiently for me to say something — it was one of the few times when he had asked me a question and really wanted an answer — and so I had said, "No, I don't think he's kidding at all. I think he's probably just looking around and wondering a little. That's not so wrong, is it?"

I could have said nothing worse. "Not so wrong!" he had howled. "At

his age? What's up with you: have you gone bats, too? Listen, by the
time you're as old as he is anybody that doesn't know what he wants is
halfway home to the booby hatch, and you can put that in your pipe and
smoke it! It burns me up! Here's a kiddo as sharp as a tack and as nifty a
lawyer as ever walked into this burg, and what does he do? He shoves
himself up off his can and down into court maybe once a month, and the
rest of the time he stays home playing beanbag with Flossie and waiting
for some half-assed Good Fairy to tell him what he really wants! Well,
that kind of baloney goes over with me like a lead balloon! He'd better
wise up in a hurry, that's all I've got to say. I'll tell you one thing: I
didn't raise anybody to be a second-rater!"

This was an unusual — in fact, an unprecedented — diatribe; it had
not been repeated. I doubt that it would have been in any case — my
Uncle Jimmy, I think, must have had sharp regrets at having so impul-
sively blasted one of his boys, even if he had done so only to me — but
now Phil had suddenly made his move: he had astonished everyone and
delighted my Uncle Jimmy by doing a complete turnabout. It had happened in this way. Shortly after my talk with my Uncle Jimmy, Charles
had decided to run for mayor. It had been a family decision rather than a
purely personal one, and in this decision Phil had participated. He had
of course been asked to help in the campaign, and he had of course
agreed. Then had come the surprise. Almost at once what had started as
a dutiful fraternal service, a matter of family obligation, evolved into
something much more than that. Phil, whose interest in local matters
had been greater than Charles's but still not much more than casual,
now had found himself fascinated by the whole intricate business of our
politics and by the possibilities of political control and reform, and although — as he had said to me on that hot night years ago, when we had
driven home from the beach together and had stopped for supper in the
awful cafeteria — he had no ambition for himself in office, his vision of
what could be done if the right person was in power was an overwhelming one. There was no question in his mind but that Charles was the
right person. The fact that he was Charles's older brother could not have
mattered less to him. He was not an envious man, and he was extremely
clear-sighted; he was sure of his own gifts and knew very well what he
could do and what he could not do; he knew that although he was a far
better lawyer than his brother, Charles in his turn had talents which he
did not possess: he was in fact the first member of his family — perhaps
even before Charles himself — to correctly assess those talents and to see
where they might lead. Accordingly he had gone into action, not only
joining Charles's campaign but taking over its direction. He was acute,
energetic, not easily fooled; he was an excellent organizer, able to cut

with quick decision into the fat and the flab that always bulks and swells behind a candidate; his work at the bar had given him varied connections which now proved most valuable. He had become not merely Charles's second in command but the ideal complement to him, and more than anyone else — more than my Uncle Jimmy and, some said, at this stage of the candidate's career, more even than Charles — he had been responsible for that first victory. Ever since that time, although he had continued to maintain a token law practice, he had been with Charles. He believed in him; he was as close to being indispensable as one man can be to another. This was a fact acknowledged by many, and among those who had always acknowledged it was Charles.

It was also acknowledged by my Uncle Jimmy, and so now, after his first quick automatic flash of belligerency, he realized of course that of all people I was not likely to talk Phil down, and all he said was, "Why should I tell you about Phil? You know as much about him as I do. You know what he does. I tell you, those two make a great team. They're going places together." Then, without breaking stride or changing his tone, he said, "I saw you gabbing with Charles just now. For a long time. He offer you a job?"

And from his expression I couldn't tell whether he knew this, that it was something he and Charles had talked over beforehand, or whether it was merely a shrewd guess. I said, "Not exactly. We sparred around the edges a little, but there was nothing definite."

"Don't give me that 'nothing definite' crap," he said. "Who cares about that, hah? He asked you to get on board, right? And what did you say? No soap?"

"More or less, I guess. You're not too surprised at that, are you, Uncle Jimmy?"

"Listen," he said, "I gave up being surprised when I was still wearing knickers. I knew then that there were some people you could hit in the mouth with a sack full of gold and they'd spit it all out into the gutter because it didn't taste good. You can't change people like that any more than you can teach a pig to pick cherries. Your old man was one of them and so are you. But I don't get sore at that any more. I just wish for once in your life you'd wise up and latch on to something when it's handed to you. What's the percentage in staying a boob?"

"You want me to hitch my wagon to a star, Uncle Jimmy?"

But he had said his piece; he was not now interested in persuading me further. I was his nephew, not his son; it was late at night and I'm sure he was tired. It was not often that I thought of my Uncle Jimmy as getting along in years, but now I noticed signs of fatigue in his little, ageless, combative face. He said only, "I want you to use the squash God gave you. But if you want to be stubborn it's up to you, Buster. It's no skin off my tail." And absentmindedly, he had done something I had never known him to do before: he had called me by the nickname he had always called my father. He looked at his watch and said, "I don't know about you but I'm going downstairs with Charles while he spouts his piece to all those free-loaders. Then I'm going to come back up and hit the hay. I've got to get out of here early in the morning; I'm going to Ireland."

And of course that was where I had my first real memory of him; I said, "Have you still got the castle, Uncle Jimmy?"

He nodded. "God knows why. It's a dump. There's nothing to do over there but go out in the rain and get wet. But Mary — your aunt — liked it so I go back now and then. Then I get the hell out. Fast. Thank God for the jets." He looked at me inquiringly and said, "You do a little traveling: you ever get over that way?"

"No, only to touch down at Shannon now and then. And once I stayed in Dublin a couple of weeks, but that was years ago." It had been in fact on our honeymoon: Jean and I had gone there, just as my father and mother had a generation before. We had had a wonderful time; we had been very happy. I said, "I haven't been in Ireland now for a long time."

"You're not as dumb as I thought you were," he said. "Well, I keep the place open all the time. A Mick farmer and his wife look after it for me. God knows what they do with themselves when I'm not around. Throw potatoes at each other, I guess. And sleep: everybody in that damned country sleeps fifteen hours a day. At least!"

And suddenly, for no reason, the name Teddy came leaping into my mind, and instantly I remembered the long-faced Irish chauffeur who used to drive James and Charles and Phil and me all around the country on rainy days, and whom my Uncle Jimmy had fired in one of his rages. I said, "Whatever happened to Teddy, Uncle Jimmy? Remember him?"

"Sad Sam," he said promptly. "I tied the can to that baby in a hurry, but I had to hire him back. He was strictly n.g. but he was better than the others. The clown I got in his place lost the carburetor. How the hell you can do that I don't know but he did! The next one drove the car right into the ocean. With me in it! So I got Sad Sam back. Your aunt liked him okay. He's dead now. TB. They've all got it over there, it's in the milk. But anyway," he said, "if you get over, look me up. I might be there."

I promised I would, and once again he swung his fist in a mock-punch at my arm; this time it was in farewell. "Keep the faith," he said, and his tone was sardonic. "That's always the Big Goodbye in this burg, right?"

He went off, stepping peppily across the room, going down to share the final big moment of the night with his son. It was his night as well as Charles's, he was obviously on top of the world, and yet on this night when he was so happy — when one of his great dreams had come true for him — it was curious that for much of the time he had been talking to me, and now as I watched him walk away so jauntily, I found myself thinking of him not as I usually did, as I had always done, but instead wondering if in fact my Uncle Jimmy, in spite of his family and all his activities and his dreams beginning to come true, was not quite often a fairly lonely man. . . .

But it was late, and in a few minutes I left too, saying goodbye to Flossie and my Aunt Gert, who by now were the only members of the family remaining in the library. As I went down the stairs I could see immediately that it was now no trick to either enter or leave the house: the front hall which had been bursting with people an hour earlier was now completely empty. Not that the party had grown smaller; it was now larger than ever, but the cargo had shifted: all those who had been out on the fringes, eating and drinking and talking together out on the lawn or in the hall or up and down the staircase, had now pushed their way into the ballroom, aware that the moment was at hand when the new Governor would tell them what they had come to hear: that he had won because of them. They were jammed so tight in the big room that it seemed, literally, that if anyone had dared to lift a hand or twitch a shoulder everyone in the room would have shivered in pain. Nothing was clearer than that if only some of the guests had chosen to stay here in the hall they would have been far better off: they would have heard more, they would have seen more, they would have done both in some degree of comfort. But this did not matter: what *did* matter was the feeling, apparently common to all such gatherings at all such climactic moments, that it was enormously important to be physically as close as possible to the man who was shortly to say precisely what everyone present knew was to be said.

Standing on the bottom step of the stairs, I could see over all heads to the bandstand, where the musicians had now been pushed back into a little clump against the wall. Separated from them by the distance due his leadership was Shep Nomad: plump, ever-smiling, watchful, he seemed frozen into a posture of anticipation and delight at a point just halfway between "the boys in the band" and the handful of men who occupied the foreground. There was no music, there was no talk: there was just plain bedlam. Charles had stepped forward and was waving to the crowd; if at that point he had said anything it could not have been heard over the shouts, the whistles, the great explosive spasms of applause. Suddenly, as if on a cue perceived by no one else, Shep Nomad dipped a plump hand, and from their cramped positions the musicians somehow managed to swing into "Happy Days Are Here Again," followed by Charles's campaign song. Impossibly, the noise from the crowd grew louder; the music itself was now barely audible; Charles, still standing in the exact center of the bandstand before the slim upright microphone, continued to smile and to wave. On the platform with him were Marie, my Uncle Jimmy, the new Lieutenant Governor, a monsignor whom I did not know, and three or four others — presumably figures of greater than usual significance in the campaign. The group was joyous but incomplete: someone was missing and all at once I realized that of course it was Phil. He was nowhere to be seen, and I wondered where he could have gone at such a moment, and why? But just then Charles turned to Marie, took her hand, and brought her forward; she waved; they stood arm in arm; the band played the terrible song their leader had written for her; there was more bedlam. Then she stepped to one side and my Uncle Jimmy came up, holding his hands clasped over his head like a victorious boxer. He stood between Charles and Marie, shorter than both of them, smiling happily; suddenly he reached out with his arms and pulled his son and daughter-in-law up close to him, hugging them hard: the crowd stamped and cheered and screamed. Clearly this gesture of togetherness, made by the tough and famous little father of the family, was the high point of the evening so far. And down on the floor, right next to the bandstand, almost brushing Charles's feet, one bright blue arm was raised in the air and waved about wildly: Edso, that experienced and well-nourished veteran of a hundred such occasions, had made it to the front and now was aching for his reward: a nod, a wink, a flick of a finger — any sign would do, as long as it came from the bandstand.

The noise continued; Marie and my Uncle Jimmy soon stepped back, leaving Charles alone before the microphone. He began, several times, to speak; the crowd would not let him. He waited, smiling, never once putting up his hand, until gradually, very gradually, the cheers and cries and whistles began to die, and then there was only an occasional diehard shout and an isolated spurt of applause, and then, at last, a silence which was deep, respectful, waiting, total.

Out of this silence Charles began to speak, and as he did so I left — there would be no more surprises from now on. The big front door was open and I walked out into the cool night air. The state policeman on guard at the door nodded and said, "A great night."

I said, "A great night." I walked out to the edge of the terrace and stood there for a moment. There was no moon: in the dark night that part of the lawn which stretched away to my left seemed black rather than green, fading off into the even blacker and barely visible bordering trees. To my right all was brighter, lit by the still gay but dying fires of the Japanese lanterns. Even though it was much cooler now the breeze was pleasant, the sharpness of full fall was not yet here, and so I stood there on the terrace, looking out into the night, listening to the sounds coming out of the house, hearing Charles's voice but not really getting what he was saying, and hearing too the applause that broke in on virtually every phrase. Out on the lawn half a dozen men moved silently and systematically about, clearing the tables, folding them up and carting them away, spearing the debris from the littered grass: the party was very nearly over. I watched for a few seconds more, and then I turned to go off across the lawn to my car when someone standing just behind me said, "It's no fair to eat and run. You're supposed to stay for the speeches."

It was Phil. Apparently he had been standing in the dark on the far side of the terrace when I had come out; quietly he had come over to me. I wondered again why he was not where it seemed he should be at this moment; I said, "You're not in on the finale: how come?"

He said just what my Uncle Jimmy had said earlier, except that his meaning may have been a little different. "It's Charles's night. There's a good reason for Pa and Marie to be up there with him. Not so for me, unless we're out to establish our family solidarity, and I don't think that's required by now, do you?"

I said, "You're selling yourself short: that's new, isn't it? My guess is that they want to see you up there with the others, that they even expect to see you."

"They've seen me," he said. "And they'll see me again, don't worry about that. They're all good party workers and sooner or later they'll all come around to find out what goodies are in the basket. And when they do, I'll be the one they'll have to see. So I'm in no danger of being overlooked. Besides, there's another thing: it's a matter of tactics. Do you know that right from the beginning I've never gone up on a platform with Charles — never, that is, when it was at all important or when he had something he wanted to get across? That's something we both agreed on — matter of fact, it was my idea. Know why?"

I didn't; he said, "It's obvious: we look too much alike. Or we remind people of each other, which comes to the same thing. Charles alone is fine; Charles with me is vaudeville. Comedy stuff: all we'd need is straw hats and ice cream pants. Charles could talk all he wanted to about Consolo or Corruption or Higher Minimum Wages or Lower Hospitalization Costs, but half of the crowd would simply be looking at us and saying to each other, 'Isn't it wonderful, Agnes: do you think they're really twins?' You can't lick that; it's inevitable. So Charles appears alone. With pretty fair results."

I was suddenly curious to know what he had thought of the whole campaign; I said, "Now that it's over, did you think he'd win all along?"

He nodded. "Sure."

"No doubts?"

"Doubts, yes, but only because you're foolish if you don't realize that accidents can happen. And probably will. But I knew that if we got our share of the breaks we were in, and in big. It wasn't by any means as hard as the mayoralty fight, no matter what you may have heard. And neither one of us ever thought for a minute that it would be. Surprised?"

"Yes, a little. I would have figured Consolo as much tougher than that on past performance alone."

"The trouble with past performance is that it's in the past. Everyone is over the hill sooner or later, and we thought Consolo had just about had it. He'd lost a lot of support where he'd always been strongest — with the Italians. When he first ran I don't think there was an Italian in the state who didn't vote for him: he was their boy. But everything changes, including Italians. We had polls taken, and every one of them showed that by now the Italians were getting tired. They didn't want just another Italian in there, they wanted a good Italian. Well, there just wasn't one around — at least, not one who could run for governor. So they voted for Charles — I don't suppose the 'Kinsella' hurt there, by the way. It was the old confusion all over again. Remember: 'Hey, are you Irish or Eyetalian?' "

I remembered: it was a family joke. When I was a boy in school I had often bitterly regretted having one of those names — Costello was another — which was subject to mortifying misinterpretation. In a way proud of the name because it was my father's, my mother's, I nevertheless longed for something clearcut: Sullivan, Murphy. But now, years later, ambiguity apparently had paid off. . . .

"Whatever the reason," he said, "when they ditched him he was dead. He had to be: without them he just didn't have the horses. Anyway, for my money he was always overrated. He had this reputation for almost supernal cunning: well, I had a couple of long sessions with him and I couldn't see it. What I could see was a rather stupid man who'd had almost supernal luck. And now the luck had run out and he had nothing — or very little — left. So that's why I figured it would be easy. On top of which we got a few breaks, we had the organization, we had drive, we had the money. And we had Charles."

First things last? I said, "In short, a breeze?"

"No," he said. "Not a breeze. Damned hard work all the way."

"No fun?"

"Well, you know: a funny thing happened to me on my way to the State House. Funny things are always happening around here: the whole state's a joke machine. But overall it didn't add up to much fun: as I say, it was mainly hard work. Not fighting Consolo; just keeping our own crowd in line. Which was no cinch, believe me."

"The celebrated coalition?"

"That's right. Labor for Kinsella, Small Business for Kinsella, Ministers for Kinsella, Negroes for Kinsella, Professors for Kinsella, Conservatives for Kinsella, Liberals for Kinsella. And — inevitably — Independents for Kinsella. You name it, we had it. It took a little doing to get them all in under the same tent, but we did it. We put them all together and then we found out we had to do something more: we had to keep them all together. And the one way, the *only* way, we could keep them together was to keep them apart: as far away from each other as possible. A slight paradox. You follow?"

"Yes, sure." It wasn't hard to follow: the rivalries, the potential clashes, the hurt feelings and the jealousies inherent in this reluctant combination were easily imagined. And now, again, I remembered the talk we had had on that night five years ago; I said, "But isn't that more or less what you wanted? You were out to take control away from the stumblebums by broadening your base: wasn't that the whole idea?"

"That's right. And we did. Of course we've still got the stumblebums — you don't get rid of an army of hacks and grafters overnight, and they're still important: look at Cogan, for one — but the point is they don't have control any more. *We* have that."

"You and the coalition."

"Yes, but we run the coalition. With some difficulty, but we do. The real trouble is that each group wants Charles all for itself. Just by the way, nobody's any worse there than the Professors. They don't want their piece of flesh, they want the whole body. One hundred per cent: they want him for their very own, they want to serve him up for dinner, they want to eat him up. And failing him, I'll do. Fortunately Charles is just about tooth-proof and I'm not so soft myself, so we survive. But it's not easy." He sighed and said, "They all want something different: well, okay, you expect that. The Negroes, of course. They're catching up and they're shooting for everything now: fine. Maybe not fine, but understandable. The poor bastards haven't had a fair shake for so long that all they want to do is grab the dice and run. But you can deal with them — at least you can deal with whichever spokesman you're talking to at the moment. And with them it all means something, it's exciting, it's real, and at least you feel you're in the land of the living. Whereas with some of the others . . ."

He shrugged, and I said, "The Professors? You don't love the egg-heads any more, Phil?"

"There's a certain kind of arrogance that puts me off," he said. "I suppose we're arrogant enough in our way, but it's not *that* way. I talked to a couple of them here tonight: they have a rather peculiar idea of their own contribution to the campaign. The fact is that it wasn't all that great. Do you know Kurt Vogelschmidt, for instance? Have you met him?" Switching to mimicry, he said, "Haff you as yet had zat disdigdt blesshure?"

"No. I know who he is, of course." This owl-faced, mountainous refugee from savage European oppressions had come to America at the outbreak of World War II. Weighing close to three hundred pounds, paralyzingly articulate, he had bullied a succession of Midwestern political science faculties into helplessness until finally, ten years or so ago, he had wound up here in the city for emergency abdominal surgery. He had remained to teach and to talk. There were rumors that he had been on the point of beginning a distinguished political career in Vienna when the war had unhappily intervened; these rumors remained rumors, but it was a fact that he was now one of the most vocal of academic political activists, and I remembered seeing his name heading a list of professors who had vigorously supported Charles. I said, "He's . . . what? To the campaign, I mean. The Brains Trust? The big theory man?"

"I'll tell you just what he is," Phil said. "He's a waste of time. He's my mistake. I got him in; I thought he packed a little weight with the others. Well, he does. But not enough. Not enough, for example, to justify calling me every other night around one in the morning to tell me what he expects of Charles on the basis of his own keen analysis of Austria before Dollfuss. The hours I've spent listening to that chuckle-head outline a strategy which would be just swell if only Consolo were Franz Josef! At first I thought he was kidding; by the time I caught on it was too late. And all the while, chirping away in the background — because she's an intellectual type too, you see — is his charming wife Elli, who weighs a cool thirty-five pounds, has bangs, wears knee socks, lives in the past, loves Bartók, hates supermarkets, and serves a special kind of iron strudel she bakes herself! It's ghastly beyond belief. It drives you right back to the stumblebums: I'd a lot rather spend my time chewing the fat with One-Eyed Danny Geegan of the Police Athletic League. At least I'm sure we got his vote. For all I know charming Elli wrote in one for Leopold Figl."

I said, "He's dead, I think."

"That's all right with me," he said. Then he smiled quickly and said, "That shows you how parochial I've become. Do you think this state is getting to me?"

"What about Charles?" I said. "How does he get along with them?"

"Better than I do. That's partly because I'm with them more. But also he's more patient and he's developed this great self-control. And that marvelous way of looking gravely attentive, as if he were really listening hard to what you were saying. That's big magic in the academic league: they're all talkers. And then they also misread Charles rather seriously. They know he's not really one of them, but they think that in a way he is, they think he values them especially, and they think that now he's the Governor they'll all do very well."

"And they won't?"

"No," he said soberly. "They can't: it's not in the cards. Oh, they'll do all right, but that's not what they want. They want a little power. They want to be right up there with Charles, running the show. They haven't got a prayer: Charles is much too smart to let that happen. He knows exactly what they've given him, and he'll make some sort of equivalent return: equivalent, but no more. Well, some of them will accept that, and others won't. But if they don't, what are they going to do about it? Support somebody else? Who? You see in a funny way they're a little like the party hacks: they may not much like what's happening to them, but where else are they going to go? And nobody knows that better than Charles."

And suddenly it occurred to me to wonder what my Uncle Jimmy had been doing while all this had been going on. He must have known of this wing of Charles's support: did he ever meet with them, talk with them, discuss the details of an overall strategy? It was a picture impossible to envision, and when I mentioned it to Phil now he agreed.

"He didn't see much of them; I kept them away from him as much as I could. You know: what could come out of that? And as it turned out, Pa had a great time in the campaign: a ball all the way." He added reflectively, "I don't know, I guess you might say Pa in politics today is a mixed blessing. On the one hand you have all his energy, his savvy, the funds, the people who get behind you: old pals of his you couldn't get near otherwise, and who really can make a difference. On the other hand, he's not quite used to the little delicacies that now have to be observed: he was born in a tougher age. So that sometimes, when he's angry, he just lashes out and to hell with the consequences. And then you have to persuade him that the NAACP doesn't look kindly on their members being called 'jigs.' Plus the fact that he's been in the saddle so long it's a little hard for him to move over. Even when it's Charles who's supposed to be driving the horse."

I said, "Pitched battles?"

He nodded. "Now and then. Well, you know: inevitable. When Pa wants his way he leans hard. But in a more subtle way Charles is quite a leaner, too. So we had our moments. As you can guess."

"As everybody could guess, apparently. The papers were always full of the real inside dope about what happened at those high-level policy meetings between the Boys and Pa."

"I know, I know. I read them all. Nothing was ever right. Where do you suppose the papers get their political writers, anyway? They used to ship them over from the sports page in carload lots: where do they come from today? The classified ads? It's pathetic. All that imaginary expertise. . . . If I read once," he said, "I read a thousand times that old chestnut about Charles and me standing up to Pa, trying to beat him down on those old reactionary ideas he kept insisting on. Of course it didn't happen that way at all. He had plenty of reactionary ideas, but the point is that he's also very skillful; it's only when you're working with him on an operation like this you realize how quick and how smart he is. The truth is that he was right half the time. It was when he was wrong that we had trouble, because he was always more stubborn then. But it all worked out in the end. Probably because Pa wanted Charles Governor even more than he wanted his own way. And probably because on the things that really count Charles and Pa aren't as far apart as you might imagine."

And there was something in his voice as he said this — or rather, something *missing* from his voice — that brought me right back again to that night years ago when he had been filled with buoyant prophecy, and had spoken with such excitement about Charles and politics and the future. Now the future had arrived, but the excitement and the buoyancy seemed to have gone: on this night of triumph Phil was strangely muted, and I had no idea why. It may have been simply that he was tired, that this was the natural letdown after the long campaign. Or it may have been that as he became more deeply involved in the endless local political tangles and quarrels he saw no great reason for excitement, perhaps discovering that no matter what he and Charles and my Uncle Jimmy might accomplish, they could hardly work the miracles he had hoped for in the beginning. Or it may have been merely that he was five years older now — or it may have been something entirely different, something I hadn't even thought about at all. But in any case it bothered me, because once again, as he was talking, I felt again that same sense of disquiet that I had felt throughout all the family party: a faint uneasiness, a troubled conviction that something in some way had gone wrong with Uncle Jimmy and his family, and now I think that perhaps I may have showed something of what I felt, because I saw Phil suddenly give me a quick and curious look. But he said nothing, instead turning away so that he had his back to the house and to me; he flipped his cigarette and it sailed in a long high curve out into the night, the little red spot of light landing somewhere on the dark lawn. He stood for a moment, looking out in that direction, and then he said slowly, "So there we are. Or rather, here we are. 'Around and around she goes, and where she stops, nobody knows.' " He turned around again to me and said, "Who used to say that all the time? Someone on the radio, wasn't it?"

"Major Bowes," I said. "The old Amateur Hour." But it was a strange quote to dig out of the past, especially now, tonight; I said, "How'd you happen to remember that? I mean, the quote."

He shrugged. "I don't know. It just came out of the blue. Bits and pieces from the past: you know the way they do." With a quick grin he added, "Although I grant you that this was an odd one. Considering the moment. Winners aren't supposed to talk like that, are they? Whatever happened to positive thinking?"

"Maybe it got used up in the campaign."

"Maybe. But to tell you the truth I wasn't thinking about the campaign. Or politics. I guess I was thinking more in personal terms."

He seemed about to say something more, then stopped, and turned away again to look out across the lawn. I didn't say anything. It would have been difficult to know just what to say, but I had the feeling that he neither wanted nor expected me to. So I stood there, looking at the tall slim back, and thinking, oddly enough, of Phil not as he was now, but as he had been as a boy, and of how he had always been the most exuberant and the happiest one of all the family, and thinking too that we were both now . . . what? Middle-aged? And by one of those queer tricks of association I found myself thinking not only of Phil or Charles or my Uncle Jimmy, but of Jean and myself, and of how we had all and so unexpectedly changed. . . .

Gloomy thoughts in the silence. The silence out here on the terrace, that is; inside the house Charles had finished his talk, the music had come up again, there were cheers and roars and a great burst of loud applause. I heard cries of "Speech! Speech!" and I wondered from whom this speech was demanded. My Uncle Jimmy? Marie? Anyone who would speak? Nothing happened immediately; then, gradually, the noise died down, and someone began to speak. Not Marie, not my Uncle

Jimmy, but someone I could not remember having heard before. The voice was heavy, the articulation was none too clear, and although I could hear words I couldn't understand what was being said. Phil had turned back to me again and was watching me as I listened; after a moment he said, "The voice of the turtle. Cogan. Recognize it?"

I didn't, but that wasn't surprising, because I hadn't heard it in years, and I had hardly expected to hear it tonight — in this house, that is, and in this way. For Charles, I knew, despised Cogan, and while it may have been logical to invite him here — to a gathering that was, after all, political rather than personal — it was not quite so logical to serve him up in this position of preference. Puzzled, I said, "What's that in aid of?"

"Class. We always like to lend the program class." In the same dry voice he said, "It's what's technically known as a master stroke." He paused, and for just a moment I thought he had decided not to say anything more, but then he said, "It was an idea Charles had. All in the interest of party solidarity. He seemed to think it would be wise."

"And you?"

"Oh," he said, "I guess I seemed to think it wouldn't."

I suddenly thought of Charles, earlier this evening, saying — lightly — that there were "cracks in the solid family wall," and now, not because I was merely curious, but also because I think I was still troubled, I said, "More pitched battles?"

"Of a different sort," he said. "Well, not really battles, because there are one or two areas where Charles isn't . . . persuadable." Then he said, "It's late, isn't it? I've got to go in and get Flossie. Jack, you'll be around for a while? Back here, I mean?"

"I think so, yes." I wanted to learn more about those one or two areas, but I knew that I wouldn't — at least, not tonight. I said, "I can work here as well as anywhere else, and also the house needs touching up here and there. I'd like to see to that before I go off again. So I'll be around."

"We'll get together," he promised. He reached out and tapped me lightly with a forefinger on the upper part of my arm; it was the way he had signaled his departure to me ever since we were boys. "See you soon," he said.

I said goodbye to him, and he walked with his long steps back across the terrace toward the house. He had nearly reached the door when I called out to him, and as soon as I did he stopped and stood, waiting. I had called because suddenly it seemed to me that there was something more to be said, but now that he stood waiting for me to say it, all I could think of was a clumsy, even rather foolish, "It's all right, isn't it? I mean, with you?"

"You ought to get together with Charles," he said. "That's more or less what he asked me a couple of hours ago. I must be radiating cheer. Anyway, the answer is yes: it's all right. It's even better than that: it's fine." He gave a little wave of his hand and said, "Thanks."

Then he went quickly into the house, and I was left alone on the terrace. It was darker now: the last of the Japanese lanterns had gone. Even in the darkness, though, I could see that the swiftly moving men had done their work, for all the tables had been taken away and of the great spreading quilt of debris only an occasional scrap of paper remained, blown by the wind in and out of sight. The lawn looked dim and deserted. The air was sharper, more seasonal, now, and in the moonless fall night there was a clear pale splattering of stars. Out in front, toward the street, there were now no shouts, no songs, no signs of activity: presumably the students and other sightseers had gone home. The only action came from within the house where, with Cogan, the speaking seemed to have come to an end, and the music was once more pounding out through the still open windows. A door at the far end of the terrace opened, and I saw a small group of people come out, the first sign that it was now permissible for the party to begin breaking up — although I knew it would be a long time yet before everyone called it a day. I waited until this first group had gone down the drive away from the house, and then I left the terrace and cut across the lawn to the side where I had put my car. There were now other cars there, parked in a long row; to get to mine I had to detour around them. As I did so I heard, suddenly and very loudly, the sound of someone shouting, and almost immediately I saw a man come crawling on his hands and knees out from between two of the parked cars. He was about fifty feet away and he was not alone; following him slowly, and looking down at him, was a uniformed state trooper. He said soothingly, "Okay now, sir, okay. Everything's going to be okay. Just try to stand on your feet. That's the boy now!"

"Don't tell me what to do!" the man on the ground cried belligerently. I was nearer now, and when he turned his head I at once recognized the thin foxy face: it was Walshie. I don't think he saw me, and it would have made no difference if he had: clearly the party with its abundant free drink had been too much for him, and he was very drunk. He pushed himself up onto his knees and said to the trooper with surprising distinctness, "By God, if you want to hold on to that badge, buddy, just you don't tell me what to do!"

And then he collapsed on the ground and lay there on his back, one hand raised and making a small and threatening fist, his face tilted to the stars. The trooper saw me; he shrugged and smiled. "Par for the course," he said. To Walshie he said, "Come on now. On your feet, sir."

From his back Walshie howled, "One more word outa you and you'll be back pounding a beat where you belong. I'm a personal friend of Governor Charles Kinsella! You just ask the Governor if he don't know Leo J. Walsh!"

"Okay, Mr. Walsh," the trooper said patiently. He bent forward, reaching down as if to put a supporting arm under Walshie, but suddenly Walshie sat bolt upright.

"Leo J. Walsh!" he cried. "Remember that name if you know what's good for you, buddy. I'm a man that's got a million personal friends! Governor Charles Kinsella! Rudy Vallee the Vagabond Lover! And more! And I got up off my ass to lick cancer of the bowels and I can get up off my ass to lick you!"

And then, as sometimes happens with drunks, lucidity deserted him and so did consciousness: abruptly he collapsed once more, this time falling face down on the ground, where he lay absolutely motionless. Walshie had passed out. The state trooper, who had been bending forward all this time, now merely reached down and picked him up easily, as if he had been a pillow; he said to me casually, "Out like a light. It's funny, it's always a poor little bag of bones like this that tells you he's going to murder you."

I said, "Want any help?"

He shook his head. "No sir. I'll just take him back into the kitchen. We're all set up for this in there. We'll sober him up some and then we'll see he gets home all right. Don't worry, sir."

He freed one of his arms long enough to give me a quick salute, and then he walked off toward the rear of the house, cradling little Walshie in his arms. And this was the last thing I saw at Charles's victory party; in a sense, perhaps, it was not inappropriate: I had begun the evening with Edso and Walshie, and now I had closed it with one of them.

"Baldini"

"Baldini"
A Memoir and a Collaboration

by EDMUND WILSON

WHEN I first knew Edwin O'Connor in the late forties, he was spending his summers near me at Wellfleet, Cape Cod. He was working at a broadcasting station in Boston and had very little money to spend on vacations. He lived in a shack on one of the "ponds" — which to us non-New Englanders seem more like "lakes" — with an equally unaffluent friend, and he rode around on a bicycle. We would see him on the beach writing, and he occasionally came to call on us. When his first book, a short novel called *The Oracle* was published in 1951, he gave me a copy and asked me to read it. It was a caricature of a stuffed-shirt radio broadcaster, and although I was amused by the ironic tone, I could not believe in the central character as a genuine human being, nor did he quite achieve the dignity of a striking comic creation. We did not talk in those days about books very much, but we discovered a common interest in amateur magic. We kept up with the literature of the subject — I find that Ed O'Connor had collected a considerable library, which was almost exclusively technical, whereas mine ran considerably more to historical and biographical material. We frequented magicians' supply stores and exchanged secrets of sleight of hand. At one point, Ed had acquired a new method of performing "the pass" — which "Professor Hoffmann," that curious Victorian broker, who became the pioneer in English of literate writing on magic, has described as "the very backbone of card-conjuring" — that was smoother than the old-fashioned method but which I was never able to master. The same qualities that made Ed a raconteur who could hold the attention of any company and keep them continually laughing made him an expert at what the magicians call "presentation," which involves a similar kind of semi-hypnotic skill.

It was only after I had gradually got to know him that we talked about literature and religion. In the meantime, I had been rather astonished by the success of his second novel, *The Last Hurrah*, which was not only so much more successful commercially than *The Oracle* had been, but was also quite three-dimensional as the earlier book was not. Ed O'Connor became not only rich but a writer to be specially noted — though his financial success was at once so conspicuous that the reviewers, in this case and in the cases of his subsequent novels, were unwilling to acknowledge this. What with a prize, a movie contract and a large advance from his publisher, *The Last Hurrah* had made many thousand dollars before a word of it had been printed; and, with the exception of the unsatisfactory interludes of the diabolic fairy tale *Benjy* and the adapted play *I Was Dancing*, his later books were also best-sellers. These, *The Edge of Sadness* and *All in the Family*, were occupied, like *The Last Hurrah*, with the Irish Catholic world of Boston, which had never before been exploited with this seriousness, intelligence and intimate knowledge. *The Last Hurrah* had dealt with the old-fashioned Irish political boss, frankly corrupt and feudally benevolent; *The Edge of Sadness* dealt with the priesthood and, in one of its most effective scenes, pitted the sophisticated and snobbish Boston priest against the sincere ascetic who has chosen to mortify himself by devotion to an illiterate and discouraging parish; his last novel *All in the Family* represents the Kennedy generation which stands somewhere between the old Irish world of Boston and the new world of cocktails and enlightenment. In all this, there is no attempt whatever to fall into the once accepted clichés and represent the Irish Americans as lovable or humorously happy-go-lucky or, except in a satiric fashion, to touch the chords of *Mother Machree*. O'Connor gives us rather the brutal and quarrelsome and histrionic sides of the Irish, and his attitude toward them, though friendly, is sometimes extremely acid. He specialized in hypocritical, tyrannical and completely self-centered old men — old Carmody in *The Edge of Sadness*, who exhibits a scene of contrition on what is supposed to be his deathbed but repudiates it when he recovers — and vituperative and wrangling old women, such as the sister in *I Was Dancing*. He composed so many conversations in which the parties were slanging and scoring off one another that I was interested to hear him say, after his first visit to Ireland, that he could not stand the literary life of the pubs — Ed did not drink at all — on account of its malignant backbiting. I was amused by his relations with Mayor Curley, who had more or less inspired Frank Skeffington, the boss politician of *The Last Hurrah*. A Boston paper sent the book to Curley, inviting him to review it. Curley looked at it and wrote the editor that he was putting the matter in the hands of his lawyer. When, however, the author by chance met the Mayor for the first time, the latter said,

"What I liked best was where I say on my deathbed that if I had my life over, I'd do it all over again." It was *The Last Hurrah*, apparently, that stimulated Curley later to write an account of his life. He there confessed to misdeeds that profoundly shocked Ed: Ed could never have invented such unscrupulous wickedness as Curley's public support of the Ku Klux Klan, let alone a public official who was shameless enough to tell about them.

Yet Ed's powers of invention were of the vital kind that not merely reports on a social group but which produces imaginary personalities. Though, for example, he knew the Kennedys and was very much interested in watching their careers, the Kinsellas of *All in the Family* are something quite other than the Kennedys. But curiosity about the Kennedys gave rise for the book to a false publicity — which Ed did nothing to encourage — as a kind of *roman à clef*. Aside from the fact that the younger Kinsellas — the family in the novel — are of the Ivy League generation of Boston Irish, I cannot see that the dramatic situations to which their respective careers gave rise have much in common with the adventures of the Kennedys. They took place entirely in the imagined world which Edwin O'Connor had created. So I found out in talking to Ed that the ecumenical priest in the Kinsella family who is always going away on missions to non-Catholic churches and of whom it is said that in his present phase he will hardly speak to a Catholic is as much a comic invention as the manager of the Dublin hotel with his ironical glamorizing of Ireland and his curious unexpected laugh. Ed was also a master of mimicry, in dramatizing his anecdotes in conversation as well as in making his creations talk. Certain of his friends and acquaintances became his favorite evocations, whom he was able to imitate so vividly that they almost became characters in his fiction. The two phonograph readings which he made from his novels — which are soon to be put on the market by CMS — show that in this capacity he might have qualified as a professional entertainer. He was very attentive to accents, and it is interesting on these records to hear the voices in which he imagined Skeffington and his other characters speaking. His one dramatic weakness, which he was trying to overcome, was his tendency to prolong conversations, making them loop around and around without satisfactorily progressing. This, I think, was his chief difficulty in writing plays, in which a dialogue must not go on too long and must take steps to arrive at some destination.

In the meantime, the effect on Ed of passing suddenly from the routine of radio to riches and reputation was to make him play a new role of humorous ostentation. I think, however, that he perhaps really reveled in his passing to this luxury from his old habitation. I remember his saying on one occasion that he had to go back to Boston in order to be "near the bank." He purchased a Mercedes, which he treasured with special solicitude and he rented — at, I learn, however, a very low rate, since the owner was an enthusiastic admirer — a magnificent residence on Chestnut Street, the property of a rich Boston art-lover who had furnished it with Renaissance Italian furniture and other foreign rarities in the taste of Isabella Gardner's museum in Boston. There was a sedan chair in the hall, and I told him that I supposed he used it to be carried up to the State House every day — an idea which he at once accepted. This establishment reminded me of a story that a friend of mine had told me of having once had dinner in Boston at the house of "Honey Fitz," a prominent local politician. There had been footmen who waited on table in kneebreeches and silk stockings. Fitzgerald called one of them over for the benefit of the guest. "See," he said, pinching the footman's calf, "two pairs." "Why two pairs?" "He's a hairy son of a bitch!" Ed enjoyed playing some such role, and I never could be sure, when I visited him, that we were not in one of his novels. He developed a slight impatience of a kind characteristic of the rich with the tiresome, the incompetent and the undependable. He later moved into and actually purchased an even more monstrous mansion on Marlboro Street just off Arlington which he said the former owner had built with the ambition of being the possessor of the biggest private house in Boston. When we first went to dinner there, Ed said as he showed us in — referring to the mansion itself — "We have to go through this gate-house first." It was a little too large for comfort. The rooms were too spacious to talk across, and one would have to group in isolated pairs that were out of communication with one another. Along the wall, beneath the high ceilings, were empty niches that should have had busts in them. It proved, however, to be too much for the O'Connors to keep up, and Ed eventually sold it at a profit.

This was not the literary life as the New York intellectuals understood it. Ed's two later novels were also best-sellers, and a literary intellectual objects to nothing so much as a best-selling book that also possesses real merit. Only Irish Catholic readers, who recognized, as one of them told me, all their "old uncles and aunts" in these books, seem fully to have appreciated them, and, except for Mr. Kelleher, in an article in the *Atlantic,* no one, so far as I know, wrote anything intelligent about them. Yet *The Edge of Sadness* and *All in the Family* went much deeper than *The Last Hurrah.* They are only incidentally humorous. In the first of these, the dreariness, the blankness, of the priest's lonely Christmas in his decaying parish represents the ordeal and the unrewarded triumph of Father Kennedy's religious vocation. I was unaware until Ed told me that Father Kennedy's dedication to this unattractive and alien neighborhood, inhabited mostly by Syrians, Greeks, Italians, "a few Chinese" and "the advance guard of Puerto Ricans," assisted by his boring and ridiculous Polish curate, who, however, is given his moments of dignity, represented an attempt on the part of the author to encourage the Catholic Church in Boston to work beyond the somewhat exclusive limits which the Irish had tended to impose on it. In his next novel *All in the Family*, he is evidently trying to deal, in a firm although underground way, with the sexual Puritanism of Irish Catholicism. The unexplained suicide of the narrator's mother is echoed and balanced later on by the unfaithfulness and flight of his wife — which, however, since times are changing, does not turn out to be equally serious, for the couple are later reunited. At the time of Ed's death, he had begun a new novel, a fragment of which is given in this volume, about an eighty-year-old cardinal — the inevitable O'Connor old man! — who knows that he is doomed to die of cancer. At his age and trained in the traditional ways, he cannot understand what at the present time is going on in the Catholic Church, and Mr. Kelleher tells us that he was to be confronted with a variety of Catholic types who would give voice to a variety of points of view.

II

At some point, when I was spending my winters in Cambridge, Ed and I decided to compose together, contributing alternate chapters, a novel about a magician named Baldini. The results of this kind of collaboration may turn out to be very curious. In 1907, at William Dean Howells's suggestion, the editor of *Harper's Bazar* published a serial called *The Whole Family*, of which each chapter, supposed to be written by a different member of the family, was contributed by a different American novelist. "The Married Son," who is an artist and hopes to study in France, was assigned to Henry James, who developed it with his usual patience and scrupulously prepared a confrontation which was to lead up to the chapter that was to follow; but it evidently did not occur to him that there would be nobody, according to the scheme of the story, to report, except at secondhand, what happened in this private interview on a bench in Central Park, and Elizabeth Stuart Phelps, a writer of religious novels, who was to do "The Married Daughter" chapter disregarded this proffered cue, and went on with no reference to what had gone before to rather a vulgar un-Jamesian monologue. So, in writing alternate chapters with Ed, I very soon ran into difficulties. He would not always accept my cues or my methods, and I found my narrative blocked. I suspected that this was deliberate, and that we were playing a game of chess, and this suspicion has been corroborated by Mrs. O'Connor's telling me that, in sending back Chapter Four, Ed had said to her with satisfaction, "Well, I guess I've got him now." One of our principal points of divergence was in that I wanted to keep the conjuring within the limits of the possible whereas Ed did not hesitate to make it fantastic. The trick, for example, of the chosen card that appears between two plates of glass is something every conjuror knows but it was plausible that Baldini at that time should not yet know that it had been found to be possible to set the trick off through an electronic device, by simply raising one's voice at a distance from the frame. Then the elephant: it was true that Houdini had been able to make an elephant disappear on the ample Hippodrome stage which had room for a very large cabinet in which the vanishing elephant could be concealed. But Ed wanted to have Baldini perform the trick out-of-doors in the Yankee Stadium "beneath the folds of crimson and gold" of an all-enfolding wrap, as is possible with the levitated girl who, covered with a similar blanket, has been floated out over the audience and then, when the blanket has been snatched away, is seen to have disappeared. I had to accept this, although I could not imagine the practical means by which the feat could be accomplished. Another thing that annoyed me though I had to accept it too, was the appearance of Derek Marchmont. I had invented him merely in order to introduce his complaint, on the grounds of good taste, of the practice of an American magician of producing a borrowed pearl necklace from his mouth which I had seen in the London Letter of the magician's magazine *The Sphinx*. I had not been prepared to have Ed bring him back in the role of an important character. We thus very soon reached an impasse, and, having then other things to do, I dropped *Baldini* for two years or so. I was planning, however, to revive it, not wanting to be outwitted by Ed, and, not very long before his death, had got the manuscript out to study it. I shall not discuss my further plans for it till I have presented the unfinished fragment itself.

"Baldini"

Chapter I
(E. W.)

JACK BALDINI was baffled.

He had seen the trick a hundred times: the chosen card with the corner torn off that suddenly appeared in the frame between the two panes of glass. But in Esmeralda's apartment there was no confederate to set it off, at least none that Baldini could see, nor could he detect any threads. She had simply taken the frame from a shelf and set it up on the table.

"A camera timer?" he asked.

"Guess again." She let him wonder a moment. "No: a new electronics job. Cute? All I have to do is raise my voice. Or a pistol shot if you want that old gag."

Without giving him a chance to examine it, she put the apparatus away.

"That's one I hadn't heard about," he was forced to admit. "It might open up huge horizons."

"It's not on the market," she said, pouring him another drink from the cloisonné cocktail shaker.

She offered him a stuffed date.

"Do they go with absinthe?"

"I love them."

He stood up, with the date in his fingers, and looked about her curious living room. He was embarrassed at her scoring off him with the new electronics trick.

"You've got some nice items here."

There were photographs of Adelaide Hermann and other woman magicians, besides several of Esmeralda — Esmeralda the Great, as she called herself, one showing her in the toreador costume in which she always opened her show. To the accompaniment of fiery music, she would maneuver with a bull-fighter's cape and produce from it a bouquet of silk flowers, a pair of red rubber lobsters, a bowl of goldfish, a bird cage with a plastic parakeet and finally a pretty Spanish dancer, who carried on with the castenets while Esmeralda changed to something more feminine: a simple green evening gown, which seemed to offer no place of concealment for the properties that magicians call "loads."

One picture Jack Baldini did not like to see: a signed photograph of handsome Derek Marchmont, the distinguished English magician, in his flight commander's uniform embellished with decorations. He had a BBC voice and accent which Baldini could not abide, and at the time when he had contributed a London column to an American magician's magazine, he had complained of the bad taste of an American performer, who had borrowed a lady's necklace, pretended to spill the pearls in an omelet, tasted a morsel of the omelet and then produced the necklace intact from his mouth. He had now returned to London after a highly successful visit to the States, during which he had appeared with Danny Kaye: but there had been a good deal of talk about him and Esmeralda, and now Baldini thought he noticed a distinct veneer of BBC overlaying Esmeralda's Middle Western accent. And her father was a circus man! He found the stuffed date rather sickening.

"But that's gimmicks, that electronic card-frame!" He turned abruptly and addressed her with a loud authority. "*You* don't need gimmicks, Mamie! There's nobody that doesn't need gimmicks like you. Won't you show me that dice routine, darling, that everybody raves about. I've only heard about it — I've never seen you do it."

"Oh, that silly old routine," she replied. "You really want to see it?"

"I'm crazy to."

She left the room. Jack resented as unbecoming what he felt was a false note of modesty that she had learned no doubt from the gentlemanly Marchmont.

He studied, where it stood in a corner, made uncanny by a mask-shaded light, a replica of the Iron Maiden of Nuremberg, which he had never seen her use on the stage and which seemed to him a little more sinister than anything he would care to use himself.

She came back with two very large dice boxes, from which she scattered on the table large dice. Then with brusque and rapid gestures, as if with impatience, she shuffled them about on the table with the dice boxes held bottom up. He admired her long expert fingers. She seemed to be shoving the dice off the table, but when one looked at the carpet, they were not there, and then, when she lifted up the boxes, they would be seen to be piled up neatly in stacks as if they were children's blocks. Later on, they all seemed to coagulate to produce two larger dice, and then these coalesced in one giant. This was a magicians' trick, which required enormous skill but — since it could not be watched on a stage — was quite useless for public performance.

"Mamie, you're out of this world!" exclaimed Jack. He took a sip of his absinthe cocktail in its queerly-calyxed green glass goblet. He thought he knew where the dice had gone, but he refrained from scrutinizing her bodice, whose contents so invited admiration. Or *did* he know? He usually could see what his masculine confrères were up to. But did she hypnotize him, or was it the absinthe that left him somewhat puzzled and dazed? He found that he was suddenly shy about bringing up the business he had come to discuss. He had to pluck up his courage. She was a master magician undoubtedly, but then, after all, so was he. They both stood at the top of their profession, and there had come to be between them a certain rivalry. But why should they not join their forces? Why not do a show together? The element of the dramatic and the picturesque was something they had always had in common. Their shows were both brilliant masquerades. Not only did Esmeralda open with her toreador "production" act, she appeared again in Spanish costume at the end of the first half of the show and sang a flamenco which ended with a flight of tumbler pigeons (instead of the conventional doves), released from a small casket, which, as she sang, contained her true love's heart; and then later, yet again, as a Castilian beauty, when she would "vanish," in magic parlance, a lover whom she had hidden behind a screen, simultaneously with a frantic husband who had rushed behind the screen to kill him: a shot was heard, and then the screen was folded up and removed — both the men had disappeared. As for Jack, he did impersonations, and, as was recognized, delightful ones: an Italian, a Chinaman, an Austrian, all imitated from foreign magicians — his bald head made wig-wearing easy; and in one of his "illusions" he sprang into a chest as a hunted Sicilian gangster, and then when the chest was shown empty, he suddenly appeared in a box, wearing kilts and a Harry Lauder cap and shouting, "Hoots, Jack Baldini, laddie, 'tis a bonnie braw act ye gie us!" and vaulted down onto the stage, to be met by tremendous applause. And Esmeralda had long exercised on Jack a queer kind of fascination; he had seen her show again and again. Though they had always been on friendly terms, she had held him off, he felt, as a male competitor, and he wanted to know her better. After years of cute little assistants, who had been chosen for their appearance in short skirts, high heels and bras as well as for some modest competence as contortionists or acrobats which qualified them to turn cartwheels at the end of an act and to compress themselves into narrow spaces for the girl who is sawed in two or the girl in the wicker basket which is run through and through with swords, he felt that he could love such a woman. Did he love her already? He hardly dared ask. With her rich and abundant black hair, her long artificial lashes, her full figure and her mesmeric gaze which made "false direction" so easy that, for her fellow magicians, no matter how persuasive, it almost appeared to be cheating, she seemed sometimes a real enchantress who possessed some power other than that of trickery when she would cause a great iridescent ball to float out over the heads of the audience or produce at command from an aluminum shaker which had previously been shown to be empty innumerable kinds of drinks. One did know how these tricks were done, but there were others of which she had never told the secret and which none of her fellow magicians could do. Jack had realized, since looking at that photograph of the so much admired Marchmont, that he could not introduce into his own new show a burlesque of a British magician.

But he now decided to take the leap. "Mamie," he began, "you and I have the only shows in magic now that are really imaginative works of art, the only shows with real personality" —

She forestalled him before he had finished: "I'm glad you came in tonight, Jack. I've been toying with the notion of a project that I think you might possibly be interested in. Since Derek's gone back to England, I don't know anybody else I could trust."

"What is it?"

She looked at the grandfather's clock which was one of the guaranteed American antiques that contrasted so oddly with her more exotic furnishings.

"There isn't time for it now, I'm afraid. I'll have to dash out in a minute. I've got to be in a benefit tonight, and I've got to get to the goddam hall to check on my props and things."

Since it was Sunday, he had hoped to have dinner with her.

"What benefit?"

"The crippled glassblowers."

This was puzzling, but he did not inquire.

"Can't you give me some idea what you have in mind?"

"I'd rather talk about it when we've got more time. Come around after the show on Thursday."

"I've had an idea, too. A kind of a dramatic show that we might do together" —

"You won't need your accents and false mustaches for the act that I'm thinking about."

He felt a little hurt.

"My public are used to seeing me in character" —

"After a minute or two, you won't be seen at all," she said. She grinned in the friendly way that always made her audiences feel that the sorceress was one of themselves — the women that she was one of the girls, the men that they could take her out.

She struck a Javanese bell with her palm, and the girl who played the Spanish dancer came in, without looking at Jack.

"Get the floating globe ready." And to Jack: "Have you seen my new one? I've got the whole geography of the world on it. It lights up from inside and looks lovely. When it's hanging in the middle of the house, it explodes and scares them crazy. It's a poor night when we don't get some screams. I can't do all that, though this evening. — Well, goodby now. See you Thursday."

She held out her sharp-nailed hand. "Not so practical for card work," he thought. "Except of course for marking the backs."

Chapter II
(E. O'C.)

BALDINI lived in a small apartment on the West Side, an apartment so small that, had it not been for the magician's cunning, it would have seemed barely habitable. Thanks, however, to a most ingenious arrangement of mirrors, the place looked easily seven times its size, and the casual visitor, entering Baldini's tiny — nine by twelve — drawing room for the first time, received instantly the impression of limitless space.

For three days following his Sunday meeting with Esmeralda, Baldini remained in his apartment. There was work to do, he did not do it. More than a month before, he had agreed to perform his wonders at a children's party, to be given by the irascible soda-crackers monopolist, Shepherd O'Brien. Moreover, in a moment of weakness, he had agreed to perform his most celebrated illusion — The Vanishing Elephant. The party was to have been on Monday. Monday came, the children gathered, the air rang with shrill voices and the crunching of a million soda crackers, but — Baldini was not there.

He had stayed at home. For the first time in his professional career, the conjurer had failed to fulfill an engagement. For a time he attempted to justify his behavior to himself by complaining of the lack of props. Elephants, he reminded himself, were in notoriously short supply these days; then too, once secured, they were apt to be something of a nuisance off-stage. Expensive, too; Baldini was not cheap, but the thought of his bills for hay alone sometimes made him shudder.

Still, the trick was a great one. The effect of a mature elephant, vanishing at a word from beneath the folds of crimson and gold with which the magician had draped it — this was something to behold! Baldini knew this, it was the trick of which he was most proud; it was the trick which, above all others, had gained him his enviable reputation — and yet, it was a trick for which he now felt something very close to hatred! For it was this trick — this same superb illusion — which had once made him a figure of fun in the eyes of Esmeralda.

It had happened nearly a year ago now. He had promised to perform the feat for her alone; he had chosen as his site a deserted corner beneath the center field bleachers at Yankee Stadium. He had performed as never before; even the fact that Esmeralda had appeared accompanied by Derek Marchmont had failed to dim the luster of his performance. The silken folds swiftly and silently cloaked Randy, the double-tusked behemoth, and then, at the single peremptory magical word *"Neh-ru!"*, the silk was whisked away, and the great beast was gone!

Esmeralda's eyes had shone, her lovely, luscious body had quivered with an admiration which was close to passion, it was a moment for which Jack Baldini had hoped for years. But alas, it was a moment which was destined to be spoiled. For Derek Marchmont, consumed with envy, nevertheless had leaned negligently on his whangee, and said, in a drawling voice, "Good show, Sabu!"

SABU! With the utterance of the dreadful word, so humiliating in its implications, a change had come over Esmeralda's face. On her full lips suddenly appeared the slightest of smiles, a mocking light came into her eyes, and Baldini, with sinking heart, knew that he was forever to be joined in unlovely combine with a dwarfish, nut-brown mahout.

From that awful day, he had eliminated the Elephant Vanish from his repertoire. It had made a difference, even to an illusionist of Baldini's astonishing versatility; the old proverb "To lose an elephant is to make a hole," has seldom found truer illustration. Yet such was the measure of his skill that he had been able to survive the calamity; his gifts for mimicry and disguise had stood him in good stead. Joining them to his magnificent technical abilities, he had remained at the top of his profession, and only Baldini himself knew how bitterly he mourned the loss of his *pièce de résistance,* and how eagerly, how passionately he had planned for some trick, a great trick, a *Baldini* trick: a trick worthy of succeeding its splendid predecessor.

And now, at last, he had found it! A trick so astonishing, so ingenious, so induplicable that, once performed, it would be his forever. His — and Esmeralda's. For in the performance of this simple yet extravagant illusion he would require a confederate. And no ordinary confederate — in a word, no "stooge" — would do. No, here he needed someone who commanded a powerful stage presence, who was at home in the great, rather than the routine, feats of magic, and who was, above all else, a *woman.*

Esmeralda, of course, who else? No one; among the prestidigitators of her sex, it was Esmeralda who stood paramount. He was eager to confide in her, to tell her at once every last detail of his scheme for their joint future, yet here he was, alone in his apartment, forced to wait until the appointed Thursday. It was a necessity which left him impatient, even mildly angry; with a frown, he filled his sword-stick with absinthe, and slowly began to drink from it. Glasses, goblets, and tumblers were all very well in their way, but when it came to serious drinking, Baldini had always felt there was nothing like a sword-stick.

After about a half-hour of steady drinking, Baldini rose from his chair and began to perform. Drink, he knew, had a retarding effect on other magicians, on him, however, its only effect was to sharpen his wits. Watching himself covertly in the multiple mirrors in which his apartment abounded, it seemed to Baldini that he had never been more brilliant. Cards poured from his hands in bewildering profusion, often, in midair, apparently changing in color and size; a live rabbit was produced, not from a hat, but from an object no larger than a tennis ball; then, turning to his genius for impersonation, he mimicked the great Chinese magician, Long Tack San, in his most renowned trick: placing a bowl of water in his hands, he completed a somersault in the air, emerging with the bowl still full and, moreover, three goldfish swimming about. Baldini, as he did this trick, became completely submerged in the character of the agile Chinese; rather short and portly himself, he seemed to gain at least a foot in height, and his eyes acquired a peculiar slant; most astonishing of all was the fact that, although he was bald as an egg, he now, without recourse to a wig of any sort, seemed possessed of a full head of lank black hair!

He rounded out his performance by doing a short but debasing imitation of Derek Marchmont. He did a series of easy, almost childishly simple tricks, and did them clumsily. As he performed, he talked. In the beginning, Derek's BBC accent was faithfully duplicated; then, as cards slipped from his fingers, as props fell to the floor, as effect after effect of the supercilious Britisher failed to come off, Baldini altered his voice so that eventually it became a revolting, supplicating cockney whine.

"Lor' lumme, Guv'nor!" wheedled the pseudo Marchmont. "I ain't 'arf bad todye, I aint! 'Arf a mo' wile I give it anuvver try!"

This pleased Baldini; as the sword-stick tilted once more to his lips, he smiled thinly and thought of the possibility of actually reducing his rival to such abjection. Perhaps when he and Esmeralda had presented their act he could somehow bring this to pass.

Meanwhile, on Thursday, there was Esmeralda. He would, at that time, inform her of his plans. And it was only now, for the first time, that he recalled her saying that *she* had some plans! Plans that, apparently, included both of them, plans that might very well parallel his own. For she had spoken, in a casual way, of the possibility of their appearing together: this was all to the good. What was *not* all to the good was the suggestion that in this act Baldini would be both silent and invisible. It was not quite what he had in mind for himself; shrewd showman that he was, he felt instinctively that if he could neither be seen nor heard, his role might perhaps be a subordinate one.

Was this, in fact, what Esmeralda really wanted? Could this be? Was it perhaps conceivable that the whole proposal had been cunningly inspired by the distant Marchmont? Baldini frowned and went once more to his sword-stick. He simply did not know; he would have to wait until Thursday to find out.

Chapter III
(E. W.)

"You were terrific, darling," said Jack, when he found Esmeralda in her dressing room after her show on Thursday night. "What gets me is that you didn't just clip those pigeons so they wouldn't get away. You taught them that circus routine so that they fly around the house and then come and perch on your shoulders."

"Oh, I hoped you'd miss that silly production act. Production is such a bore. I've put in some gags to make it even sillier so people will begin to laugh: the sausages and the cabbages and the lobsters. I've been playing with the idea of a chamberpot. Let it slop out and then pretend to empty it on the audience." She made a brusque gesture of flinging the contents.

"I don't like it. I'd cut all that out. It's beneath the dignity of a show like yours. Just build up the pigeons and the dancer. Maybe a big silk with a bull's head. That thing that you wave around suddenly turns out to have a bull on it."

"I'd like to have a real bull, but they're not so easy to handle as elephants."

He was silent a moment. Was this a sneer?

"Have a bull with a man inside, if you really want to be that comic. Then Irena could dance with the bull."

"Irena isn't a comic. She wants to be taken as a serious artist. I wanted her to skip rope with the sausages, and it made her furious."

"What about your floating ball? It didn't explode tonight."

"I haven't got it rigged right yet, and I didn't want to spoil the act."

"Sardi's restaurant," said Baldini to the taxi driver.

"Let's go where we can be more private." She gave the man another address.

It was a dark little restaurant in the West Fifties where Jack had never been before. She led him to a corner table.

"Let me hear *your* idea first," he said, when they had ordered spiced beef sandwiches and Pernods.

She demurred for a moment, reflected. "If you've got something to say, say it now."

He needed the support of the Pernod, and he drank it all down in two draughts.

"It's this idea I've had for a show. Now, you're the biggest woman magician that the world has seen since Adelaide Hermann."

"She wasn't so hot," said Esmeralda, chewing a bite from the sandwich. "She just used Hermann's old illusions after his death."

"All right then — there never was a woman magician who was in the same class as you — and very few men, I may add." As she stared at him, not recognizing a compliment, he was sorry he had added this. "Well, there've never in the history of magic been two top flight magicians who worked together — a man and woman would make it sensational. I've been thinking that you and I could put on a show that would mark a new summit in magic."

He paused. She was attentive, perhaps interested.

"Of course, you'd have some wonderful ideas, and I've got a few myself. Here's my conception of the second half. The Queen of Sheba comes to see Solomon. She comes in on a richly caparisoned elephant with a bodyguard in beautiful costumes and ladies of the court and all that. Solomon bows low and greets her in a guttural ancient Hebrew accent — he speaks like old Schildkraut when he was playing in English. Long handsome beard and scepter and a huge high crown on his head. She smiles at him graciously and proudly dismounts. Solomon flourishes his scepter, and the elephant disappears. My old gag, but it'll do to start with," he added in a deprecatory tone. "Waiter, two more of these. — Well, Solomon and Sheba are both magicians, and they vie with one another giving presents and performing miracles. He gives her a big bowl of goldfish — we'd have to have it made a special shape so it wouldn't look too much like a party for the kiddies — and she whips out a purple silk shawl with the Star of David on it. He comes back with an ostrich-feather headdress, and she counters with a couple of dwarfs that play leapfrog and turn handsprings. He lets fly with the tumbler pigeons that go to perch on her shoulders. Then Solomon claps his hands, and a banquet appears from nowheres — the attendants all have flowing robes. Sheba takes a jug from one of her maidens and asks Solomon what he'll have to drink: white wine or red wine or mead or myrrh or whatever they drank in those days. He says he'll have a highball — that brings a laugh — and she pours out a mahogany-colored number. She says she always starts with Pernod, and she pours out something cloudy. Then comes the Sauterne and Burgundy and she asks the major-domo what he'll have. He says a Bloody Mary. Solomon raises his eyebrows. 'You must have been out with the Golden Calf,' he says. Then what will her chief lady-in-waiting have? 'A very dry martini, please, Your Highness.' 'Olive or onion?' she asks. 'She was out last night, too,' she says to Solomon, 'but Charmian's a girl who can take it.' Of course we'll do better than this — I'm just improvising at the moment. While they're dining, the dancing girls dance — that gives Irena a chance for her act — and when the banquet is over, the major-domo pulls the cloth away from under the things on the table and begins to juggle with the cups and plates. I've got a topnotch juggler, and he can sail plates out over the audience. What happens at the end we'd have to decide. I've got one new stunt that I'd like to have you see."

She had listened without interrupting, smoking her cigarette. Yet, he felt that he had not succeeded in communicating to her his own enthusiasm. But now she said. "Maybe I've got it," looking down and flicking the ash.

He was taken aback for a moment: his heart had been set on the trick on which he had been working so passionately; but after all they might use them both. "What do you have in mind?" he asked.

"Well, you know the old challenging problem that nobody has ever solved: how to make a man disappear, without any drops or traps, in full view of the audience."

"It could be done with mirrors but hard to manage."

"Mirrors are out," she said. "How do you get him behind them without having something to hide it — and then, anything that's near enough is going to be reflected in the mirrors."

"My juggler might distract attention."

"I think I've got the solution."

"She vanishes the major-domo." He was fitting it into the spectacle.

"I need a good magician. It would have to be you."

"And then Solomon appears in a box, and he makes a majestic bow like Chalyapin in *Boris Godunov*." Demonstrating, he bowed from the waist and, trailing his right arm, saluted from the level of his cheek.

She did not comment.

"Well, what's the gimmick?" He gave her the smile of a man of the world.

"I haven't got it all worked out yet. It's a little bit tricky — I've been

getting into things that you can't always depend on for a public performance. Let's talk about it later."

"But you think that our show's a good notion?"

"Let's think about it. I'll call you up."

"Well, let me tell you the idea *I've* been working on."

"I've got to get home," she said. "Irena's got some kind of bug, and I
sent her home to bed after the opening act. You tell me about it next
time."

He concealed his disappointment and paid the check.

"Why the glassblowers?" he asked as they were going out.

"That benefit? Oh, I'm crazy about them. It fascinates me to see them
do it — making vases and goblets and things. And I like to see them
swell and swell and then go off."

"The glass, you mean?"

"Yes, they blow those big glass bubbles, and if they keep on blowing,
the bubble explodes. I used to know a professional glassblower, and I
used to make him do it for me."

"He was the only man you ever loved," said Baldini on a tone of ban-
ter.

"I had a passion for him," she said, "while he lasted. It makes some
people nervous to watch it." She laughed. "And if the pieces fall on you,
they burn — it's molten."

Baldini was silent.

"Don't take me home," she said.

"Of course I'll take you home. — We might have that in the show,"
he said as they were sitting in the taxi, "It's another of Sheba's entertainments. There's your perfect distraction. The glassblower makes vases for
Solomon, and then when one explodes, he vanishes."

"I'm working on it, but you have to have a furnace and a lot of apparatus."

She smiled warmly when he dropped her at her door, with a caress of
her velvet eyes.

"I'll hear from you? — I can get the backing."

It was too early to kiss her, he thought.

Ah, what a queen she would make, riding in on his well-trained elephant!

Chapter IV
(E. O'C.)

THERE followed two weeks in which Baldini did not see Esmeralda. He
talked to her once over the telephone; she had called him to cancel a

dinner date. It was during this call she had announced, disquietingly, that she had had second thoughts about "Solomon and Sheba"; she was now against it. Furious, he had asked why.

"Physically, Sheba's not right for me," she said. "With that long nose and everything."

As patiently as he could, he explained to her that she was thinking not of Sheba, but of Cleopatra.

"Oh, well," she said negligently, "what's the difference?"

It was a maddening question. Baldini was not an intellectual snob, but he had majored in history at Long Island University. Only the fact of Esmeralda's beauty saved her from a cutting and well-merited rebuke.

And yet he was not as upset about this as he would have been a week ago. The simple truth was that the "Solomon and Sheba" routine had begun to seem less attractive to him — considerably less attractive. He was unwilling, as he grew older, to work his old Elephant Vanish. Not merely because Derek Marchmont had once poked fun at this feat; not merely because there was some slight element of danger to his person; but more because with age his skill increased, and he had now reached the point where he feared that one day he would perform so skilfully that the elephant would indeed vanish in fact, instead of simply *appearing* to do so. And if *this* should happen — if, thanks to his magic, the elephant *really* disappeared and could not be returned — it would mean that he would lose a fresh elephant with every performance! Baldini was not without private means, but he was reasonably certain that such an expense would soon prove burdensome.

He went back, now, to some of his old tricks that he had experimented with years ago, but had abandoned. Levitation in particular captured his attention once again. He envisioned Esmeralda, placed in a handsome mother-of-pearl sarcophagus, drifting slowly over the heads of the audience — could this be done? He thought it could, and if so, it would be a far more effective trick than her own proposed feat of vanishing a man or woman without the use of drops or drapes. Indeed, as a showman, he had a certain contempt for this trick; privately he thought it good enough for a woman magician, but not quite up to the standard he had established for himself.

He called Esmeralda at the end of two weeks.

"Mamie: tomorrow at eight?"

She had agreed — it seemed to him reluctantly.

"Is it terribly important?" she said. "I'm really not in very good shape."

"Your shape always looks good to me," he sniggered. As soon as he said this, he knew he had done it again. It was his weakness: the coarse streak which occasionally cracked through his otherwise impeccable veneer. He suspected that in the past it had cost him employment at several children's parties.

"Good night," she said icily. Though of Hungarian birth, she was always the perfect lady.

The following evening, Baldini took a taxi to Esmeralda's apartment house. As usual, he proposed to the driver that they toss for the fare: double or nothing; as usual, the driver accepted; as usual, thanks to his manipulative skill, Baldini paid nothing. It was a way he had of cutting down expenses.

He went up to her apartment quickly, and a little nervously. Would she be angry still, following his coarseness of the evening before? He hoped not, but if she were, he was confident that what he had to tell her would melt her wrath.

To his surprise, he heard voices, laughter through her door. He pushed the buzzer; there was a silence, then the sound of scuffing, then, finally, the door opened, and there stood Esmeralda, her eyes shining, a glass in her hand.

"Why, Jack!" she said. "That's right you were coming tonight, weren't you?"

He nodded; he did not trust himself to speak.

"Well, come in, come in," she cried. Possibly because she was a European, she added, "*Entrez!*" Her hand shot out in a beckoning gesture; from her fingers seemed to flow a succession of gay, multi-colored silk flags.

What a ham, thought Baldini morosely: always on stage. And with those lousy, childish tricks! But he went in, and as he crossed the threshold, he stopped short. For there, lounging negligently on the long expensive couch that he — Baldini — had given Esmeralda for her birthday, was Derek Marchmont!

"Hello, Goldoni," he drawled. "Long time no see!"

Goldoni! It was the last straw! Baldini boiled with rage, he wanted more than anything else in the world to reach out, grab this insolent British mountebank, and beat him into insensibility. Unfortunately, he could not do this. His innate good manners forbade it; also the knowledge that he would receive a severe trouncing.

He stood there, seething quietly. Marchmont rose languidly from the couch, unexpectedly performed a front somersault, and came up smiling and bearing in his hands a small fish bowl, filled to the brim, and with a single goldfish swimming around in it.

"My compliments," he said mockingly, handing the bowl to Baldini. "Think of it as a tranquilizer, old man; it will help you while you seethe."

"Now now, boys," said Esmeralda prettily. "Let's all be friends and have a party. After all, Jack, Derek's just flown over from England. He's only been here a few days."

"I didn't expect to be here at all, actually," drawled Marchmont. "But duty called: I had to give a command performance at the glassblowers' benefit."

Baldini stared at Esmeralda. "The glassblowers' benefit? But that's the one *you* were —"

She cut in smoothly; too smoothly, he thought. "Imagine my surprise," she said, "to find Derek on the bill with me. And all the time I thought he was in England!"

"England couldn't contain me, dear lady," said Derek, with a flourish, "as long as you and the glassblowers were here!"

If it weren't for my rage, thought Baldini, I would be nauseated. Fighting a desire to drown them both in a cascade of vituperation, he said, as calmly as he could, "I see. You performed together, then?"

"Quite," said Marchmont. "And brilliantly, may I add. Not a rehearsal, everything improvised, yet it all went like clockwork. Even Esmeralda's pigeons seemed to take to me; it was as if we'd worked together for years!"

"Yes, it was lovely," Esmeralda said, and Baldini noticed that a glow came into her eyes as she said this. He felt like running her through with his sword-stick. Continuing, she said animatedly, "In fact, Jack, Derek and I have something to tell you!"

"I wonder if you can guess what it is?" asked Marchmont nastily. "Eh, Goldoni? You should be able to, you know: a man with your professional background. Didn't you once do a mind reading act? Extrasensory perception and all that sort of thing? Well, think hard, old man, and see if the master-mentalist can't put two and two together and come up with four. Look here, I'll even give you a clue!"

And with just the trace of a sneer on his thin aristocratic lips, Marchmont began to juggle a series of thin golden bands, finger-size, in the air; at the same time he hummed nasally a tune which Baldini, after a moment or two, recognized as "The Wedding March." He stared, first at Marchmont, then at Esmeralda, with horrified eyes; thanks to his training as a Master Mentalist, he was beginning to glimpse just what the despised Marchmont was driving at.

"Get it, old man?" said Marchmont, smirking unpleasantly. "Not too subtle for you?"

"Oh, Derek, you're such a clown!" cried Esmeralda, giggling happily.

It was the first time Baldini had ever heard Esmeralda giggle; it struck him as a most unbecoming sound. It was the last sound he heard before slumping to the floor. Jack Baldini had fainted.

I MUST not finish the story along my own lines now that Ed cannot contribute his chapters; but I shall give a brief summary of what I intended.

My next chapter was to take place in a New York shop that dealt in magic supplies. Attached to it, as is often the case, is a workshop where "illusions" are manufactured. The craftsman who makes these and the proprietor of the shop are discussing a rather curious order which Esmeralda has just put in. She has supplied certain specifications but has not explained what she wants to do, and the man who constructs apparatus is in some doubt as to how to proceed. It comes out in the course of the conversation that they do not quite like Esmeralda. At this moment, Esmeralda herself arrives to inspect what is being done. Baldini now also drops in. Esmeralda is not very cordial and does not talk about her project; but Baldini, who is mesmerized by her, is deferential toward her reticence, since it is customary for inventive magicians to keep their secrets at first from their colleagues. I do not know what Ed would have made of this, but my idea was to have it later suspected by Baldini when he is coming to rebel against Esmeralda's domination, that, in pretending to make him disappear in full sight of the audience, she is preparing to do something dangerous. He is put on his guard by the men in the shop, who are coming to have some inkling of the nature of the contemplated "illusion." What has happened is that Esmeralda has learned from the head glassblower, whose hobby is physics, how to vaporize in an instant on a limited scale. A flash and some smoke will be seen by the audience, and Baldini will have disappeared. Esmeralda, it turns out, is a fanatical manhater, on account of having been sent, as an orphan, to live with an uncle who raped her. The new destructive powers she has now acquired are prompting her to give vent to her lifelong antagonism by more and more extravagant feats. Could she not make the glassblowers themselves disappear? They are to open up the performance with a prelude for what is to come, by blowing up their glass bubbles till they burst with a bang. Why not vaporize Derek, too? He along with Baldini are to be permitted to put on individual acts and to have their little applause before her own great feats of annihilation. Why not — her madness accelerates — turn the wonder-gun on men in the audience, too. She comes out in a sweat as she thinks of it. She tries to control herself, assure herself that the disappearance of Baldini alone may be accepted as a magician's secret, and his subsequent non-appearance be explained away as a retirement from the profession on account of illness. She has yielded to Baldini's desire for the Solomon and Sheba spectacle. She, as Sheba, will top Solomon's magic by making him vanish in a puff. She grimly enjoys this prospect. But Baldini, by the time of the performance, has been tipped off by the magic-shop men that Esmeralda is mad as a hatter. He has had her watched; a diary has been read, and her lethal intentions have been discovered. Just before the Solomon and Sheba act, her gun has been confiscated. She is arrested and put under restraint barely in time to avert the massacre. But the show must still go on. It is announced that Esmeralda is ill, and one of the girl assistants acts as her understudy. Irena has had also to be restrained and has bitten a policeman's wrist. The performance ends successfully with the spectacular finale, which involves the girls doing cartwheels, the appearance of cobras from baskets and the production of national banners, including both the Israel and the Arab flags but not those of the Communist countries or Franco's Spain. Baldini in the costume of Solomon is the hero of this dazzling number and takes the bows at the end, with a speech in a heavy Yiddish accent. But Derek Marchmont has climbed up on the elephant, which has been made to reappear, and is waving the Union Jack.

At the time that Ed and I were discussing the revival of Baldini, I received the following letter accompanied by a glossy photograph of a very third-rate-looking dancer majestically posed in a lace mantilla:

January 24, 1967
(NEW STYLE)

My dear, dear Mr. Wilson,

I am writing to you on this occasion because I have only in the week just past received the most joyful news that you are proposing to lend your magnificent talent to a book about my son, otherwise perhaps known to you as "Jack Baldini." Surely you will sense at once with your keen eye that this is a genuine letter from an A-Number-One mother, for the accompanying photograph, taken only a *very few years ago*, is my darling son's favorite of me, which he always kept very close to his person in his boudoir.

I must tell you I took the occasion to write first to your friendly collaborator, Mr. Edwin O'Connor, that highly gifted man. He said I should immediately write to you because of the purpose of my entreaty. He said to me, he said, "Wilson is the money man, my dear lady; I deal only in ideas!"

Accordingly then, to you I write. Naturally a book provided by you for the markets of the world, about such a son of such a mother, can be expected to realize much in the way of valuable moneys. Although I am of course an *artiste* and under most circumstances cannot trouble my pretty head with such bagatelles, just for fun, for a singing lark, as you Americans sometimes express it, I think I would like to ask you for a small part of those moneys. A novice in these crude affairs, I hardly know what next to say; perhaps "fifty per cent" would not be amiss?

My my, what a happy time we will have, all working together! I intend to spend most days of the spring and summer months very close to you on that blessed spit of sand, Cape Cod. I will be in residence at the Hotel Holiday from Memory Day, May 30th; I will be accompanied by a young Polish boy of nineteen whose spiritual counsel I now feel indispensable. It is sad I will not have the distinct pleasure of seeing Mr. O'Connor there, as he has courteously explained to me that frequent family deaths oblige him to journey to Japan for most of the coming year.

Goodbye for now, dear Mr. Wilson! How I look forward to receiving a missive in your own hand, addressed to me in care of my attorneys-at-law, Greenbaum, Wolf & Ernst, in the city of New York, N.Y. Such pleasant men they are, to be sure, but how harsh and unforgiving if a crafty person should attempt to deprive a deserving and quite beautiful woman of what is so rightfully hers.

> With all my cordiality,
> [Signature undecipherable]

III

This nonsense was not to be continued, and the break with all the other elements in one's friendly relations with Ed, the abrupt obliteration of his presence, his personality, was shocking to all who knew him. His death made a terrible vacancy in our little community at Wellfleet. As Mrs. Arthur Schlesinger has written, in an article in the Boston *Globe*, he had become a kind of center of our life on the beach, where he knocked off to read in the afternoon after doing his work in the morning. One always had with him entertaining conversations, and his sustained imaginative activity was backed by an impressive physique. He three times saved bathers from being swept away. I once saw him swim out and pull in a raft with two girls which was being carried off to sea. I was struck by the fact that many people on the shore who had stood around watching this immediately disappeared when the raft had been safely brought in, without anyone's making any move to inquire about or offer anything to revive the two girls and Ed, who were lying on the sand exhausted. He scolded the girls for their recklessness, and the last time he rescued one of these greenhorns, he swore that he had "had it" as a lifeguard and would never rescue anyone again. He had undergone, before his marriage, a serious operation, the removal of a part of his stomach, but he seemed to have recovered so completely that one forgot that his condition might still be precarious. Since he has gone, I have been constantly reminded that Ed's death was a serious personal loss when I have from time to time caught myself still thinking, "I must tell Ed that," or, "I must ask Ed about this." I had by that time become interested in what was happening in the Catholic Church, and in talking to Ed about it, I found that he was capable of being just as sardonic about its ministrants as he was about anyone else. I believe that the explanation of his satirical children's fable *Benjy* — the story of a horrid little prig who makes trouble for everyone else — is that Ed was always on his guard about letting people be conscious of his virtuous habits because he realized how easy it would be for these to become obnoxious. He neither smoked nor drank; he was considerate and incorruptible. Though he never at all emphasized this and though he reacted very strongly to a badly performed Mass, he remained a practicing Catholic, and he was one of the few educated friends I have had who struck me as sincerely attempting to lead the life of a Christian. It was only when he died that one realized how much he had become in Boston a kind of public figure. His funeral was almost on the scale of that of a respected bishop or cardinal; and it was not merely his literary talents, his enlivening wit, his conspicuous commercial success and his sympathetic capacity for fellowship with all classes and callings in the city that had made him such a popular personality but, together with all these attractive features, the reassuring sense that came through, from behind his satiric humor, of decency, reliability and an unwillingness to take ignoble advantage of the failings and misfortunes of other people. In spite of the egoistic old men, the virulent old women of his novels, he could hardly have allowed Esmeralda to have become such a monster as I was projecting, and I believe that it was partly this divergence of temperaments that brought our Baldini to a standstill.

For Whom the Novelist Writes

(This article appeared in the April-
May, 1963, issue of *The Critic*.)

I WANT to talk about a kind of relationship which exists between the men and women who write novels, and the men, women, and children who read them. You will have noticed that I did not mention "children" when I spoke of writers — this was not an oversight. The truth seems to be that children are not normally great novel-writers, except of course in France. In that extraordinary country the child-novelist is a common fact of life. Nowhere is the difference between our two cultures more clearly marked than here. At the very hour when the American teen-ager is at home, industriously putting a fine edge on his switch-blade, his French opposite number is just as industriously reading the reviews of his third novel. When the French speak of a juvenile delinquent, they do not mean some youngster who beats up old gentlemen in public parks; they mean, instead, one who uses a past participle badly.

In this country, however, we are confined to chronologically older novelists, and it is about them and their public that I propose to talk to you today. This public is most important to the novel, and there are those who say it is quite as important as the novelist himself. Not many novelists really support this view. Still, the fact remains that while it is the novelist who brings the novel to life, it is the public which keeps it there. If the public is too small, the novel will die; if it is smaller still, so will the novelist. This may not matter much to the public, but if you are the novelist, it matters very much to you.

In a sense, then, the public *belongs* to the novel: it is the tail-end of every novel, the completion of the process. This process is one we all know at least a little about. It begins with the writer: it begins when he gets an idea, or a series of ideas. He thinks about these ideas, they grow in his mind, his imagination; before he writes a word a whole world may have taken shape, sometimes in roughest outline, sometimes in astonishing detail — depending pretty much on what kind of novelist he is, how he works, what his writing habits are. Then the writing starts, and this may take a week or it may take several years — and there is no guarantee at all that the book which has taken the several years will be better than, or even as good as, the one which has taken the week. But finally the book is written, it goes to a publisher, and here it is either published or it is not published. If it *is* published, it goes to you. It goes to the public, and it is at this point that we become concerned with it.

A question of definition arises: just what is, what makes up, a writer's public? I suppose you can say it's made up of the people who read a writer's books. And yet, curiously enough, we hear of writers who are said to have enormous publics, and in reality they are very little read. Quality is no particular gauge here; this can happen to very bad writers as well as very good ones.

For example, some years ago a famous business man wrote his autobiography. It was published; it was sold. It was in fact on top of the best-seller list for some months. Yet surely very few people sat down and read this book. Perhaps no one did, outside the author's immediate family. And me. I read it: I was sick at the time, it was given to me in the way that bad books are given to the hospitalized. No one wants them around the house, so they are given to those who are thought to be too sick to care. This is doubtful therapy, but it happens all the time, and it happened to me with this book. It was a terrible book and I read it with fascination. As a writer, I realized I was in the presence of a kind of classic: a monstrously bad book, which would nevertheless sell millions.

On the other hand, and to return to the novel, there was the case of *Dr. Zhivago*. When that novel was published in this country and swiftly became a success, it was widely assumed that Boris Pasternak had acquired a great American public overnight. This was not true. Virtually the same thing happened to this novel that happened to the bad autobiography: a great number of copies were sold, and very few were read. I think it's quite safe to say that a very small percentage of those who bought *Dr. Zhivago* actually read it — or even read more than a few pages of it. In contrast to the autobiography, though, this was a genuine loss, for *Dr. Zhivago* is a marvelous book, and yet, like many best-sellers, it was bought for reasons that really had very little to do with the quality of the book itself. So it is entirely possible for a writer to become well-known, even famous — for one of many reasons — and still remain comparatively unread.

But even if we assume that the public we're speaking of *is* a reading public, it is of course a mistake to speak of it as if it were *one* public: a great, single, undiversified mass. It isn't; for every novel there are several publics; they range enormously in taste and in intelligence and in sheer size. The novelist knows this. He knows that when his book is published it will be placed before a great public which is in fact a layer cake of smaller publics. Each layer will respond to him — assuming, that is, that it responds at all — in its own peculiar way, from its own distinct point of view, and with its own separate demands. The writer is fully aware of this, and he is aware, too, that not all of these responses will be of equal value to him.

There is, for example, the response of a very small public, made up, usually, of no more than a handful of people. These are the writer's colleagues, and not just his colleagues, but particular colleagues. Some of them he may know well, some he may know slightly, some he may not know personally at all. But all are among those very few writers for whom the novelist has a special feeling, for whose work he has a particular admiration, and for whose good opinion he cares a great deal. If, when he publishes a book, one or two of these respond with appreciation, perhaps even with enthusiasm, then this gives the novelist a kind of pleasure, a kind of reward which he will get from no one else.

Such a public is, of course, a professional one: its few members are all likely to be working writers. They are insiders, so to speak: they know what the novelist is trying to do, they appreciate the way in which he is trying to do it. But there is another public which is also professional, and is quite different. It is much larger, for one thing; it is also infinitely more uneven. This is the public which consists of those critics and reviewers who write about fiction for newspapers and magazines. In a way, this is a strange reading public. In the first place, its members are *paid* to read. They are not paid much — and in the newspapers, this is at least half the trouble — but they are paid: this makes them professionals. And they do not read for themselves. That is, while some of them may read the books for their own pleasure and instruction, their job is specifically to read them for someone else: to pass on their findings, in print, to others. They serve as a kind of bridge between the novelist and the general reader. From time to time there have been those who have questioned the structural soundness of this bridge.

I would say, speaking mildly, that this is not an age distinguished for its critics. Book reviewing in the magazines is apt to be on a higher level than that in the daily or Sunday papers, but this is a faint compliment. Generally speaking, the magazines have their old reliable workhorses who over the course of the years have become familiar, but not necessarily trustworthy — and certainly not inspiring! There are the specialists, who often write with brilliance about their particular hobby horse, but care nothing or less than nothing for the rest of the merry-go-round. There are the poets who, resting up between poems write about poems, or about novels as if they were poems. There is Leslie Fiedler, who writes about Leslie Fiedler. There are the old Marxists, for whom everything of value in life came to an end when one day the armies of the Soviet Union invaded Finland; they write about everything, but they write in the cold, disappointed prose of ghosts. And there are the professors, perpetually engaged in the most pleasing of academic pursuits: the slaughter of one's colleagues: "It is, however, surprising that so eminent an authority in the field of the novel as Professor Harold Stringtoe should have failed, in his own first novel, to advance beyond the primitive technique of the picaresque. . . ."

All this and more — in the magazines. In the newspapers, the situation is even more disappointing. In the last few years, I think I have seen the book pages — or half-pages, or quarter-pages or columns — of most of the newspapers in this country; with very few exceptions, they are unimpressive. And to say this is to be kind. The pages themselves are physically unattractive; one would think their primary aim was to repel readers at a glance. Quantitatively, the book pages of these papers are bad; qualitatively, they are worse. Quite frequently, the reviews in the smaller papers are faintly disguised steals from reviews which have previously appeared in larger papers; quite frequently, too, they consist largely of quotes from the information sheets supplied by the publishers — scarcely non-partisan material. In some papers very long books are reviewed in a very short sentence; other papers, with a taste for the concise, do not feel the need even for that. A phrase will do: ". . . rip-roaring farce," or ". . . a corking tale of derring-do."

This sort of thing goes on everywhere and all the time. And the fault is not the reviewers'; it is those who employ them who are to blame. The average newspaper publisher looks upon the book page with no enthusiasm. He knows that in some mysterious way that he does not quite understand, it has worked its way into his paper; he does not quite dare to get rid of it altogether: it is thought to have a certain "prestige" value; but he also knows that it does not pay its way in terms of dollars and cents. Accordingly he is unwilling to spend money on it, he gives it the worst space available, his reviewers are given nothing for their efforts but the books they review — and sometimes even the courtesy of a signature on the review is denied — and the final slipshod page serves as nothing but the perfect mirror of the publisher's distaste for the whole enterprise.

The novelist is wise if he pays very little attention to any of this. He is even wiser if he decides, quite early in his career, not to reply in print to his critics. Sometimes this is not easy. No one likes to be attacked, and the first impulse is to retaliate. But my own feeling is that this serves very little purpose. If a novelist feels the need to justify himself, he can do it much more thoroughly through his own books than he can through the limited confines of the correspondence columns of a magazine or newspaper.

Not all writers would agree to this. I know of two or three who are celebrated for the swiftness of their reaction to any critical attention; their names are old familiar friends to the man in charge of the Letters to the Editor: "Dear Sir: In his curious account of my book, *Ashes in My Mouth*, your reviewer, Seymour Mandelman, makes the statement that it is '. . . a thoroughly inexpert job from beginning to end.' I'm afraid a careful reading of his review must raise certain questions as to Mr. Mandelman's own astonishing lack of *expertise.* . . ."

And so forth. Letters of this kind run pretty much to a pattern. They are intended to serve as withering rebuttal, and their main fault is that they really don't wither much of anything. The Seymour Mandelmans of this world do not obligingly dry up and blow away — they write letters back. They *always* write back. And these letters, it appears, must be answered in turn or else — so the novelist feels — he will suffer public humiliation. And so the correspondence continues until at last a halt is called, not by either of the feuding parties, but by a weary editor.

All this wastes time and produces little, but as I say, there are a few novelists who seem to take pleasure in it — who seem, indeed, to find it necessary. I think this is true — that it is necessary, I mean — but I think it's true only because these novelists are not primarily novelists at all. That is, they write novels, but they're not really interested in those novels as such; what they *are* interested in is in having those novels — and themselves — written about and discussed. There is an odd reversal here: what is important is not the novel, but what comes after the novel — the letters, the articles, the protests, the denials, the heated speeches at the cocktail parties. The novel itself is merely the springboard from which one leaps into the stimulating pool of literary controversy. Which is a way to do things, admittedly, but I'm not so sure that it produces very good novels. Or very good novelists.

In my opinion, the novelist is best off when he leaves the critics alone. There are few critics, only a few, whom he can read with profit — for me, they are men like Edmund Wilson or Alfred Kazin; other writers have their own favorites. But for the most part, the writer can afford to ignore the rest. If they write about him, he may read them; indeed, he *will* read them — in my experience, most writers read what is written about them: the novelist who scorns to read his notices is pretty much a creature of legend. And in reading them he may be amused or annoyed or pleased or outraged, but he is not likely to be influenced one way or the other. This is not because he is above improvement or superior to correction; it is simply that he knows, quite early in the game, that the great majority of critics will tell him nothing about his own work that he does not already know.

But the public made up of critics and reviewers has at least one thing in common with that other public we spoke of earlier: that one which consists of the few colleagues whom the novelist values most highly. They are both specialized publics, and they are both small. By far the greater part of the novelist's readers belong, of course, to what is usually meant when "The Public" is spoken of: that large public which has as its distinguishing component what Dr. Johnson called "the common reader." The common reader of today is not quite what he was in Dr. Johnson's day, for the readers of books are now stratified into layers and categories which would have been unthinkable in that less complex age. Yet he exists, and he is important, for it is he, in fact, who buys, rents, borrows and presumably reads the novelist's books — on the simplest level possible, it is he who pays the bills. As I say, this is a simple level; it is a level on which the novelist often thinks. He may not be the canniest fellow in the world, this novelist, but he knows that when he goes into his tailor's for the delivery of a suit, if the tailor says, "Eighty-nine fifty with the alterations," and if he answers "Did you see what they said about me in the last *Kenyon Review?*" an interesting stalemate will result.

For some novelists there are a great many common readers; for others, not so many; for still others, very few. Yet, in whatever numbers, they exist; the novelist knows this, and is grateful for them. And if, suddenly or slowly, their numbers start to grow, to expand, the novelist does not become less grateful. There is, I think, some misunderstanding on this point; there is occasionally a willingness to credit novelists with a greater fastidiousness than perhaps they possess. There exists a persistent suspicion that any novelist worth his salt becomes uncomfortable and possibly even angry if his public threatens to increase.

This has not been my experience. I know many novelists, and some are fairly rarefied figures. I have not noticed that as their sales increase, they grow more resentful. Their first reaction may be one of pleased surprise; the second is usually a quick telephone call to the publisher to ask for more advertising, so that their sales may increase still further.

The truth is that most novelists like to reach as many people as they can; they are not remotely interested in any voluntary restriction of their audience. This is not to say that they will change themselves in order to secure more readers, a greater audience. Any move made in that direction is inevitably perilous. The air of history is filled with the moans of writers who have deliberately set out to placate a public — who have, to put it less nicely, sold themselves and their talent down the river. No; pandering to a public is cheap, is wrong, and is dangerous. But if the writer continues to write as well as he knows how, he certainly wishes to be read by as many people as can read and understand him. It is not his goal to write in isolation or comparative isolation; he wants as large a public as it is possible for him to have, and still remain himself.

To suppose anything else is to be hopelessly romantic. For example, let us take a book such as *The Magic Mountain.* Let us take another book, such as *The Carpetbaggers.* Obviously these two books were written on very different levels; obviously one is literature, and the other . . . well, it is not literature. Yet I think Thomas Mann, if he were alive today, would be neither outraged nor insulted if he found that a few of the readers of *The Carpetbaggers* had bought *The Magic Mountain* and were reading it; he would not for a moment consider that he had lost stature as a novelist. A writer can be supremely confident of his own abilities, and still be pleased when he learns that more and more people are finding his work of interest.

Of course, if in gaining this larger and quite different public, he should happen to lose his original one, then that's something else again. To continue with the somewhat unlikely example of Thomas Mann, if he had awakened one morning to discover that all the old admirers of *The Magic Mountain* no longer read him, and that he was now enjoyed by the followers of Harold Robbins . . . well then, he would have had to ask himself some rather pointed questions, the answers to which might not have been comforting.

In general, we can say that the novelist wants to reach as large a public as he legitimately can. We can also say that the novelist of today has certain advantages and disadvantages, in relation to that public, that his predecessors did not have. On the plus side, he has enormous potential readership. There is now near universal literacy; in his wilder moments, today's novelist can almost persuade himself that if nearly everyone can read, perhaps nearly everyone will read *him.* In more lucid moments, today's novelist realizes that despite this, he will never, no matter what he may do, confront and captivate his public as did his predecessors of one hundred years ago.

The nineteenth century was the Novelist's Century in a way in which the twentieth century never comes close to being. One hundred years ago novels formed the great popular entertainment. They were read then as they had never been read before, and as they would never be read again. One reason is an obvious one: in this age lived the greatest novelists. It was the century of Tolstoy and Dostoevski and Turgenev; of Flaubert and Balzac; of Jane Austen, of Thackeray, and of Dickens. This is not a bad reason for a century's being called the Century of the Novel.

But it was more than the novelist; it was the public as well. For the public of that time did not read novels; they devoured them. A book was often spoken of in the same terms as food, and consumed as gluttonously. All classes did this, even those who could not read — for the novels of Dickens were read aloud to groups of illiterates. The novel was Everyman's meat, and Everyman ate heartily. And along with that went a sense of *belonging* to the novel in a way approached by no reader of today.

This was mainly because novels were rarely produced in those days as they are now — as complete books. They came out in parts, and as each part appeared on the stands, the public would seize it, read it and then respond by making their feelings known to the author. They were not at all shy about this; they knew what they wanted, and they wrote to the author, demanding to get it.

Dickens, for example, brought out most of his novels in monthly installments. When the January installment of *Nicholas Nickleby* or *Little Dorrit* appeared, there were many other installments which remained to be written. This gave the public plenty of room to move. It was a more emotional age than our own, and the readers responded emotionally and directly. They wept, cheered, stormed, applauded or cursed, all according to whether or not the slowly developing turns of plot pleased them. And if they protested in sufficient numbers, even the most eminent of novelists sometimes gave in. Dickens did; so did Thackeray. They knew their relationship to their public, and every once in a while, they heeded its suggestions.

I don't recommend this as the approved procedure for the writing of novels, but the fact is that it was done, and done by some of the greatest novelists of all time. The dangers of such a practice can easily be seen, and indeed even then these novelists were sometimes severely criticized for it, but the point is that the public of that time, both because of their tremendous appetite for novels, and because of their involvement with those novels as they were actually being written, could be much closer to the novelist, and could exert far greater pressures on him, than any public before or since.

Certainly no novelist of today has anything like this rapport with his public. Is this a loss? In a way, yes. It is at least a flattering thing for a writer to have visible, tangible and almost limitless evidence that he is directly affecting a great many people, that he is — if only for a short while — deeply penetrating their lives. On the other hand, this involves certain obligations; a public, so aroused, may penetrate right back. Response is fine; every writer wants it, and yet, in order to work, he also wants a certain privacy. Speaking as one who writes novels, and who has at least the normal concern about his public, I can assure you that while readers may not react in quite the vigorous, unbuttoned fashion of a hundred years ago, they are not shy, nor are they silent.

Nor would the writer want them to be. Still, there are limits, and I can remember thinking, only a month or two after *The Last Hurrah* came out, that for me those limits had been just about reached. It was at this time I discovered what I had no need to discover until then: that an unlisted telephone number can be man's best friend.

I am, fortunately for me, a writer whose books happen to be fairly widely read. I am grateful for this. A great many of the people who read my books write and tell me that they do, and I am grateful for this, too. I am not so grateful that I answer these letters, however, and I don't answer them because the business of answering letters, in any kind of conscientious spirit at all, with anything more than perfunctory notes, can be an extremely consuming one, and the writer, if he is not careful, will find that he is writing more than ever before, but writing letters rather than books. Especially if many of those letters come, as they do, from students whose only object, as far as I can see, is to get the writer to do their homework for them.

I think a novelist has certain obligations to his public. I think, too, that those obligations should never be allowed to interfere with his work at hand. Because, in the end, what must matter to him most is none of the public we have talked about so far today, but still another one which has up to now remained unmentioned. This is a public which must always be obeyed, no matter what it demands. This is the only public which he can afford to placate, which he can — and indeed, must — set out from the very beginning to please. This is the most important public of all, and, strangely, it is also the smallest public of all. It is so small that it consists of just one person — and this is the novelist himself.

Egocentric as it may sound, the novelist knows that with his own work, he comes first. We have been talking for some time now about the novelist and these separate publics, these different layers of the one great public, each of which responds to a writer's work in its own way, each of which brings to the writer its own kind of reward. But in the end, when a novelist has finished his book, if he can pick that book up, and if he can begin to read it, and continue to read it with the feeling that this is not so bad, that it might even be pretty good; if he can read it, not with *complete* satisfaction, of course — I think no serious writer has ever felt that — but at least with the satisfaction that he has done as well as he can at this particular time, and that the book he has before him comes fairly close to being the book he had originally intended to write; if he can read with that feeling, I say, then he is pleased in a special way, and no matter what else may come to him from others as the result of this book — whether fame, or money, or appreciation — it is quite likely to be this special private pleasure, this special satisfaction which he feels alone, and which he can share with no one, which will be his greatest reward.

A Meeting on Sunday

(This is the text of a talk, given as part of the
Christian Culture Lecture Series, sponsored by
the Paulist Fathers, in October of 1963.)

Aᴛ the beginning I should say that I'm afraid this is going to be a bit
of an intra-mural talk. That is, if it's going to be of any interest at
all, it will be of interest mainly to those of you who are Catholics, because it's concerned with a matter which is rather peculiar to Catholics.
I think, however, that most of this audience tonight *is* Catholic, and
for those of you who aren't I can only apologize for what will undoubtedly seem a most parochial subject — a subject which was chosen
for no better reason than that it is one which has been bothering me
for some time.

I want to talk to you about what happens to the average Catholic in
this country on Sunday morning. Now what is apt to distinguish the
average Catholic from, let us say, the average Protestant — and bear in
mind, please, that this is a figure of convenience: we all know that there
is really no such creature as an average human being — on Sunday morning is that the Catholic is more likely than not to go to church. This is
not to say that Protestants do not go to church; it is simply to say that it
is a matter of fact that the percentage of Catholics who go regularly to
church is far greater than the percentage of Protestants who do the
same.

I think that this is unarguable. Most Catholics would claim it to be so,
most Protestants would admit it to be so — although they would not
necessarily assign to it the significance that the Catholics might. But in
any case, here we are with all these millions of Catholics going to church,
Sunday after Sunday, usually in the morning, but now often in the afternoon or evening, and doing this from the time they are little children
until the day they die, or until they are too incapacitated to fulfill their
obligation any longer.

For that is what it is, isn't it? An obligation: among our earliest memories is that of someone taking us to Mass, telling us that we must always
go to Mass, that to miss Mass on Sunday, knowingly and willfully, is a
grievous sin. And so we go to Mass: it is the core of our religion. We go,
every Sunday, to re-live, in a certain way, the Sacrifice of Our Lord on

Calvary. Unquestionably, this single trip on Sunday is the most important religious act we perform during the week, and there have been those unkind enough to say that for most of us it is the *only* religious act we perform during the week.

Well, tonight I want to talk to you about what happens during the time we are in church on Sunday. I want to talk, not about the Mass itself, or about what happens to us as a result of our participation in that Mass — I have neither the intention nor the presumption to attempt to discuss that with you. I'm not a theologian, and despite the sound of what has been said so far, this is not a sermon. But what I would like to look into is what happens *besides* the Mass — what happens, in other words, when the priest turns from the altar and speaks, as priest to layman, to the congregation. He may speak for one minute, he may speak for fifteen; he may speak for any length of time between these two extremes. But however long he speaks, he is the priest meeting his flock, and it is this meeting, this encounter, that I propose to discuss now.

Now this meeting is, or should be, an important one, and for a very simple reason: it is virtually the only occasion on which the priest confronts the people who are under his spiritual care. To be sure, there are other meetings, but these are likely to be social affairs — card parties, communion breakfasts, and the like — and really the only time the priest talks to his people in what we might call his *official* capacity is during these few minutes on Sunday. It's self-evident, then, that this is a singular moment, and one which should be of the greatest importance, not only for the people, but for the priest as well.

At this point, we may stop and ask ourselves two questions. First, is this meeting in fact that important? And second, is it in fact important at all? Different people would of course answer these questions in different ways, but I think few of these answers would be entirely reassuring. To put it as mildly as possible, I think that it might be concluded that this meeting, this moment, rarely lives up to its promise. To put it another way, and not quite so mildly, I think it might even be concluded that this meeting is more often than not a failure, and sometimes comes very close to being an outright disaster.

I want to go into what I think are some of the reasons for this. In doing so, I would like to make my position quite plain. This is not the cry of a disgruntled layman, and it is not the beginning of a bill of complaints about how poorly the clergy are serving the laity. This would be ungracious — particularly in this setting — and worse, it would be untrue. But I do think it is necessary to point out something which has become increasingly evident to many laymen, and also, if I can judge from my conversations with them, to many priests as well. And that is that the priest in the pulpit on Sunday morning fails so signally and continually to come through to the people.

We're all familiar, of course, with the pattern which is invariably followed in the pulpit each Sunday. There are first of all the prayers: for the sick, for the dead or dying, for the friends of the parish. There are the announcements — announcements which make mention of parish activities and parish needs. There is the reading of the Sunday's Gospel in English. And, finally, there is the sermon.

Let us take first the matter of the Sunday sermon. Sermons are shorter than they used to be, and there are not so many of them. In some churches they have been virtually eliminated. Is this a bad thing? Certainly there have been few cries of protest from the congregations; it is perhaps not unfair to say that this curtailment or even absence is looked upon as more of a blessing than a deprivation. And if you cast your mind back over some of the sermons you have heard, you will see, I'm sure, that there is nothing mysterious about this. It is a quite natural reaction.

Think of those Sunday sermons for a moment. Don't think of any special one, or two, but think instead of them in a long procession. Try to remember, if you can, your reaction to them in general. Were you angered by them? Pleased? Embarrassed? Delighted? Edified? Or outraged? Did you want to get up and walk right out the door? Or were you stirred to repentance? These are all possible reactions, but I think that in the main the Sunday sermons have not really affected us in these ways. I think that instead they have done something far worse: they have not affected us at all. They have bored us, left us indifferent, rendered us apathetic. I say this is worse because it seems to me that one of the greatest dangers we face today when it comes to religion, when it comes to a matter of what we ultimately believe, is precisely this danger of apathy: of simply not caring.

It is my impression that the impact of the average Sunday sermon is so slight that it can hardly be called an impact at all. How rarely does it happen that any one of us remembers for more than five minutes what Father So-and-So has said from the pulpit? At best, I suspect it might be remembered and even mentioned briefly in the car going home from church; usually it is not remembered or mentioned at all. Or, if it is, it is likely to be mentioned in a way which is distinctly unflattering to the preacher.

Well, why do these sermons not have a greater impact? Why do they not stir us, why are they not remembered? These are not easy questions to answer, and even to begin to answer them fairly we should try, first of all, to put ourselves in the position of the priest, and we should remind ourselves that the priest of today, in talking to his people, has no simple task before him. It's not just a matter of getting up, saying a few words about religion to a group of selected friends, and then sitting down. In delivering a sermon, the priest of today has a far harder and more complicated job than did his predecessor of, say, fifty years ago.

This is because the whole relationship between the parish and the parish priest has changed. I'm not sure that the extent of this change is always realized — by either the priest or the parish. But it is very great. Fifty years ago, when a priest stepped into the pulpit to address his flock on a Sunday morning, he occupied a position of wide authority (which he does not occupy today) and he had a sense of intimacy with the parish (which he does not have today). For one thing, he had the immense advantage of being one of the people — of coming, that is, from the same stock that they did. When I was a boy the parishes were still all divided along racial lines: an Irish pastor in an Irish parish, a French pastor in a French parish, and so on. This still obtains to some extent, but by no means in the old way. Fifty years ago most of the parishioners knew that they were regarded by many of their neighbors as something of an alien band. The priest was their natural, tribal leader, as well as religious leader. Also, he was quite likely to be the best-educated man in the parish. Thus his authority extended over the broadest possible area; he spoke on Sunday to his people on many matters, and when he spoke, he was listened to. In a book I once wrote I had a priest — a modern priest — look back rather wistfully on those days, and remark that then the priest really mattered to his people, really penetrated their lives, in a sense in which he certainly does not today.

So then, here was the old-time pastor, up in the pulpit, speaking with every conceivable authority to an audience, most of whom he knew, most of whom stood in some awe of him, and most of whom took whatever he said on whatever subject as the gospel truth. You do not need me to tell you, I'm sure, that this blessed state of affairs no longer exists.

Today, the average pastor — the average priest — looks down from his pulpit on Sunday and sees faces that he recognizes, but a great many that he does not. The parish is not the stable unit it used to be; there are many and rapid population shifts; the old intimacy between shepherd and flock, the intimacy that can come only from long, steady, mutual knowledge of each other, is no longer there. And something else has happened as well: his flock has come up in the world. The college education, instead of being a rarity, is now a commonplace. The priest is no longer almost by definition the only man of substantial schooling in the parish. There are now many in his congregation who are as well educated as he; there are others who are far better educated than he. Whatever else this may mean, it certainly means that the priest of today seldom speaks with the assurance that the priest once did on all manner of subjects. And indeed, even when he speaks on the one subject on which he can count on superior knowledge, the one subject for which his training has uniquely qualified him — the subject, that is, of man's relation to God —, even on this subject certain difficulties arise which simply did not exist years ago. For the priest of today, when he speaks to his congregation, must speak to many different levels, and speak to them at one and the same time. He now has to speak to a group which may have in it, all at once, doctors, lawyers, stevedores, scrubwomen, professors, policemen, politicians, janitors, housewives, physicists — really, a great layer cake of people, each layer representing something different in the way of training, in the way of intellect and imagination. It is up to the priest to address himself to all these layers at once — and be understood by them all. There is an obvious problem here; he cannot pitch his talk too high or too low. He has to find some sort of happy medium; he must, if you will, be somewhere between Father Teilhard de Chardin and the nun I once had in Sunday School, who told us that Saint Peter hung out the stars every night and took them in in the morning.

Well, let us agree that to give a good sermon today is not easy. But having agreed to that, let us also agree that it is not impossible. It *can* be done. What I find troubling is that it is done so rarely. We come back to our starting point: that most of the sermons we hear on Sunday are poor, and some of them are shamefully bad. And for this I think there is an explanation — although I do not necessarily think that where there is an explanation there is also an excuse.

Certainly there is not the excuse of insufficient subject matter. The priest in the pulpit is not in the least like some schoolboy called upon suddenly to give a classroom talk; he cannot in justice panic and say, "I don't have anything to talk about." He has everything to talk about. He has an almost infinite choice of subject matter; within his proper province he is positively engulfed with material; in the Epistles and Gospels alone he suffers from an embarrassment of riches. And yet how seldom does this richness reach us on a Sunday morning? How rarely is the wisdom, the strength, the consolation of the Scriptures brought home to us in these few minutes? How infrequently do we find the men who are in intimate and daily association with the Mass expounding, for the rest of us, something of the glory and the magnificence of the liturgy? How seldom do we hear a sermon, a sentence, even a phrase, which makes us sit up straight and say, "But this is for *me*. It is not just something stated nearly two thousand years ago; it is a truth which is relevant to me, to my time, to my own daily circumstances. *What this priest is saying now affects me."*

How often is this said? How often is it thought? And if it is not said or thought, why is it not? Well, of course, one of the reasons is an obvious one — that is, that what the priest has chosen to say really does not affect me, really has no meaning for me. I hope you will not misunderstand me when I say I find it shocking that with so much that is deep and meaningful and relevant to our own salvation to talk about, so many sermons should continue to be rooted in trivialities. I don't mean that the priest should attempt to compete with the editorial columns in commenting on current events that shake us all; we do not go to the Cathedral to hear about Charles de Gaulle, J.F.K., or the emergence of The New Africa. But we do go there — there, and other churches as well — in the reasonable expectation of hearing something which has some application to our daily lives as adult Christians, and not just another version of those old familiar sermons which we first heard in catechism class, and have been hearing, year in and year out, ever since.

For example, this year one of the most remarkable men of our time died. He is of particular significance to us as Catholics, because he was not only a remarkable man and a world figure of the greatest importance — he was the head of our church. He was The Pope. Pope John, I think it's safe to say, in a few years had a greater impact on the world than any religious figure within our immediate memory. The approaching death of this extraordinary man was a matter of very real concern, not only to Catholics, but to enormous numbers of people outside the Church, people who indeed had shown no previous sympathy with anything or anyone connected with the Church. I saw the greatest literary critic in the English-speaking world today, a man always avowedly anti-Catholic, come up to me and say, "This man is dying and I think it's awful; I can't tell you how shaken up I feel." And I think this sort of thing was felt and expressed all over, by those who would not normally feel or express themselves in this way. And so, on the Sunday before the Pope died, but when everyone was well aware that he was very soon to die, I went to Mass wondering what would be said from the pulpit about this greatest figure the modern church has seen. I did not have to wonder long. Nothing was said about him. He was not mentioned in the prayers, he was not mentioned in the announcements, and when the time for a sermon came round, there was indeed a sermon given, but it was not a sermon on Pope John. It was our old familiar friend: the sermon on Dirty Books.

I found this at the time literally incredible. But what I have found even more incredible is that since that Sunday — apart from one day in the middle of the week, when the memory of Pope John was universally honored — I have not heard a single Sunday sermon on the subject of Pope John and his brief but magnificent reign, during which we were all so privileged to live. I have been to many churches since then; I have heard this sermon in none of them. It may be, of course, that some of you were luckier than I and have had a different experience. It may be that I was simply unfortunate. If so, I was doubly unfortunate, for while on these subsequent Sundays I did not encounter any mention of Pope John, on two occasions I did again run into the sermon on Dirty Books.

I think the trouble here really is a lack of judgment, a lack of a sense of first things first, and finally, a lack of proper preparation. How many priests, I wonder, prepare their sermons? I mean, *really* prepare them? Really go over in their minds, for a long time, just what they should talk to their people about? How many priests do this? And if they do, how many of them then sit down at their desks and write their sermons? Not just dash them off, but *really* write them: write them with care, taking pains with each word, trying for exactness, for clarity, for freshness of expression, so that the truths behind the words will come to the listener with a new force, a new vitality, and not as something that he has heard a hundred times before. How many priests actually do this, I wonder?

I know some priests who never bother to write out their sermons in advance; it is even a matter of quiet boasting with them that they do not need to do so. They have been giving sermons for so many years that they feel quite confident of their ability to extemporize on any subject the moment they put the Gospel down. It seldom seems to occur to them that more often than not these hastily improvised sermons are in fact rather badly organized, with little orderly procession of thought, so that after a very few minutes all over the church the devout listeners are in reality dreamily making bets with themselves about whether this is really the last sentence or whether there is more to come. It's a natural thing to do: sermons like this usually have no logical beginning and middle, and they can end anywhere. On the other hand, sometimes these spur-of-the-moment speakers know they can, at a moment's notice, fall back comfortably on sermons they have given many times before. Such sermons have the advantage of being well-organized, of making some perceivable point; however, the fact that they have been given so many times before is precisely what's wrong with them. All the juice has gone out of them; the priest has spoken these same words so often that his spark is dimmed, he is merely repeating what he has repeated too often, and all that is left is routine recitation which may begin well, but ends by capturing no one.

Now all this, I think, is carelessness — or perhaps "laziness" would be a better word. Because for the most part it does involve an avoidance of hard work on the part of the priest. Writing, good writing, is hard work. I am a professional writer; I write every day of my life. I can assure you that to put down in written form just what you want to say in just the way you want to say it is very hard work indeed. It involves a great deal of time, energy, and discipline. There is an old saying that easy writing is bad writing. This is not always so, but it is almost always so. And all too often the sermon, when it is written, is easily written, is badly written. All too often it is padded out with specimens from that long list of tried and true pastoral clichés, which aren't any good any more, but which have the great merit of coming immediately to mind. The result is phrase after phrase which long ago lost any meaning they might once have had. And all too often, along with this, goes the reliance on the standard tricks of the tired orator — the trick, for example, of meaningless repetition, of saying the same thing thirteen ways: "This miserable man, this unhappy soul, who was so soon to die, who was so soon to breathe his last, who in a matter of moments was to meet his Maker face to face, nevertheless faced his final seconds upon this earth in a cowardly fashion, in a manner deprived of all courage, with an attitude, we might almost say, of fear, of fright. . . ." Well, really, nothing has been said, but it took twenty-five seconds to say it. A few more of these and a surreptitious glance at the old wrist watch will give the preacher the welcome intelligence that once again he has come to the end of his weekly instruction to the assembled faithful.

This brings me to the matter of the delivery of this instruction. Not *what* is said, but *how* it is said: the style, in other words, of the speaker. I am informed that in the seminaries of today many courses are being offered in the hope of improving the level of pulpit oratory. I am all for such courses; in fact I can hardly wait for their effects to be felt. The problem today is that the priest who talks to an audience, a congregation, almost necessarily talks to people who have grown used to fairly good talkers. The old-time priest was quite likely to be one of the few orators the people were exposed to; today, thanks to radio, the moving pictures, and above all television, the public is regularly exposed to speakers who may not be miracles of eloquence, but whose speech has certainly a professional competence. This means, among other things, that when that public is in church, it is apt to be less tolerant of slovenly speech or a droning voice or shouted declamations than was the public of years ago. To use a not entirely satisfactory word, it is a public more or less *sophisticated* in the ways of oratory, and the people who make up that public shift uneasily in their seats if the priest begins to mumble along in an incomprehensible monotone, or, alternately, if he suddenly begins to shout at them — the kind of pulpit shout that was so much admired years ago, and was popularly supposed to be at its best only when delivered by a Redemptorist on a Thursday night. You know the kind of thing I mean, I'm sure. It begins with a priest standing there with his arms folded, frowning down at the congregation. He is waiting for silence; he gets it, but still waits, just for effect. Then suddenly, he explodes into sound: "Were not ten healed? *Where are the nine?*"

It has been my experience that any sermon which begins in this manner will be almost unbelievably painful to listen to. Fortunately, this appears to be the opinion of a good many priests as well, because this style has been pretty much — although not altogether — abandoned, and today, if the pulpit orator has a fault, it is not that of flamboyance. It is that of casualness, of dullness, even of an apparent lack of interest, and I think I can best illustrate what I mean by asking you to consider, once again, the pattern which the priest follows in the pulpit on Sunday: the prayers, the reading of the announcements, the Gospel, and the sermon; Now, thinking of these four divisions, which would you say was the most important? Or rather, which would you say was the *least* important?

For my own part, I would think it fairly obvious that the announcements would rank in importance rather far behind the prayers for the dead and dying, the reading from the Gospel, the sermon, or the spiritual instruction, given by the priest. Yet it seems to me that it very seldom works out that way. We were speaking just now of the preacher's speaking style, his delivery; it has occurred to me from time to time that the reading of the announcements often has a surprisingly beneficial effect on this delivery. The style at this point quickens and comes to life — indeed, very often these announcements — particularly those which have to do with ingenious methods of raising funds — seemed to be delivered with an eloquence, even a passion, which is somehow absent from, let us say, the reading of the Gospel.

One Sunday in summer, some years ago, I went to Mass with a non-Catholic friend of mine. This was a mistake. I think that in general it is likely to be a mistake to introduce a non-Catholic to the Mass via the channel of the summer parish. All too often the pastor's eye may be on the tanned faces before him, but his mind is on the fuel bills coming up next winter. These bills must be paid; the best way to pay them is to harvest his crop during the bumper months of July and August. Few priests in this position can resist the temptation to make hay while the sun shines; this is understandable, but sometimes the way in which it is done is not quite wise. On this Sunday, as we left the church, my friend said to me, "Those prayers the priest said when the Mass was over — the ones at the foot of the altar? Were they in English?" I said that they were; my friend said, "I thought they were, but I couldn't really tell. I couldn't hear him; he went so fast he slurred over all the words. Isn't that an odd way to pray?" I said hurriedly that it was, but that this did not necessarily imply a lack of devotion, that undoubtedly the priest had naturally a rather quick, slurred speech. My friend said politely, "I suppose that's it." And then, after a moment, he added, "Still, when he was talking about the Food and Needlecraft Sale, and about the special collection for repairing the rectory roof, I could understand everything he said. He didn't seem to slur very much there, did he?"

Which was a fair enough observation — I think that most of us would agree that announcements of this kind are usually delivered with both vigor and clarity. And I think it might also be agreed that as the years have gone by, announcements of this kind have increased substantially in number. We are now accustomed to a state of affairs where in some churches it is possible to hear, from the pulpit, quite as much about the Interest on the Parish Debt as about The Holy Ghost. And this isn't only a matter of total minutes; it's also a matter of emphasis. I mean no irreverence when I say that in the animation, the energy, the forcefulness behind the words allotted to each, I think we might find that the Holy Ghost is not always the winner.

I once thought of writing a magazine article on this very subject. I didn't write it, but I did get as far as the title. It was a good title, too, because a good title suggests, in a few words, a rather clear picture of what the article is to be about. My title, I think, would have given just such a picture to most Catholics now in this country. It was, "The Second Collection Today Is . . ."

Well, I bring this up for only one reason: I think it indicates a tendency which is growing, which is wrong, and which, in the long run, is dangerous. Let me make it quite clear that I realize that the priest is faced with a very real problem here. It's not a question of greed. To be sure, there are some greedy priests, just as there are greedy men in every walk of life; ordination is not in itself a guarantee against this. But in my experience such priests are very few, and by far the greater number of priests who appeal to us for funds in what may often seem a rather relentless manner do so because they think it necessary to do so. Whatever else life may be for them, it certainly is not free. There are salaries to be paid, a convent to be run, a church and rectory to be kept in decent repair, a school to be maintained, and that fuel bill we spoke of a few minutes ago is always there and has to be paid: your friendly oil man's friendliness sharply decreases if he is offered a few prayers in place of good hard negotiable currency.

So that there is this problem — a problem which is further complicated by the fact that, in general, we do not help the priest meet that problem as well as we could. Which is just another way of saying that, Sunday after Sunday, we don't give as much money as we could — and as we should. There are a few spectacular donors, to be sure, but by and large we are in no danger of embarrassing the clergy with our largesse. We give, but I suspect few of us give till it hurts, or even come close to that. I know that; you know it; but what's worse, the priest knows it, too. And so he tries to persuade us to give more, Sunday after Sunday.

My objection to this is simple. I certainly do not feel it is wrong to appeal for funds which are required to run the church; it is quite another story, however, if those appeals are made so often and in such a way as to disturb the atmosphere within the church itself, if these appeals are allowed to assume such proportions that they seem to be, not just a part of what the priest is saying, but the part with which he seems most deeply concerned.

Yet I am convinced that this is exactly what happens, over and over again. It is my belief that more often than not there is an unfortunate and improper equation between the spiritual and the material in the address of the priest to the people on Sunday. I further believe that this has become so habitual that many of the priests themselves do not grasp the frequency with which it occurs, nor the extent to which it is now regarded as a commonplace. A week ago this past Sunday, I came back to Boston from Cape Cod, and went to an evening Mass. When the priest turned from the altar he told us that there would be a meeting this week of some parish society; he told us that this was fire prevention week and read a letter to that effect; he told us that this Sunday there would be only one collection but kindly to remember that expenses were heavy; he told us that the Los Angeles Dodgers had just won the World Series. He did not give a sermon. It was the last Mass of the day; we were out in twenty-five minutes.

Now, I don't know why the sermon wasn't given; certainly under the circumstances there was no pressure of time, and so the old excuse of You-have-to-get-them-out-so-the-others-can-get-in did not apply. I've never been quite comfortable with this excuse, by the way. Probably because I've never been quite convinced that the Sacrifice of the Mass and the rapid turnover principle are entirely compatible, and also because it seems rather odd to me that in order to achieve this rapid turnover it is always the sermon which is sacrificed. I can never remember the announcements being similarly omitted for this purpose.

So, as I say, it is my belief that there is this imbalance in the pulpit on Sundays, and to me the prime illustration of this imbalance has always been the appearance of the visiting missionary, who comes in from some remote, wild, and inhospitable area to appeal to those of us who are more fortunately situated. Like you, I have seen many of these missionaries; they do good, and some of them even do heroic, work. Their lives are hard. It would be unkind and un-Christian to begrudge them what they ask for. And yet, as I've listened to these missionaries in different churches over the years, and have been frequently moved by their stories of disease and danger and hardship in far-off places, I have also found time to wonder why it is that in their appeals, all these missionaries spend ten seconds asking me for my prayers, and one hundred times ten seconds asking me for my money.

". . . Now first of all, my dear friends, we need your prayers. Without them we could do nothing. All of us hope that you will continue to remember us, night and day, in those prayers. But along with your prayers, my dear friends, we need something else. We need . . ."

And at this point I always have the uneasy feeling that it is only now that the missionary is getting down to work, that it is only now that he is saying what he came to say, and that while he undoubtedly meant what he said prior to this, he didn't mean it in quite the same way. It was only an hors d'oeuvre, so to speak, to the main course.

Now I am sure that these missionaries do not for a minute discount the power of prayer; their lives and their sacrifices are evidence of that. Yet when they speak to me, it doesn't come out that way; the prayer is always cast in the role of the junior partner. And while I know these missionaries need funds in order to support themselves in their work, I cannot help thinking that it would be both appropriate and novel — indeed, unprecedented — if once, just once, a missionary would step into the pulpit and say, "My dear friends, we need your money. We need as much as you can possibly spare. We need it because it costs money to live and to run our missions. It doesn't cost much but it does cost something. And for that something we depend on you. But because we are priests, and because our work is concerned primarily with the saving of souls, we need something more than we need money: we need your prayers. We need them badly, and we need them constantly. . . ."

And so on in this vein, with the emphasis unmistakably on the need for the members of the Christian community to be praying for each other. I cannot believe, if this were done, that the collection would really suffer so greatly. And yet it never is done; at least I have never heard it done, in a good many years of listening to missionaries. And from time to time, I must say, the fact that it was not done struck me as rather strange.

I think that one of the troubles is that there is a fundamental misunderstanding here — a misunderstanding between the priest and the people. This misunderstanding is rooted in the fact that priests really lead quite different lives from the rest of us. Now this is obvious enough, but some of its implications are perhaps not so obvious. What I'm getting at is this: because of the differences in our ways of life, sometimes we are not in as close touch with each other as we should be, and sometimes we forget things about each other we should remember. For example, it is quite possible that many priests, who live in and around the church most of the moments of their lives, who celebrate Mass daily, who so frequently are in the presence of the Blessed Sacrament, whose whole way of life is permeated, so to speak, with the *things* of religion, forget to what extent most lay people are deprived of — or, if not exactly deprived of, are at least absent from — those same things of religion.

Most of us live, day in and day out, in a society which is completely secularized. From Sunday to Sunday the great majority of Catholics do not enter their churches, and while it is always unwise to guess at the spiritual life of anyone other than ourselves, it might safely be said, I think, that a prayer in the morning and a prayer at night — or several prayers — constitutes the extent of our religious acts throughout the week. The rest of the time we find ourselves engulfed, not by the ultimate concerns — such as how we must live, how we must die, how we must behave in the eyes of God — but in the hard and ever-pressing immediate concerns: the payment of rent, what to have for dinner, taxes, the possibility of promotion, insurance premiums, and when to pay the doctor's bill.

These are the things we live with every day. They are what I have called our immediate concerns. And the only time we get away from them, really, the only time we find ourselves — or expect to find ourselves — in an atmosphere where these immediate concerns do not rule, is on Sunday, when we go to church, when we participate in the Mass, when we listen to the priest as, from the pulpit, he confronts us with quite other concerns, deeper concerns, reminding us of their existence, refreshing us as to their meaning, pointing out to us their relevance to us all.

Now, I don't want to romanticize here, and I'm not for a moment suggesting that the average Catholic layman looks forward to Sunday morning with shining eyes, and that on Saturday night, just before going to bed, he says to his wife, "Oh, I've waited all week long for this: tomorrow morning at ten-twenty Father Casey's going to talk to me about Eternity!" Because of course he doesn't say this, and he doesn't feel it, either. All the same, if on the following morning he finds that a good part of what Father Casey says to him is said dully or hurriedly or haphazardly and seems in any case to be a repetition of something he has vaguely heard many many times before, and if, in addition, another and somewhat livelier and clearer part of Father Casey's address is not substantially different from what has been said to him earlier that week by the chairman of the United Fund or by the smiling lady who told him that the Red Cross has its needs, well then, while he may not give any outward expression of discontent, he is quite likely to feel that somehow something has gone a little wrong. And if this something goes wrong often enough, after months and years of it the layman will almost certainly cease to pay any great attention to anything the priest says from the pulpit. He will, in effect, be bored in advance; he will feel that the same old record is about to play again; and he will see no point in listening.

The conclusion is obvious. If this sort of thing happens often enough and to enough people, the priest can be said to have lost his audience. You may have gathered by now that I think that this is pretty much what *has* happened. It's not a particularly pleasant conclusion, and this alone is enough to set it apart, for we are surrounded these days by optimistic conclusions in the department of religious observance. Each such conclusion is buttressed by a set of cheerful and unarguable statistics. More people are going to church now than ever before. Until World War Two, there was not a single Catholic Church in the main downtown district of Boston; now there are several, offering many Masses every Sunday, every *day*. The ticket windows may close in the South Station, but there is a chapel where the old newsreel theatre used to be, and it remains open. The number of weekly communicants has increased tremendously; the dialogue Mass has been introduced and the sale of Sunday missals is up to a figure inconceivable a generation ago.

I don't deny these statistics; I don't deny that they may point to something that is worthwhile and good. But statistics never tell more than a partial story whenever human beings are involved, and this is especially true in religion. For statistics of their nature deal only with what is measurable, and what is valuable, what is essential in religion is not measurable at all. It is not possible to calculate devotion on a mathematical scale; it is not possible to weigh a prayer. And it is not possible scientifically to estimate the guidance, the help, the enrichment, the benefit all these many church-goers receive from the priest as he talks to them, Sunday after Sunday, from his pulpit. No statistics at all are available for that sort of thing, and I realize that I am speaking most unscientifically when I say that if they were available, I do not think they would be entirely comforting.

The "Cardinal" Fragment

Introduction
by JOHN V. KELLEHER

ONCE I said to Ed O'Connor, "You know, half my trouble with the church is that I have no sense of *ecclesia*, no feeling for group worship." He said, "I haven't either."

We were not arguing at the moment. Neither was he agreeing with me. He was just noting a similarity. That of course made the remark the more puzzling, for after all he was a steadily religious man, a frequent communicant, and I was a grumbling satellite. There was nothing for me to do with the statement then but file it for later rumination, and presently we were talking about something else.

Needless to say, I have thought about the remark often since, and I think now I can understand what he meant. He was describing without pride or regret the kind of Catholic he was, one kind among many, not better and not worse than those for whom group worship was a spiritual or emotional necessity. He would never imagine himself as somehow separate from the body of the congregation, for the congregation was made up of individuals, all sorts of men and women with all sorts of particular needs, and the priests were almost as varied as the laity. When we did argue about the church he always insisted that the clergy not be judged by standards that would make human foolishness specially reprehensible on their part. "They're only men, too. The church as we see it in daily life is a human institution liable to all the faults and mistakes any other institution is liable to. God Almighty, the sacrament of Holy Orders doesn't make a man eight inches taller or eight percent smarter. It makes him a priest. It doesn't make him any less a man."

(Here I will omit my counter-arguments which are out-of-date anyway, based as they mostly were on rage against the arrogant or heedless misuse of clerical power that was common enough not too long ago but seems now to have gone quite out of fashion. Besides, he generally resented these displays too, or observed them with a groan of impatience. He did not defend them, he explained them on premises different from mine, which made these discussions difficult and short.)

Because he saw priests, bishops, cardinals, and popes as men, with all that that implies, he was not inclined to expect supernal wisdom about earthly matters from any of them, though he was grateful when sometimes it seemed to be manifested. By the same token he was never unduly disturbed when a few priests proved morally obtuse or even downright dishonest. One of his favorite reminiscences was about a priest, the proctor of his dormitory at college, who filched his sweater, his radio, and his electric razor, and who, Ed professed to believe, died of chagrin because, though he regularly concealed sausages, bacon, pats of butter, and so forth under his pancakes when he bought breakfast at the cafeteria, he could never figure out how to sneak a glass of orange juice in the same way. Of another and singularly saintly figure, a grand old man of the campus, who every day tottered down with a few slices of bread to feed the swans, he averred that the holy ancient only wanted to lure them ashore and strangle them. When we first knew each other we used to fool about jointly writing a volume to be called *Eminent Curates I Have Known,* but we never got anywhere with it because he knew too many, every one of them with enough mannerisms and foibles to stock an early Dickens novel. Quite a few turned up in his books anyway. When Father John Carmody in *The Edge of Sadness* comments on a colleague, "He was a good enough old halfwit. He was the dumbest priest I've ever met. And think of the territory *that* covers!" he could be the author speaking in certain moods. Yet only in certain moods, recurrent but fleeting. Ordinarily he felt that the great majority of priests did a far better job than the rest of us had the right to expect, especially considering what they were up against — namely, us.

In fact, he was fascinated by the priesthood and by its peculiar problems and temptations and rewards, and I think a good part of this interest came from a knowledge that though he fully shared their faith he could not have been a priest himself, even had he wanted to be. The priest's job he regarded as wholly real, wholly necessary, and, except to certain gifted natures, nearly impossible. Therefore he was not inclined to carp at those who, with the best will, were unable to perform it perfectly — few jobs being perfectly performed in this world, even by critics. Some priests, he knew, became uncertain of their vocations and fumbled the job because, when youthful enthusiasm was past, they discovered they had not the temperament they thought they had; others, because as happens with so many men in every condition of life, their temperaments simply changed with the years. He recognized too that a man may be rather a bad priest without being a hypocrite, because he is too dense or insensitive to know that he is unfit. Above all, he was acutely aware that there is a vast difference between what is required of a pious layman and of a true priest. It was all right for him, as long as he attended to his religious duties, to have no sense of *ecclesia*, no feeling for group worship. In a working priest that would be inadmissable. However much a priest may depend on private devotion for sustenance and spiritual refreshment, his duties nevertheless are public and pastoral, and at the risk of mortal sin he may not withdraw himself from them. That indeed is the main theme of *The Edge of Sadness*, differently illustrated in Hugh Kennedy, the narrator, who by grace and luck and his inherent vocation recovers his long failure, and in his envied friend John Carmody, the perfect priest, who fails disastrously. Both are to be measured against those who do not fail, the ebullient curate, Father Danowski, and the bishop, each of whom manifests his grace by attending selflessly to the job.

Still, it might be wondered why O'Connor himself, if his inclinations were toward private devotion, was so regular a church-goer. There were any number of reasons besides his firm faith in the Catholic creed, one of them being that he felt that a man could not make it on his own. The Our Father, with all those pronouns in the first-person plural, is not a do-it-yourself manual. He was moved both by the richness of the church, its rituals, its theology, its long history and intricate organization, and by its direct services to the poor, the lonely, the sick, the dying, the uncertain and bewildered. It ministered also to the self-important, the cocksure, the proud and unfeeling, both in health and prosperity and when they too were sick or dying and bewildered. As a man and as a novelist he was equally fascinated by the endless variety of his fellow men and by their unfathomable vulnerability. In his books the range of his feelings about people is very wide, from sardonic disgust to happy amusement to pity, and the most constant is unobtrusive compassion for what each individual soul can and usually must suffer. Thus he was constantly grateful for whatever could bring comfort to the lonely soul and shield it from despair. He saw the church as the best instrument for doing just that.

But there is plenty to life besides sickness and despair, and a lot more to the church than the administration of the last rites. For all his reserve, and he was a much more reserved man than his easy affability might be thought to indicate, he got great pleasure out of watching what was going on. He loved the surging confusion of life and took no grudging attitude toward it. I suppose that is one of the reasons he was insistent on not being docketed as a Catholic novelist, since in our time the Catholic novelist is so often one who presents life as the eighth deadly sin or who detects essential holiness only when it is mystically conjoined with homicidal homosexuality or kleptomania. O'Connor had a somewhat sunnier notion of God's mercy and doubted that He loved only the lost sheep. He was willing to think that sodality ladies with marvelous hats might be saved, and taxpayers and monsignors and, stretching it a bit, even editorial writers and professors of education. So in this novel, had he gone on writing it, the panorama of this imagined diocese in a time of crisis in the church would have been crowded and active. The entire diocesan ministry would have been examined with appropriate degrees of sympathy and irony, as well as the responses of each character, cleric or layman, to those aspects of the current renewal that impinged on his own interests or habits. The novel should have been a great document, all the more valuable because of his natural concern for the common and quotidian. From none in the church was he more remote in spirit than those Catholics who delight in knowing, and retailing, only the inside story of rectory or chancery, commonly Machiavellian, commonly wrong. The whole drama was what interested him, because only in what you could encompass of the whole could you hope to discover the humanity and truth of the particular.

A month or so before his death he had set the book aside to work on the other story of which we also have a fragment, the one about the little boy, which he found with excitement was coming with unprecedented ease and sureness. (Mostly he wrote very slowly, polishing and repolishing each sentence, reworking each paragraph till it declared itself right, letting the story discover itself to him by its own small changes of direction. It was a painful and uneconomical way of writing which he cursed and accepted. Like character it was fate, the only one he had, and he didn't presume to tinker with it. This means, however, that each of the two fragments, as far as it goes, is in finished form.)

I think, though, the cardinal novel might have been difficult for him to resume because of the acceleration of radical change within the church. Obviously the book was begun in response to that change, but it was begun two years ago and was conceived in terms of what he could then discern or foresee. His feelings at the time were not unmixed with dismay, and the dismay was growing as he saw so much that he cherished threatened by reformers whose sincerity he took for granted but whose common sense he somewhat mistrusted. Of course he was full of hope and keen interest, too. Still, if at fifty he had come back to the book and tried to get it moving again, he would have been faced with a situation already markedly different from that he had started with. The central principle of the novel, the study of how grace recurs in all kinds of circumstances, would of course be unaffected, but to describe the constantly evolving debate and the hurrying cast of debaters and yet keep the description from fading almost at once would be quite a problem. After all, it isn't only among laymen now that present issues are declared irrelevant before they are half defined and that nothing is less rememberable than the fervors and indignations of the day before yesterday. To a master craftsman, however, the pleasure of any job lies exactly in its difficulties and in finding ways no journeyman could devise of overcoming them. I cannot imagine how he would have solved the problem, but I know that whether he succeeded wholly with it or not he would once again have proved the lively growth of his powers.

But that is only speculation. The fragment itself is the reality. Short as it is, it gives us a lot: a glimpse of a new, swifter, more nervous style, the promise of a rangier construction. Chiefly, though, it presents the firm outlines and precise coloring of a compelling portrait. Readers will recognize that the cardinal is essentially the man already partly depicted as the bishop in *The Edge of Sadness*, O'Connor's ideal of a priest, a man of unpretending faith and integrity, intelligent, compassionate, and humorous. He knew there were men like that in this rascal world, and he liked to affirm them.

The Fragment

ONE

Oɴ this day the Cardinal celebrated his Golden Jubilee: he had been a priest for fifty years. . . .

It had been a long day. Too long, thought the Cardinal, too long, too long, too long. As always he had risen at five-thirty; he had said his mass in his private chapel; then he had walked down the long hall to the small bright morning room where he knew his breakfast would be waiting. It was the time of day he had come to enjoy most; in this first hour of the fresh and silent morning, before he met or talked to anyone, before, really, the day began, he was quite likely to feel for just a few moments that he was — well, not young, of course, but young*er*, and sometimes in these moments he almost was convinced that if he so wished he might rise from the table and with a springy, hard-muscled step walk right out of the house and into the morning, and then walk and walk and walk, as fast and as far as he liked. Probably through all those old parts of the city where he'd once known all the buildings and most of the people — parish census: "Hello, yes, by all means I remember you: your good husband Michael, isn't it, and the two children: Timothy and Agnes?" — but where he hadn't been now for years, and where now he would continue to walk, noting changes, making plans, observing but unobserved, and then at the end of the day coming back home, tired, yes, but not really tired — the pleasant lassitude of the athlete in training —, and curiously satisfied, just as if the whole world was once again before him, long and still undefined and full of all sorts of possibilities.

It was a small, recurring, oddly comfortable illusion: the Cardinal, ordinarily not a man to cherish daydreams, nevertheless, for some reason he was not sure he entirely understood, did not resist this one.

And then he ate his breakfast. Always, as he ate, he read: the front page on this morning of his Jubilee had been divided about equally between assorted disasters and himself. It was this paper that he read every morning: he found it uniformly terrible. He never failed to remind himself that it was the only paper available to him at this hour, and yet he knew that even if it had not been, even if there had been ten other papers on hand, he still would have looked at this one first, for no better reason than that he had been reading it all his life. He had grown up with it: it was one of those old associations from which he had long ago ceased to derive either pleasure or reward but which, gradually and mysteriously, had become so much a part of him that he might just as easily have tried to discard his veins or his bones. It was a paper miraculously immune to time. Here in the age of volcanoes, when every day the Cardinal heard fresh rumblings and felt the earth move beneath his feet, the paper — apart from certain superficial changes: meat had gone up, different people died — seemed exactly the same as when he had first read it as a boy. Still short on hard news, still remarkably long on what it chose to term "human interest," it remained unappeasable in its appetite for the trivial and snuffled the world for the insignificant detail. Was there, wondered the Cardinal, was there any other metropolitan daily anywhere in the country today capable of exploring with zest the simple-minded stories behind such headlines as "SINGLE-ANTLERED ELK ZOO'S NEWEST ACQUISITION" or "ELEVEN-YEAR-OLD BASSO DUPES MARINE RECRUITING SERGEANT"?

A queer survival, he had thought, reading. And then he thought: Well, like calls to like. . . .

The paper's interest in him had begun with his consecration as bishop; it had flowered — exploded, really — when, fourteen years ago, he had become the Cardinal. At first he had been baffled and even appalled by the endless procession of flabby improbable stories, so fawning and cosy in their tone, so totally unreal in their substance; now, however, he read them exactly as he would have read legends, the central figure of which — the benign hometown hierarch, majestic yet folksy, forever beaming at freshly baptized pickaninnies, or waving at departing pilgrims, or leading three hundred lumberjacks in the recitation of the rosary — was in some way vaguely familiar to him but was no one he had ever met. Characteristically, the paper concentrated on the homely minutiae of his daily routine, and on this morning, as the Cardinal had eaten his breakfast he had found himself reading a detailed account of what it was that he was eating.

("Nowhere does this beloved prelate reveal his Roman training more clearly than in his preference for the frugal 'continental' meal with which he begins each day: a single unbuttered roll, a dab of honey, a half-cup of black coffee. This monastic fare . . .")

The Cardinal, whose training in Rome had in fact amounted to less than eight months, had read this while slowly making his way through his unvarying breakfast: a large glass of orange juice, a plain omelet, three strips of crisp bacon, two slices of lightly buttered toast, two cups of coffee with heavy cream. He read with some amusement and with no surprise: his opinion of the accuracy of journalists was not high.

The breakfast had represented almost his last private moment of the day. From that point on he had been on public view and in constant motion. He had celebrated and preached at the Solemn Pontifical Mass in his cathedral; it was the official marking of the day, and as the long procession had filed into the sanctuary he had glanced out into the huge and for so long unfashionable church and noted that for the first time in years it was crowded: policemen were at the doors, people were standing on the steps outside. This *had* surprised him. He had a clear head and was not in the least sentimental about himself; it was his conviction that, today, the term "beloved prelate" could in fact apply to very few; he did not think himself among them.

After the mass he had gone back to his residence and here he had welcomed, first, his close friends — priests, for the most part: those few old men who, like himself, had been in the seminary nearly sixty years ago. Then had come the deputations from the various parishes, the religious orders, the fraternal societies, the police and fire departments. The governor of the state and the mayor of the city had paid their courtesy calls. He had been interviewed by the press and had appeared — twice — on television; he had visited three hospitals, two parochial schools, a convent and a children's home; he had eaten lunch with the inmates of a prison.

That night he had gone to a banquet. It had been *his* banquet, a testimonial to him from the city, and because it was at least a quasi-official celebration it had of course been picketed. As his car had pulled up to the curb the Cardinal at once had spotted the by-now familiar figure: fierce, feminine, orange-haired and sneakered, trudging implacably up and down the sidewalk, holding aloft the worn poster (a priest in the lower left-hand corner, an American flag in the lower right, a jagged bolt of lightning striking between the two and dissolving in the legend "SEPARATE CHURCH AND STATE!"). The Cardinal had sometimes wondered, as he came across her in his scheduled appearances — she was everywhere, waiting —, who she was, who she had been. Catholic? Non-Catholic? He did not know; these days it was impossible to tell.

The setting of the banquet was the slightly faded, once-splendid ballroom of a slightly faded, once-splendid hotel — all right, thought the Cardinal: fair enough — and from the beginning the evening had matched his expectations. He was a veteran of these civic dinners; one was very much like another; looking about him tonight, he had seen no qualitative difference between his banquet and, say, the annual Good Heart Luncheon, which this year had honored Augie Manciullo, an aging Sicilian thug with mad and murderous eyes, whose recent astonishing benefactions — Conscience? Unlikely, thought the Cardinal. Income tax problems? Ah! — had secured him late respectability and had won him the preposterous nickname of "Mister Charity."

In keeping with the entertainment traditions of a pluralistic society, the Cardinal had been seated between an Episcopalian bishop and a rabbi. (Fair play.) He had been repeatedly toasted, saluted, cheered; a fat bald tenor, incorrectly described as "formerly His Eminence's favorite altar boy," had sung what had been incorrectly introduced as "His Eminence's favorite hymn ('Mother Dear, O Pray for Me')"; Mister Charity had approached him and invited him to come out to The Track ("Any day!"); the Cardinal had spoken, briefly; others had spoken, not so briefly; the rabbi had called him "tolerant." It had lasted a long time.

And now he was back in his study: a small, white-haired old man with pale and slightly protruding blue eyes and a clear, smooth, polished skin. A large and gently curving nose had seemed to grow large with the years; in his earlier days his colleagues had called him "The Beak"; today, he knew, subordinates more circumspectly did the same.

It was ten-thirty; he was alone; he was eighty years old. His shoulders ached and so did the small of his back; his feet hurt. He was tired and wanted to go to bed. Still, he could not, Not yet. . . .

His secretary came in: a young monsignor with the thick wide body of a fullback and gray-blue eyes in a flat face. Almost certainly a Slav, and yet, the Cardinal thought, so much for certainties: the monsignor's father's name was Donnelly and his mother's had been Keohane. His hair was long — or, at any rate, longer than had been worn by any young priest in the Cardinal's day — and the color of dark straw; mysteriously, it seemed always slightly damp, and the Cardinal, puzzled, had in the beginning wondered if the monsignor, before every appearance in his superior's office, had found it necessary to take a shower or wash his hair.

It was a small point which the Cardinal continued to notice but about

which he no longer wondered. For moist hair was merely one and perhaps the least of the many incomprehensible aspects of his secretary. He
had been with the Cardinal for more than a year now; he had come
recommended as the brightest of the bright young priests returning from
their studies in Rome. The recommendation had been made by those
the Cardinal trusted; he had believed it; since then nothing had happened, really, to lessen that belief. His secretary *was* bright. He was more
than that; he was efficient, he was careful, he was in every way immeasurably more competent than the man he had succeeded: the middle-
aged Monsignor Concannon who, even before his tragic collapse (d.t.'s),
had become as erratic as he was congenial and disarming. So that, clearly,
as a secretary Monsignor Donnelly was miles ahead of Monsignor Concannon — no argument there. Then why, thought the Cardinal, why did
he wish, every now and again — or to be strictly honest, rather more
than every now and again — that poor Jack Concannon was back? Why?

In a way it was a pointless question because the Cardinal knew the
answer very well. But he backed away from it now, put it out of his
mind, partly because he felt it was not quite fair to his present secretary,
partly because he suspected that he didn't come out of it any too well
himself. All the same. . . .

Monsignor Donnelly, now at the Cardinal's desk, arranging papers,
flipping them through his tremendous hands with an astonishing grace
and speed — banana fingers, thought the Cardinal, on a riverboat gambler — said, "These telegrams, Your Eminence: have you seen them
all?"

The Cardinal had. There were hundreds: they had come from all over
and from everybody. Earlier in the day Father Charlie Crimmins had
dropped in, coming up for a few hours from the retired priests' home,
and for a moment, when all the others by some miracle had left and
when he and the Cardinal were alone, he had plunged happily and
greedily into the pile of telegrams like a child stomping through leaves
on an autumn morning. There were so *many* of them, and not only that,
not only that. . . .

"Oh my my!" Father Crimmins had said, mouth-breathing, his
poached old eyes watering down on a sample yellow message, and the
Cardinal knew that what he was really saying was, "Look who *this* one's
from!" As indeed he was, for in the next moment he added, "As busy as
he is! Well, I voted for him the last time and now I'm glad I did. Oh yes,
very glad. They say all sorts of strange things about him, don't they, but
there's something about him all the same. Something in his face, I
mean. Do you know what I mean, Joe?"

"I know what you mean."

"Something *good*, you know. You get so after a while you can tell things from faces, don't you think? Well, anyway, I suppose he must be one of the most powerful men in the world now. Did you have any idea you'd hear from him today, Joe?"

The Cardinal had said drily, "I thought I might." He knew — slightly — this powerful and extremely adroit well-wisher; to his smooth and elaborately courteous greeting he attached no meaning at all. Thereby, he was sure, perfectly matching the mood of the sender.

"The burden of the world is on his shoulders," Father Crimmins had mused. "And Joe: do you know what they're saying about him these days? They're saying he's coming very close to the Church! Very *very* close. Oh Joe, wouldn't it be grand if —"

He had gone on talking this sort of nonsense, and the Cardinal had half-listened for a bit. He wondered if Charlie were going a little crazy, like old Father LeClair, a semi-mad French Canadian charlatan who years ago had turned up in Saint Raymond's Monastery — God knows how or why. At the time it had been widely reported that, like the Curé d'Ars, he could look into the hearts of men; in 1952 he had announced that Harry S Truman had been a secret Catholic for twenty-five years. So that just possibly Charlie was on the same road — except that who could imagine Charlie looking into the heart of anybody?

They had been boys together, they had been ordained together, the Cardinal had known Charlie Crimmins longer than he had known anyone: a simple chatty boy who had grown into a simple garrulous man. He was a familiar figure throughout the diocese, for he had served in many parishes, being transferred from one to another with unprecedented rapidity. A certain misty incoherence in the pulpit, a wandering irrelevance in conversational style, a general incapacity for even the smallest practical matter had led many of the laity to believe that he was perhaps a saint; his superiors and fellow-priests, living with him, working with him, *listening* to him, had arrived at a different assessment. (It was Bishop Reid, the Cardinal's chancellor, who had once used Charlie in formulating a famous local definition of Hell: "Heaven — with Charlie Crimmins as your roommate!"). Charlie was not everybody's cup of tea: there was no doubt of that; the trouble was that there were too many moments when the Cardinal wondered whether Charlie was even *his* cup of tea. Because to anyone in authority he was not merely a problem, an embarrassment: he was a series of embarrassments — the Cardinal remembered very clearly exactly what had happened when, nine years before, a feeling of guilt overcoming judgment, he had uneasily given Charlie a parish of his own. It had been his greatest single administrative mistake — rectified in time, but just barely. So here was Charlie, seldom a comfort, never a counsel, the boyhood chum grown up to drive a man mad — and yet, the Cardinal reflected, if ever he had been pushed up against a wall and held there and pressed to identify his oldest friend, he knew that unhesitatingly and automatically he would have named Charlie. Lately he had often wondered why. Was it — as much as anything else — a matter of simple endurance? Of habit, of old-time association? Did the same principle apply to Charlie that applied to his choice of morning paper?

He had thought of this in his study that afternoon when Charlie had been sitting there, fumbling through the telegrams, oohing and aahing and looking slightly unfocused and older than ever and a little like Goofy, the Disney dog. Up until a year ago the Cardinal had never really paid any attention to the way Charlie looked — he had known him too long for that. And then one day, on an afternoon very much like this one, Charlie had come calling, entering the study unannounced as always, coming in talking and with that peculiar sideways modified trot which looked so deferential and tentative but which would have broken through a regiment of guards, circling past the secretary — the Cardinal remembered that young Donnelly had just come on the job and had been expertly feinted out of position by Charlie's weaving and bobbing and false moves: "Oh no no, don't bother, don't trouble yourself at all, Father, I can find my own way, His Eminence and I are old friends, old friends, yes yes, oh hello Joe, there you are: well well well!" — and then plopping down into the chair in which he always sat. He had continued to talk, of course, burbling away about the day the sun stopped at Fatima and the time Al Smith had said hello to him at the World Series — two favorite subjects — and the Cardinal, silent and abstracted, had suddenly and to his complete astonishment found himself looking at his old friend as if he had never seen him before in his life. At that moment he felt the strangest sensation, not simply of disbelief but almost of awe, as if something in him were unable to accept the fact that this tremulous and chattering figure, this ancient composite of smoke and bones and failing flesh, was really Charlie Crimmins, his own exact contemporary!

The experience had been unsettling. Partly — he later realized — because of the coincidence: on that very day he had been thinking a great deal about old age. His own, to some degree — although he took this calmly enough: his health had held up surprisingly well (appendix, yes; hernia, yes; otherwise, nothing), his memory was strong, his mind clear — but largely old age in general. Like most old men the Cardinal read the obituary pages. He had been doing this for years: often what he read gave him pain, and sometimes — increasingly, now — a sense of personal loss. But lately catastrophe had come in clumps: in the three weeks before the day of Charlie's visit the Cardinal had presided at the funerals of half-a-dozen men and women he had known well, people who had helped to shape the immediate world in which he had grown up and in which he had always felt so thoroughly at home. The latest of these funerals had occurred only that morning. After the mass the Cardinal had gone back to his chapel; then he had returned to his study. Charlie had arrived while he was thinking of this group of men and women, all of an age — all, really, of *his* age —, whose roughly parallel lives had ended so sharply and so close together that they might have been the common victims of some mysterious and highly selective blight. And it was while he had been thinking of them, and of what they had meant to the city, to the diocese, to him, that he had looked up and there, as if to underline all somber thought, was Charlie, an all-but-unrecognizable Charlie, a Charlie who in the twinkling of an eye had somehow grown older than anybody, a Charlie who was obviously coming apart at the seams! For that one shocked instant the Cardinal could do nothing but stare, while Charlie, unaware of having produced this special effect — unaware, indeed, of having produced any effect at all — had happily gone on talking as the Cardinal, still staring, had wondered what could possibly have gone so wrong so suddenly, and wondered too if Charlie knew or if he even suspected.

He said finally, cutting in, "Charlie, stop a minute. Tell me about yourself. How are you feeling?"

"Hah? What? Feeling, Joe? Why, I feel fine! Just fine, never better, never better. Why?"

"No special reason. It's a question I ask everybody these days. When you're nearly eighty it's the kind of thing that comes into your mind." Then he had said, "I'm thinking of sending all priests in for compulsory physicals. I suppose that would include you."

And of course Charlie had been on this like a cat, two old hands pushing out in instant protest, banishing even the possibility of the "check-up." Shaking his head, ducking down low, he had said, "Oh no no, there's no need of that for me, Joe, no no, none at all. Not for me! I never go near doctors, you know that!"

"Yes. My thought was this: you could always start."

"Oh well, Joe, I don't know about that, I really don't. Doctors, I mean. I've got nothing against them as such, they're some of our finest people, I know I know, but I've got no call to go to them, no no. They're for the *sick*, Joe, and take a look at me: I've never had a sick day in my life. Well, God is good. Oh, I don't say I haven't had my ups and downs, the same as everybody, I don't say that at all, we all have our aches and pains. Last week I had a sty. Right here on my left eye. Well, for a while there I thought I might be in for trouble, you know what sties can be like, but then, you know, it went away. The way sties do. What I did was, I used *plenty of warm water. . . .*"

He had talked for a while about sties. The Cardinal, familiar with Charlie's inability to dissemble even slightly, had been satisfied that whatever was wrong, Charlie knew nothing about it. Which was just as well: the Cardinal had spent a good part of his life hustling to hospitals and rest homes and the bedsides of the moribund; he knew a dying man when he saw one. And so, on this day of the consideration of old age and death, he had seen Charlie, and when, after the first shock, he had been able to take in the full, blunt, terrible fact — that it was *Charlie* who was dying, that this exasperating, baffling, decent, good-hearted man who had never *not* been around, would soon, in a matter of weeks, conceivably even days, be gone forever — he had instantly felt a sharp, spearing guilt (Had he, ever, given Charlie his due? Had there ever been anything more than the poor return of inattention, impatience?), which gradually had given way to a much stronger emotion, one so rare in him that he had last felt it forty years before, on the day his father died — it was sadness, but a peculiar sadness rolling in fast like one of the great coastal fogs, it was silent, isolating, depthless, and overwhelming. For the rest of the visit the Cardinal had been without words; fortunately, Charlie, being Charlie, had not noticed.

All this had happened a year ago; since that time nothing the Cardinal had so surely foreseen had taken place.

Charlie's visits had not come to an end — nor had Charlie. He dropped in to call as often as before; his spirits were constant and high; nothing was clearer than that he was not in pain. The Cardinal had watched carefully for the signs of further disintegration: there had been none. Charlie looked no better; he looked no worse. The Cardinal, perplexed, faintly hopeful but troubled, had continued to press for an early visit to the doctor; he had even gone so far as to arrange appointments. Charlie, evasive, surprisingly stubborn, had on one clumsy pretext or another, broken them all. The Cardinal, annoyed and apprehensive, had from time to time thought of stepping in firmly and forcing him to go, but as often as he had decided to do so he had been sidetracked by one of a series of staggering problems. In his eightieth year he had found himself busier than he had ever been before: the archdiocese was expanding, the Church was changing, the laity was confused (Why not, he thought, why not? So is the Cardinal), the older priests were unsettled, even frightened, the younger ones were churning, not quite sure where they were going, but definitely on the march ("Red meat!" Bishop Reid had said, throwing up his hands. "They smell it: they're in for the kill!

All they want is everything!") And so the months had slipped by, and the Cardinal, while of course never really forgetting Charlie, had never really found the time to come to grips with him, either.

Then, at last, he had. It had been on a day only two weeks ago. Charlie had come in as usual, but for once the visit had been opportune: he had arrived in the middle of a rare breathing space. The Cardinal, sitting quietly, not thinking about anything in particular, had stared out of his inactivity at his guest, and the sight had suddenly and vividly reminded him of just how much time had gone by, and of just how little — in fact, nothing, absolutely nothing! — he had done. Abruptly he had mentioned the matter of the medical examination once more, and this time, as soon as Charlie had begun to shuffle his feet around and to mumble that this was a good idea, a fine idea, yes yes, a *very* fine idea, the only trouble being that right now, *just at the moment,* he couldn't quite see his way clear to doing it, no no, the Cardinal had cut him off and had explained that this was no longer merely a suggestion.

"It's an order, Charlie," he had said flatly. "Like it or not, you're going. And that's that!"

And Charlie, cornered, open-mouthed, helpless, had listened while the Cardinal, now quickly atoning for his neglect, had picked up the telephone and called his own physician; he had arranged for him to see Charlie that afternoon. In fact, right away. The Cardinal did not anticipate insubordination; nevertheless he was a prudent man.

"I'm not busy this afternoon," he had said, "so I might just go along with you. If you don't mind."

"Oh well, Joe, it's not that, it's not that at all! It's not a question of minding, no no, you know that! I mean, why would I mind? It's just that there's no need, it's out of your way, I mean, there's no *reason.* . . ."

"I'll supply a reason," the Cardinal had said. "I'll get myself examined while we're at it, if that will make you feel better. I'm about due anyway. Now come on: I'm not too busy but I haven't got all day."

They had been driven to the doctor's office in the Cardinal's car, with Charlie silent and obviously terrified. On the way a rosary had appeared in his hands; glancing across the rear seat he had seen the Cardinal looking at him; there had been a weak flutter of a panicky smile and the rosary had been popped back into his coat pocket; the Cardinal thought: he prays like a child stealing cookies. Once at the office, Charlie had gone in trembling, nodding dazedly at the doctor, barely able to respond to questions. The examination had been expert, thorough, and surprisingly swift: when it was over the doctor had simply and crisply congratulated him on his good health and Charlie had almost broken down in babbling relief.

Privately, a few minutes later, the doctor had said to the Cardinal, "It's an odd case; we run into them occasionally. I don't imagine Father Crimmins has seen a doctor in thirty years; for all I know he may never have seen one. The point is, it hasn't hurt him."

"He's all right, then?"

"He's fine. Oh, he's not twenty-one or even fifty-one, and we still have a few tests to hear from. But on the whole it's safe to say he's in good shape. Remarkably good shape. He looks like the devil, of course, but that doesn't necessarily mean a thing. Particularly at his age."

"Yes. Which is my age."

"That's true. But there's a difference, Your Eminence. We have your history. We know. . . ."

The doctor was now a middle-aged man who had begun attending the Cardinal when the latter was still a parish priest; in the twenty-five years of their association, intimacy had not ripened. The Cardinal respected the competence of his doctor and placed absolute trust in his professional judgment; beyond that, he did not go. Once, many years ago, after he had been examined, he had lingered in the doctor's office, and he had begun to ask the doctor questions — in his earlier days he had been fond of asking a great many questions of most people he knew: he had always been genuinely curious about the lives and interests of those who had a kind of knowledge or experience which he had not —, attempting to converse with him on a variety of subjects: everyday subjects, perfectly ordinary subjects (Travel, War, the Shape of Government), but quite apart from the field of medicine. It had been a disconcerting experience; astonished, the Cardinal had thought: *I might as well be talking to a baboon.* On all subsequent visits the talks had remained within professional limits, although over the years the Cardinal had sometimes reflected upon this skillful man with his intelligent face and his delicate, extraordinary hands who, apart from his work, apparently lived in a kind of desert. Where, presumably, some plants bloomed. Some years later the Cardinal had met the doctor's wife: a breezy, broad-shouldered woman who rode horses. She had told him a joke. The Cardinal had tried to think of *her* as a plant. He had not been successful.

Still, he thought, he did not go to doctors for their small talk. Or for their quiet wives. And there was not the faintest doubt that as a diagnostician he was all by himself, first class. . . .

". . . all about you," said the doctor. "Every six months. You're very faithful, Your Eminence. Now, if you're ready? This shouldn't take long."

But in fact the examination took somewhat longer than either the Cardinal or the doctor had expected.

The Cardinal, by this time accustomed to the step-by-step procedure of the examination — touch, thump, breathe, stop, cough, probe — had noticed something new: the smooth progression had been interrupted as the doctor had reached his neck. The deft fingers had moved lightly up the side, then had paused suddenly in their passage. They moved on, then returned to the same spot, about an inch or two below his jaw. Here they had remained: touching, exploring, slightly extending their pressure. The Cardinal had not recognized in this concentrated lingering a part of the pattern; he had said, curious but without apprehension, "Something wrong?"

The doctor, pressing, palpating, had said only, "We always watch for any slight changes."

"Yes," the Cardinal had said impatiently. "Are you telling me you've found one?"

The doctor, seeming to pay attention to the tips of his fingers rather than to anything the Cardinal was saying, had said absently, "A small lump I hadn't particularly noticed before. A node. . . ."

He had continued pressing. The Cardinal had felt the pressure; there had been no accompaniment of pain, none at all. He had been barely aware of this; stone-still, he was thinking only of what he had just heard. Like many men who have had long association with doctors, hospitals, the Cardinal knew the neutral words which, in medicine, were rich with ominous suggestion. He had repeated, "Node?"

The doctor seemed to have finished pressing; he looked up and said, "Yes. A knot, a small lump. . . ."

"I know what it is. What does it mean?"

The doctor had shrugged slightly. "It's hard to say at this point, Your Eminence. I think it's something we ought to look into. As a matter of routine."

"Yes. What's your guess about it now?"

Here in his study, two weeks later, the Cardinal wondered: had the doctor really hesitated? Or had it been only that the Cardinal had expected him to? At any rate, when the answer came it was brisk and easy enough. "Very often it turns out to be a tuberculous gland. We see quite a bit of that these days, especially among people in your age group: there doesn't have to be any history of tuberculosis. It may have been picked up as a child, settled in a gland, and remained dormant for years, for a very long time. Then suddenly it comes to life — why, or what activates it, we don't quite know — , the gland swells, and that's the first indication we get. It could have been picked up from milk. When you were a boy of course milk wasn't pasteurized; all sorts of things were. . . ."

He went on about impure milk, the Cardinal watching and listening, thought: he's talking too much. After a minute he had said, "And that's what you think this is: a tuberculous gland?"

The doctor had said, "I think that's a distinct possibility."

"I see." Then he had said slowly, "There's also another possibility, isn't there?"

And he could see right away that the doctor had an answer for this, ready and routine; he opened his mouth immediately, but then, as the words began to come out he looked directly into the Cardinal's face, and whatever he was going to say had not been said. Instead, he said, "There is another possibility, Your Eminence, yes. But no more than a possibility." Reinforcement came with repetition; he said, "No more than that."

For a moment all talk died. The Cardinal had stopped looking at the doctor. He was seated on the edge of the examining table, bare to the waist; he looked down at his old and entirely unremarkable body: it seemed to him now not a bit different from what it had been for years. To himself he had said: Well. Well well well. He found that in this moment he could not think very clearly. In fact he could not think at all: all kinds of thoughts, bright and flashing, seemed to pass before him, but too fast, too fast; he reached out but could not catch or touch. And then this interval had passed, and he looked across at the doctor again and said, "Well . . . what's the next step?"

The doctor, for the first time since the Cardinal had known him, had not seemed entirely comfortable or at ease with himself; he had said, "I think a biopsy is indicated. That's —"

"I know what a biopsy is. When?"

The doctor, still uneasy, had said, "Of course no one loses if these things are looked into as quickly as possible. I'd say as a matter of principle the sooner the better. . . ."

"Now?"

The doctor had been startled; he had said, "By now you mean, *today*?"

The Cardinal had nodded; the doctor had said, "You understand it means hospitalization, Your Eminence. Not for long: a day or two. But the arrangements have to be made with the hospital. . . ."

The Cardinal had said drily, "I think that might be done. If we try."

And of course what he was really saying was, "Whose hospital is it, anyway?" A bit arrogant, perhaps, but he had suddenly wanted to cut short all talk. The doctor had got the point; the arrangements had been made immediately. Charlie had gone back alone. He had been sent off in the Cardinal's car, still beaming and babbling; he had said triumphantly, "Oh, Joe, I told you so: never a sick day in my life! Oh yes yes!"

And he had waved goodbye and disappeared down the drive. He had not asked why the Cardinal was remaining; he had not even seemed curious; he had been too full of his own amazing victory. The Cardinal had understood: he had neither begrudged him this nor had he thought it odd. Poor Charlie, in his long career as a priest, had not had many victories in which he could rejoice. All the same, the Cardinal thought, all the same, wasn't it strange, wasn't it a queer, fantastic twist — a joke, almost — that, all things considered, *this* should be the victory that Charlie was rejoicing in now?

Less than an hour later the Cardinal had been admitted to the hospital. The biopsy had been performed — after some unforeseen and apparently unavoidable delays — just before the dinner hour. Twenty-four hours later the Cardinal had learned that he was going to die.

TWO

No one knew. The Cardinal had given the firmest instructions on this point; he was reasonably sure they would be obeyed. He had been released from the hospital and had gone back to his residence; almost immediately, the following morning, he had picked up where he had left off. Most of the morning he had spent with his Vicar General and his Chancellor, discussing the shifts, retirements, and appointments of pastors; he had lunched with the financial chairman of his Building Fund Drive (Optimism: "Over the top, Your Eminence! What we plan now — with your permission, of course — is a good solid close with six Have-A-Heart Sundays!"); he had officially opened Our Lady's Center for the Sisters of Saint Ambrose, a group of nuns newly arrived in the archdiocese; he had attended a meeting of the trustees of the Public Library; he had gone to part of a baseball game, a CYO Championship Game, where the young son of his Korean gardener had pitched a shutout (Newspaper caption: "Cardinal Smilingly Looks On As Young Chinese Protege Hurls Goose Eggs At Blessed Sacrament . . ."); there had been Benediction at the seminary; in the evening he had introduced a progressive and rather peppy Dutch theologian as the principal speaker at an Ecumenical Lecture sponsored by the Ladies Auxiliary of the Corpus Christi League. He had not stayed for the talk, but for a few moments he had remained near the stage, concealed in the wings, not listening so much as watching — with a mixture of amusement and sympathy — the faces in the audience. For the most part they belonged to women with extraordinary hats. The Cardinal knew these women — or if not them, exactly, many like them; they were not young, and he had known them for a long time. He knew that tonight they were here with their heads, yes, but their hearts were at the whist parties of thirty years ago. (". . . on Monday night the regular monthly meeting of the Holy Name and Junior Holy Name Societies. On Wednesday night at 8:00 in the school auditorium Father Wilfred O'Brien, O.P., the noted

Dominican, will deliver another in his popular series of public lectures. Wednesday night's talk will be titled "The Unknown Ireland," and will be accompanied by slides taken by Father O'Brien. Admission is one dollar. On Friday night at 7:30 in the Parish Hall there will be a Bridge-Whist sponsored by the Ladies Auxiliary of the Corpus Christi League. New members of the Auxiliary are particularly urged to attend, and the proceeds will go towards defraying the parish debt. . . .")

Sunday announcements. All gone, thought the Cardinal, horse-and-buggy stuff. Or almost. And here were the ladies tonight, with their hats, looking increasingly mystified and resentful as they listened to the barely penetrable accents of the young Dutchman who was explaining their religion to them, largely by informing them that the majority of their life-long devotional practices were now considered to be worthless. The ladies, he thought, were trying valiantly to keep up with the times. As was their Cardinal. . . .

In this way he filled his days, and more than once he found himself thinking: Where's the difference? Because, obviously, his life was different now, it had to be, and yet what surprised him more than anything else, what he never failed to regard with a kind of wonder, was that most of the time there seemed to be no difference at all. Day after day he did exactly what he had been doing for years: there seemed to be no change in his routine. There seemed to be no change in *him*: he looked the same, he even felt the same. Since the time of his examination he had been preternaturally watchful for the first sign, the faintest shiver of alarm: it had not come. The truth was that he had not known a moment's pain nor had he felt anything new in the way of fatigue. He moved about at all times in apparent health; the illusion was so strong that during the first few days he had often been tempted to wonder if maybe the whole thing had not been a mistake: it was not impossible, these things had happened before. The temptation had persisted, but suddenly the Cardinal had ceased to wonder. For his own doctor had now been joined by a team of doctors; they had not disagreed. They had been tactful but positive, and now the Cardinal knew, beyond any doubt, that he had at best a few months, at worst a few weeks, to go.

He had said to them thoughtfully, "It's the *speed*: I had no idea it could travel that fast."

But it could, it could: gently, kindly, they had made that quite clear and he had been convinced. And so, convinced, he had set about putting his house in order. The archdiocese was in fairly good shape; he was not a bad administrator, he knew that, and twenty years ago, he reflected, he could have felt confidence and even pride in what he was leaving behind him. Now he was not so sure. Suddenly the new age had come in, and with it had come the new demands: had he met them? At all? What would his successor find?

Sometimes, usually late at night, when he had finished his work for the day, when he was alone or just before he went to sleep, he thought about this successor. At this point he would have given a great deal to know who he would be; as it was, however, he had no idea. He considered the possibilities, all the names that had been mentioned and speculated upon, over and over again, for several years now — when you're nearly eighty, he thought drily, the subject comes up — and in the end, he supposed, the likeliest of them was still Frank Degnan. The Cardinal knew Bishop Degnan well, for he was in charge of the adjoining diocese. Tall and silver-haired, he was nineteen years younger than the Cardinal: a middle-aged, middle-of the road figure who walked the tightrope well. In these years of Revolution in the Church he was at one moment claimed by the liberals, at the next by the conservatives; there were even those moments when, after a more-than-usually elliptical address, he was claimed by both at once. He was an effective preacher; he had few enemies; his resemblance to photographs of John Henry Newman, taken during the latter's middle years, was said to be remarkable. The Cardinal, in thinking of Bishop Degnan, realized that he had always had only one reservation about him: he thought he was a boob.

A boob but a possibility: even a strong one. The Cardinal knew that, and the thought of this majestic empty barrel rolling regularly down the center aisle of his cathedral gave him some pain. Still, nothing was settled: there was that to be thankful for. In his experience, Rome was apt to be at its most mysterious in matters of this kind. Frank Degnan might be an odds-on choice, but he was certainly no shoo-in. Nor was anyone else. They might come up with any one of a number of bishops, they might even come up with a dark horse, someone no one in his right mind would have thought of at all. It was a possibility the Cardinal of all people could not dismiss, for come to think of it, in his day, this was really what he had been himself. The darkest of the dark. . . .

And then, too, there was also this: when the moment arrived, would the decision still belong to Rome? Five years ago, even a year ago, the question would have been without point: it would have been like asking if water was still wet, or if the Grand Canyon was still there. But now . . . well, he thought, strange time, stranger changes, and as one who had sat in the Councils, observing the changes and even helping to make them, he was by no means sure which ones were coming next. In this he did not think that he was alone.

The "Boy" Fragment

ONE

WHEN I was a boy, growing up on what were then the outskirts of the small and rather ugly mill city where I was born, the one person I thought about almost all the time was my father. I worshiped him, and in a way this was strange because I very rarely saw him. He was always away, traveling, working — "Your father's on the road, dear," my mother said —, and when he came home it was only for a few days at a time, and as soon as the few days were over he went away again, and then it might be weeks or a couple of months before he came back home for another few days.

Whenever he went I missed him a lot, and I knew that my mother did, too. Usually she didn't talk much about him — usually she didn't talk much about anybody: she was mostly a quiet woman with lots of red hair and with green eyes that could look at you for a long time without blinking and with big smooth white arms that were covered with freckles —, but every time he went away, for a couple of days afterwards she talked about him all the time, and in a way that made me sure she missed him just as much as I did. Sometimes, when I was small, she would stop right in the middle of whatever she was doing around the house (we had a maid named Alma, a small slow woman with sad eyes, who did most of the cleaning up, but my mother was always busy sewing or fixing things for my father and me, or cooking, or polishing the special Waterford glass that she kept in the tall china closet and that my grandfather had given to her when she married my father), and she would call out to me, or come over to wherever I was, and say, "I was just thinking about your father, Joey." And then she would tell me different things about him. Sometimes they were things she had told me before, but I didn't mind; I liked to hear them over again. Her favorite story was about the time she first met him, when she was at this dance in the Saint James Parish Hall. She was sitting down at the side of the hall watching them dancing, and talking to some of the other girls, and all of a sudden somebody she'd never seen before came over and without even looking at the other girls just told her his name and asked her if she would dance with him!

"Just like that!" she said. "And I'd never danced with a stranger in my life, not once! But, I don't know why, I said yes, I would, and the next thing you know there we were, out on the floor, and everybody was watching us — or at least I thought they were —, and we were dancing away just as though we'd known each other all our lives! I can even remember the song we danced to. I suppose it was an old chestnut even then; it was called, 'Every Little Movement Has a Meaning All its Own. . . .' "

Once, when my father was at home, and we were all sitting in the living room after supper, I asked my father if he remembered this song, too. He said, "Joey, that's like asking me if I remember my father's name or my own birthday!"

And he stood up and went over to my mother and pulled her up on her feet. She got all pink in the face and told him not to be silly, but she was smiling and I knew she was happy. They started to dance around the room together, with my father singing:

> *Every little movement*
> *Has a meaning all its own*
> *Every little whisper*
> *Has a secret all its own. . . .*

When my mother told me about this dance she usually told me too about how my father had never been in our city before and was just staying overnight in the Stafford Hotel on his way to someplace else, and about how somebody had told him about the dance and he had looked in because he liked to dance, and about how she was the only one he danced with all night long. And that was the way they met.

I said, "And then did you get married?"

"Well, not right then, of course," she said. "Not for the longest time, in fact. But that night I remember thinking that I never met anyone I wanted to marry before. And that he was going away in the morning and might never come back. But," she said, "he did. He did!"

And she told me too that he was the handsomest man she ever saw. I guess he was: at least he always looked very handsome to me. He was pretty tall, with dark blue eyes that were almost black, and black hair that was combed down very smooth with a part on one side. I don't think I ever saw his hair mussed up, not even after we had been fooling around together. He wasn't a very mussed-up man anyway: he always wore blue or gray suits that looked as though they had just been pressed, and very fresh and clean white shirts with two gold cuff links that my mother gave him, and he always smelled good, from the after-shaving stuff he used. He had a soft kind of voice — I mean, you could always hear him fine, but he never yelled or anything like that —, and sometimes when he looked at you and got ready to say something to you he would start to smile a little, and at first you thought that meant that he was going to say something funny, but then after a while you knew that it might only mean that he was glad to be here talking to you and that he was going to tell you something that would be good to hear.

Still, he said funny things, too: plenty of them. He made me laugh more than anybody I ever met, and even my mother, who seemed to be mostly serious and thinking to herself when my father was away, began to laugh a lot when he was at home. He told jokes and stories and all about the different things that had happened to him while he was on the road. But what I really liked best were the stories that he made up out of his own head, stories that I wouldn't read or hear about anywhere else except from him. Some of them had the same people in them over and over again, but the stories were always different and they were always good ones. The ones I remember most of all were the ones he used to tell me late at night when I went up to my room and got ready for bed. Then my father would come up, sometimes with my mother, and would hear me say my prayers — "Slow down, slow down," he would say, if he thought I was hurrying through them too fast. "The story'll still be there." As soon as I finished blessing myself I would jump into bed, pull the blankets up around my neck and look up at him, waiting for him to hurry up and begin. He would look at me for a minute with a solemn face, and hold up one finger as if he was telling me to pay attention to every single word, and then, slowly and in a creepy voice, he would start. These stories were almost always about a man named Lord Crispin Trafalgar of Scotland Yard, who was so lazy he stayed in bed all day but who had England's Finest Brain, and his chief assistant Sir Chutney Lal, a midget Indian who wore a red turban and had a monocle in one eye and was always running around trying to get Lord Crispin Trafalgar out of bed so they could go out and catch criminals.

"For this was their mission!" my father would say, in his creepiest voice. "*To Rid All England of Crime!*"

What this meant mostly was that they were trying to rid all England of one Master Criminal everybody called The Toad, but who Lord Crispin Trafalgar and Sir Chutney Lal knew was really the famous actor, Stilton Mandrake. Because Stilton Mandrake was such a good actor he had all kinds of disguises nobody could see through, and so he got away with huge jewel robberies and smuggling secret formulas out of England to sell to other countries and killing prime ministers and generals and bishops by poison darts that dissolved and didn't leave any trace. Everybody always knew whenever The Toad did one of his crimes because he always left behind him a black box with a red band around it, and inside the box was a small live toad with golden eyes! Lord Crispin Trafalgar and Sir Chutney Lal were always thwarting Stilton Mandrake, and Sir Chutney kept trying to get Lord Crispin to get up and put on his clothes so that they could sneak up on the secret Scottish Island which was Stilton Mandrake's headquarters and the place where he raised his toads. But Lord Crispin always said it was too boring a journey and that he would much rather just use his Wits, and that was really what all the stories were about: Sir Chutney running around and getting into hairraising adventures while Lord Crispin thwarted The Toad with his Wits.

They were my favorite stories, and so exciting that sometimes I could hardly go to sleep. But the next night I always wanted to hear another one, and my father always told it to me. They were the best stories I ever heard.

Every time my father went away, on the night before he left he would do a whole show of his magic tricks. Sometimes he would do them just for my mother and me, but other times friends of mine I went to school with or played with would come over and we would all have cake and cookies and milk in the living room. And then, when Alma had cleared the glasses and dishes away, my father would come in, all dressed up in a tuxedo, as if he was going out to a party, and the magic show would begin. He would take a pack of cards out of his coat pocket, and the next thing you know black cards were turning into red ones right while we watched them, or we would think of a card and my father would tell us which one it was, or I would take a card and put it in my pocket and a second later my father would find the same card in Charlie Ferguson's pocket, or else he might throw all the cards, the whole pack, up in the air, and they would all come floating down and go scattering all over the floor, except the one we had picked out — and that was still up in the air, only now it was stuck to the ceiling! He did tricks with nickels and dimes and water glasses too, but the card ones were the ones we liked the best. And all the time he did them he kept talking and smiling and saying things that made everybody laugh, and when the show was over and everybody had to go home they always said they had a swell time and they all wanted to know when my father would be coming back again.

The next morning he always got up very early, and then he would call me to come into his room. My mother would be downstairs, getting a special breakfast for my father. We would go down into the front hall together, with my father carrying his new black suitcase that my mother gave him for Christmas, and me carrying his old canvas Army one, with the leather straps around it, and his name "J. DUNPHY" on it in painted black letters which were almost all faded out by now. Before I was born he had to go into the Army, but then the Kaiser gave up after a while, and he came home.

One time I said to him, "Did you ever get shot at?"

"No," he said. "Not even once."

"Did you ever shoot anybody?"

"I wasn't allowed to."

I said, "Huh?"

"Well, you see," he said, "I was always a pretty good shot, and when the Germans found out I was coming in, they started to kick like mad. They said it would spoil everything, that it wasn't fair. Apparently they had a big debate about it, and finally President Wilson said, 'Oh, all right, all right. Nobody's going to say I'm not fair.' So then he told General Pershing not to let me shoot anyone, and General Pershing came around to tell me. He said, 'I hate to do this to you, Dunphy, because I realize it may cramp your style. But I have my orders.' So he saluted me, and I saluted him, and he went back to his tent. After that everybody kept a pretty close watch on me, just to see that I didn't try any funny stuff like putting real bullets in my gun or anything like that. Oh, I tell you, Joey, it got to be a mighty rough war for me!"

I knew from the way he was talking he was only kidding, the way he always did when he really didn't want to answer what I asked him. So I never did find out if my father shot anybody or not.

Anyway, on those mornings we would go downstairs and sit down to breakfast with my mother. My mother wouldn't say very much, and my father would talk mostly to her, because I would be going down to the station with him. After a while we would hear the horn outside, and I knew it was Mr. Lacasse, who drove the taxi we always took. My father would get up and get ready to go, and then my mother, who never wanted to come to the station, would walk with him to the door, and at the door, just before we left the house, she would put her big smooth arms around his neck and hold him for a minute. Then she would give him a quick kiss and say, "Come back soon, Jack."

"Sooner than that," my father would say, and then he would hug her hard and give her another kiss, and we would be off down the front sidewalk, with my mother standing in the front doorway, waving, until we drove away in the taxi and turned the corner and she couldn't see us any more.

In the taxi my father would talk with Mr. Lacasse, who had also been in the Army and had won a medal for rescuing some soldiers that a horse had fallen on. He was a French-Canadian, like a lot of the people in our city — on account of the mills, my mother said — and when he talked fast, which was most of the time, I could hardly understand him, but my father always seemed to know what he was saying.

"I went down dere a couple of time," Mr. Lacasse said, shouting over his shoulder back at my father. "I tol' dem, 'Doan' forgot, I'm a Veterans!' An' I'm gonna tol' you dis: *dey doan' give a gosh-dam!*"

"It's a tough world," my father said.

"It doan' make no difference 'oo you are, you gotta do it, de bot' of it!"

"Right, right!" my father said, and while Mr. Lacasse went on shouting my father looked over at me and gave me a little punch on the arm. "Hi, buddy," he said.

When we got out of the taxi at the station Mr. Lacasse waited in it for me, because he would take me back to our house when my father left. My father and I went into the waiting room, which was high and gloomy and smelled of old boards and varnish. There were windows high up near the roof that were like big portholes; the sun came in through them now and you could look up and see the dust shining in the air. There were a couple of posters on the wall near the penny peanut machine that told you about how you could save money by going round-trip to places. My father stopped in front of the peanut machine and said, "Peanuts?"

It was only nine o'clock; I said, "So early?"

"Listen," my father said, "do you know what time means to a peanut? Nothing!" He put in a couple of pennies and got two handfuls: they were the little red salty kind. He took some for himself and gave me the rest, and we walked over to the window where my father was going to buy his ticket from Mr. Driscoll, an old man that had been married two times.

When my father left, he almost always went to Chicago, and then sometimes he stayed there, and other times he went on to other cities. He used to carry a map of the United States with him, and after he got his tickets we would go on board the train and sit for a few minutes in his compartment. Then we would go over the map, and he would draw with a pencil the line showing the cities he would be in — cities like Los Angeles, or San Francisco, or Saint Louis or Kansas City — before he came home the next time.

"Is that where you do your magic shows?" I said. "In all those cities?" Because by now I knew that the magic shows were what my father did for a living.

"Every one," he said. "The hand is quicker than the eye in every blessed one!" And then he would pull just a single card out of his pocket and hold it up in front of me, and suddenly it would disappear. He showed me the front of his hand and then the back, and then he kept turning it back and forth, and I knew that the card was there somewhere, but I could never see it until he stopped and let me.

Then he pulled me down on the seat beside him, and we talked for a while, and pretty soon the conductor would shout, "B-o-o-a-rd!", and I knew it was time for me to go. My father walked out onto the station platform with me, and gave me five dollars, telling me to spend one dollar for a present for my mother, and to keep the rest and spend it on myself. Then the conductor shouted again, my father ran his hand over my head, mussing up my hair, and then gave me a fast tight hug and swung himself back onto the train, sometimes even waiting until it began to move. I ran along after it for a while, but then it started to move too fast, so I stopped and just watched it and my father waving from the back platform until it went under the bridge and out of sight, and then I went back to the taxi and Mr. Lacasse.

TWO

Every once in a while my father would say to me that some things were very hard to change, but that if somehow he could only work it out right, then he might be able to be home a lot more. But I guess he could never do that, because by the time I was ten and going into the fifth grade at Grover Street School he had to be away just as much as ever. When he was away there was usually only my mother and me in the house, along with Alma. Alma lived up in her room on the third floor, and when she wasn't cleaning up around the house, she spent all her time up there, playing the radio that my father gave her. We had two other radios in our house: the big one in the living room (which we didn't tune in much because my mother, who liked to listen sometimes at night to orchestra music, said she would rather listen to our Victrola, which didn't have static and a lot of people talking nonsense) and the one I made with Charlie Ferguson out of an old oatmeal box and a crystal and a cat's whisker and a set of earphones. When my father came home one time he put a long wire up the side of the house and onto the chimney for an aerial. That night I went up to my room with Charlie and we were both all excited, not just because we were going to listen to the radio, but because it was one we made ourselves.

"How far do you think we'll get?" Charlie said.

"I don't know," I said. "Maybe a hundred miles."

"Will we get different cities?"

"I guess so. It says that all you need is a good aerial and ours is a swell one. So we'll probably get lots of them."

So Charlie took one of the earphones and I took the other, and we both listened, not knowing what was going to happen, while I moved the cat's whisker, very slowly, over the crystal. Right away we heard something like a crackling sound and we looked at each other, knowing that it was working, and I kept moving the cat's whisker around and then, all of a sudden, we could hear, very weakly, "Dah dit dah dit!"

"Oh boy!" Charlie said, and I did too, because we both knew that what we were getting was Morse code.

"Maybe it's sending out SOS!" Charlie said.

"It's probably a ship in distress!" I said.

"And suppose we're the only ones that hear it!" Charlie said. "Should we tell somebody?"

I said, "Let's listen some more first." So we did, and I kept moving the cat's whisker around, most of the time getting nothing but the crackling sound, and then coming back and getting the "Dah dit" again. By now we had looked it up in a Boy Scout book I had, and found out that it probably wasn't an SOS, and it didn't sound like any kind of message at all. So we kept listening for a couple of hours, and nothing else happened, and then we tried the next night and everything was just the same, with the crackling sound most of the time, and every once in a while the "dah dit" going over and over again. After this we listened some more nights with nothing different happening at all, except that one time Charlie got all excited and said to listen, listen, because he just heard some music. So I listened but I couldn't hear anything except what I heard all the time, and then Charlie said he wasn't really positive that he heard it after all. Finally one night we didn't even get the "dah dit" and after that we didn't listen much any more, because it was all getting kind of boring, and anyhow, we had lots of other things to do.

But Alma never stopped listening to her radio whenever she was up in her room. She had regular times for what she called "my favorite programs," and she fixed her work so that she could look at the big man's watch she carried around with her and all of a sudden put down the dry mop or the dust cloth and hurry up the stairs. My mother said that this was all right because it didn't happen too often and besides, she said, it was the only chance she got to see Alma move fast. So that what happened was that she went up to her radio about three times every day, but the program she really liked best of all didn't come on until early at night. It came on every night just after we finished our supper, and as soon as Alma cleared the table and put the dishes in the sink I could hear her start to run out of the kitchen and up the back stairs, going fast so that she wouldn't miss the beginning of "Amos 'n' Andy." Sometimes I went up to listen, too, because she said I could any time she had her favorite programs on.

When I did we always sat the same way, with me on the foot of the old iron bed that had been painted white, and Alma all scrunched back in the broken-down old easy chair that was all stained and lumpy and covered with the kind of scratchy green cloth they have in trains. This was her chair that she brought with her when she came to work for us.

"This used to be my Pa's chair," she told me one time, "that he gave to me the day he died. Bessie wanted it and so did Dorothy and so did my Aunt Helen, but he didn't give it to them. He gave it to me. 'You take it, Alma,' he said. 'It's yours!' So I took it. I took this chair right out of that house that very day. I never go anywhere without this chair. It was my Pa's Good Luck Chair!"

I said, "Did your Pa have lots of good luck?"

"Not so much as he should of," she said, "with all the praying he did. Morning, noon and night, it was just the two of them: God and him. My Pa didn't drink and he didn't smoke, and all his life he belonged to the De Molay and the Masons. But he died poor. He didn't care beans. 'The world belongs to the wicked, Alma,' he'd say to me, 'and I ain't wicked, so that's that! Praise Him from Whom all blessings flow!' My Pa was a fine man. He could of been a millionaire. But he wasn't Wicked!"

I asked my mother why Alma talked so much about praying and being wicked and my mother said it was because she was a Protestant. We were all Catholics, but we never had any Catholic maids, and I think this might have been mainly because of my grandfather, who kept on saying it was crazy to have Catholic maids working for you.

"You all know how I feel about Ireland," he'd say, "but I tell you this: if you've got one of those little Irish girls in the house, you've got a bum buy! They gab all the time about your business to the other little Irish girls! They've got to have time off on Sundays and holy days of obligation so's they can go to Mass! That means just when you need them most, they're never there! And then just when you've broken them in so they're the least bit of good to you, off they go to marry a fireman! No no, get yourself a good Swamp Yankee! A good homely Swamp Yankee! She may not go to church every five minutes, but I tell you you'll get your money's worth!"

After this I asked my mother if Alma was a Swamp Yankee, but she just told me she didn't want me to say things like that, and that it was only my grandfather's way of talking. And from the way she said it I know that Alma *was* a Swamp Yankee, even though I still didn't know what a Swamp Yankee was.

Anyway, on these radio nights Alma would run up to her room, take off her regular shoes and put on her old brown cloth carpet slippers with the Indian beads stuck in them that spelled out "Grand Canyon," and then she would sit in her Pa's Good Luck Chair and listen to "Amos 'n' Andy." I would listen too for a while, but I really didn't like it very much, so while Alma was sitting there looking at the radio and listening with her mouth hanging open, hearing everything that Amos said and that Andy said, and every once in a while making a funny choking sound that was like a laugh, I would walk around the room, looking at things. There wasn't very much to look at: just some old furniture we used to have downstairs that Alma had wanted — a big bureau full of drawers with a mirror on the top, a beat-up cedar chest, a couple of wooden chairs, and a hatrack that she took up from the back hall that didn't have anything on it. Everything in the room — except her Pa's Good Luck Chair — belonged to us, but none of it looked like ours any more, and in a funny way the whole room didn't look or feel as if it belonged in our house at all. This was probably because Alma had had it all by herself for so long.

About the only interesting thing in Alma's room was a picture she had, but it was a picture you weren't even supposed to know she had. One night when I was up there, walking around and balancing myself on one foot, I slipped and banged up against the bureau. That was where she kept her Bible, and this time it must have been too close to the edge, because now it fell over onto the floor, and when it did a picture which must have been inside it came out and landed right next to my feet. The noise made Alma jump and she got up to pick up her Bible, but I don't think she knew yet that the picture had fallen out. So I picked it up and it was a picture of a man with slick black hair parted in the middle and a thin black moustache under his nose and his eyes half shut as if he might be going to sleep. Right across the bottom part of the picture was writing in white ink that said, "Ever yours sincerely, Ricardo Cortez." I held it out to her and said, "Who's this of?"

And when she saw it she got all red in the face and ran over to me and snatched it out of my hand.

"Never you mind who that's of," she said, and she went over and put the picture in the top drawer of her bureau and shut the drawer tight. "That's none of your business," she said. "That's *my* picture."

"Did I ever meet him?" I said.

"No," she said. "Nobody around here's ever met him. He's famous."

"What's he famous at?" I said.

"He's in the movies," she said. "He's a big movie star."

"Is he a good friend of yours?" I said.

"I didn't say that," she said.

"Then why did he send you his picture?"

"Never you mind," she said. "I guess that's my business."

"Is he going to marry you?"

She got all red in the face again, and started to duck her head. She was nice but kind of homely, with a long skinny head and dead-looking hair.

She took off her glasses and looked in the mirror for a second, and then she put them back on so she could see and went back to her Pop's Good Luck Chair.

"You just mind your business," she said. "That's all."

And then she went back to listening to Amos and to Andy, who by now had almost finished. But most nights when she listened she could listen all the way through without stopping, and when it was all over she would get up and turn off her radio and keep on shaking her head from one side to the other.

"Those two coons!' she said. "They're a caution!"

She told me that Andy's father used to be a slave, but I didn't see how this could be, because Charlie Ferguson's father, the foot doctor, who listened all the time to "Amos 'n' Andy" and who knew all about them, said that they weren't Negroes at all, they were really white people who only pretended to be Negroes. But when I told this to Alma she said it was the craziest thing she ever heard.

"I know how white people talk," she said. "They talk just like you and me. And I know how coons talk. They talk just like Amos 'n' Andy. That's just common sense. You don't want to believe everything people tell you!"

Then she asked me which one I liked best, Amos or Andy, and I said I didn't know, because when I listened to them half the time I didn't know which was which.

"That's because you don't pay attention," she said. "Amos is the best one. Oh, Andy's good, but he's a bluffer. Amos is the one that owns the taxi. The Fresh Air Taxi. And goes 'Ah-waa!' " And she would stand by her radio and do an imitation of Amos, opening her mouth wide and saying "Ah-waa, ah-waa, ah-waa!" It didn't sound very much like the Amos on the radio, but I guess she liked to do it anyway, because some times, on nights when I didn't go up with her to listen, I would be downstairs lying down in the living room, reading, and every once in a while I could hear her up in her room going, "Ah-waa, ah-waa," right through the door and everything.

Most of the time, though, when Alma was downstairs, she never talked about her friend Ricardo Cortez or Amos and Andy or anything like that. She would either go around by herself, cleaning up the house and sometimes humming parts of Protestant hymns to herself, or else she would be talking to my mother about things like how her feet used to hurt her until this nurse she knew told her about a different kind of shoes and now she was okay, or about how she knew a dentist once who killed a man by giving him too much Novocain, or about how her Aunt Helen was still in the hospital after two years only now she was going crazy and thought she was only twelve years old, or about how her sister Bessie who was famous for her pound cakes but had got sick all of a sudden and now had to go to the bathroom every hour. My mother would go on doing whatever she was doing, and every once in a while she would say things like "I see," or "I know," or "Well, she has her own life to live," and Alma would keep on talking until my mother got tired of listening and either went out in the yard or else went to the phone to call Mr. Lacasse to come in his taxi to take her out shopping. And, if it was Saturday, or some other day that I didn't have any school, or if Charlie Ferguson was busy or his mother wouldn't let him come out, I would go out and walk up through the fields until I came to Cary's Pond, and then I would take the shortcut down along the Doremus Canal that took me to the old part of the city where my grandfather lived and where he had his drug store.

THREE

My grandfather, who was my mother's father — I never got to meet my other grandfather, partly because he didn't come from around here, but also because he died when I was little — was quite a small man, but you never knew this when you went into his drug store and saw him sitting down on his chair in the back room. This is where he was most of the time, because from this chair he could look out through a peep hole in the wall — from the front you couldn't tell the peep hole was there unless you knew about it: it was just a tiny little hole about as big as a dime, next to the Castoria bottles and right over the witch hazel — to see who was coming into the store. Then, if Fred, the other druggist who worked for him, was busy, or if Onesime the soda clerk hadn't come in yet, my grandfather would get down off his chair, put on his starched white druggist's coat, and go out into the store to wait on the customers. When he did this you were always surprised to see how small he was standing up, because sitting down he looked like just a normal-sized man.

Still, even though he was so small, quite a lot of people seemed to be scared of him. He had a loud voice — which might have gotten that way from talking to my grandmother, who stayed mostly at home and was deaf —, and when he said anything to you, you could tell from the way he said it he was positive he was right and that he didn't expect you to argue much with him. I never knew anybody but my mother who would answer him back, and that was only at special times when I heard them talking about my father. I never knew what they were saying, because even when I could hear it I couldn't understand it, but I knew that whatever it was my mother didn't like it, because all of a sudden she would say, not shouting, but fast, and interrupting whatever he was saying, "Stop it! Stop it now, Pa! And I mean right now!" And whenever she said this my grandfather would look at her for a minute, his face all mad, but he *would* stop it, and then he would start to talk about something else and in a voice that wasn't quite so loud. But this didn't happen too often, and mostly my mother would just listen and knit or do something else while my grandfather was talking about how the city wasn't as good as it used to be, or about how Father Corrigan was getting too big for his britches, or about what everybody was doing that was wrong.

My grandfather was pretty old by now, of course, with a high, bony, kind of hollowed-out face, and a long droopy moustache which was partly white but which had been stained all brown in the center because of all the cigarettes he smoked. He had thin white eyebrows and light blue eyes — sometimes, when he looked at you, if the sun was shining in his face, it almost looked as if his eyes had no special color at all. His hair was white, and at first you thought he had a lot of it, but then after a while you could see that what had happened was that he had pulled some long white hairs from low down on one side of his head up across the top and down to the other side, and when he bent his head toward you, you could see right down through all these thin hairs to the pink skin underneath. You had to be careful when you did this, though, because my grandfather didn't like to have people looking down through his hair, and if he thought that this was what you were doing he would straighten right up and look at you with his light blue eyes and ask you in his loud voice if there was something special you were staring at.

Usually when I went to see him in his drug store I would go right in past the soda fountain and the high stools and the four white marble tables where people who didn't want to drink their sodas or eat their college ices up at the fountain could sit, and up past the boxes of chocolates and then past the cigars and the hair tonic and stuff and then in through the doorway that had the heavy brown curtain across it and that led into the back room. When I got in the first thing I always saw was my grandfather sitting on his chair, and I knew that he had been watching me all the way in through his peep hole.

"Hello, boy," he would say, and no matter who was there he would always hold out his cheek for me to kiss it.

"Hello, Grampa," I would say, and then I would go to him and kiss him on his high bony cheek, and he would turn his head and kiss me back, and I would always smell his special smell, which was moustache and peppermints and cigarettes.

He would hold me back with his arm then and look at me and say, "How's your Ma?"

"Fine, Grampa. She's fine."

Then he would turn to whoever else was there and say, "You all know the grandson, I think? Peg's boy?"

And usually they all did, because usually they were the same people that were always there when I came in. There was Mr. Cleary, the undertaker, and Mr. Williams, the policeman, and Dr. Brady, who sent all his patients to my grandfather to get their prescriptions filled, and Mr. McManus, who had the hardware store and was thinking of becoming Mayor, and Mr. O'Donnell, who didn't do anything special but whose shoes were always shined very bright and who always had a new flower in his buttonhole. All of them weren't always there together, but they would come in and go out, with always a few of them there at the same time, and then there might be some men from out of the city who were salesmen — "drummers," my grandfather called them — who worked for different medicine companies and who came in to give my grandfather samples of what they were selling.

After I had said hello to all of them I would go over in the back so that I wouldn't be in the way, and I would sit down on one of the Simple Syrup barrels that hadn't been opened yet, or else on the steps that went up to my grandfather's little upstairs office. I would just sit there and listen while all of them talked. It was pretty nice, being there, especially on summer days, because even though the front part had two big fans in the ceiling that were always going around slowly, here in the back it was always kind of dark and cool and full of a good drug store smell. My grandfather would keep talking, along with all the others, and while he talked he kept measuring and mixing and pouring things from different colored bottles, or grinding up other things with his mortar and pestle. He didn't stop or look up much, except when he wanted to see what a prescription said, or when somebody didn't agree with what he said and wanted to argue with him. The one who argued with him the most was Mr. Cleary, the undertaker. He was a big fat man who laughed a lot and always was poking Dr. Brady in the ribs and calling him, "my partner in crime." He was always talking to my grandfather about what happened to people after they died, and all the others would always listen to him when he talked about this, because that's what he did for a living.

"A simple question, P.J.," he said. P.J. was what all the men called my grandfather. "A very simple question: *how do we know?*"

My grandfather, not looking up, said, "I'll give you a simple answer, Cleary. *We know because we know.* Now if that's too simple for you, I'll put it another way. We know because we're told. We know because we have faith. We know because we believe. And we know because it's only common sense. *That's* how we know. Fred, the *nux vomica.*"

Fred was the other druggist who only mixed things and filled prescriptions when my grandfather was out. The rest of the time he just ran around getting my grandfather what he needed and carrying heavy bundles up from the cellar. He was very tall and skinny with little pale hands, and he didn't talk very much. When all the other men were here with my grandfather he didn't talk at all. Anyway, Mr. Cleary said, "I know what we're told, P.J. And I know what I see. Every day and every night of the week. And I've never seen anything to tell me what we have waiting for us on the other side. For all I know it could be blue skies and an eighteen hole golf course, or it could be the big black hole without any bottom!"

And he laughed at this and gave a big wink to Dr. Brady.

"I'll tell you what's on the other side," my grandfather said, still not looking up. "I won't tell you what's on the other side for *you*, Cleary, but I'll tell you what's there for normal human beings. In general. There's heaven. There's hell. There's purgatory. And there's limbo if you're a child."

"That's good sound doctrine, P.J.," said Mr. O'Donnell, wiping some dust off his shiny shoes. "That's straight from the Baltimore Catechism. As I remember it."

"Well, here's something straight from Arthur Cleary," said Mr. Cleary, who's seen more dead people than anybody who ever had anything to do with the Baltimore Catechism or the Detroit Catchism or the New York City Catechism. "And I tell you that in all my years of wheeling them in and shipping them out and pumping them up and fixing their faces so they'll look ten times better laid out than they did when they were alive, I've never gotten the slightest hint that anything was happening at all! Oh, I couldn't tell you the times I've been all alone in my little beauty parlor in the middle of the night, putting the final polish on someone I'd tipped my hat to only the day before, and now he was cold as a mackerel! And I couldn't tell you the times I've just reached down with my two thumbs — just like this! — and pushed back very carefully on the eyelids so I could look right down into the eyes and say, 'All right: *is there anything to it at all?* You're there now; you know. So if there's anything there, show me! *Give me a sign!*' "

He said this in a whispery voice, and even though I knew I was here in the drug store, and could look up and see my grandfather and everybody else standing around, it was still scary and spooky, because all I could think of was Mr. Cleary, all by himself with the dead man stretched out on a table, bending over him with his big thumbs pushing up his eyelids, and his big face all swollen and laughing and whispering his questions while he kept looking into the dead man's eyes! I scrunched back as far as I could on the steps, but I didn't want to leave, either, and I just kept holding my breath and looking at Mr. Cleary until all of a sudden he said in his normal voice, "Well. The point of it is, you see, that in all those years and from all those eyes, do you know what I got in return? Nothing! Not so much as a flicker!"

"Well well well," Mr. McManus said. He lit his big cigar and said, "Tell me this, Arthur: do you use much *lignum vitae* in your work?"

Mr. Cleary looked at him and said, "What?"

"*Lignum vitae,*" Mr. McManus said. "For the coffins, you know. *Lignum vitae* is the hardest wood known to man. Or so I'm told. I believe it's extensively used in the manufacture of bowling balls."

'If you come right down to that," Mr. Williams the policeman said, "what's the matter with oak? I mean, if it's hardness you're after. Something that'll last. For anything like that you can't do better than oak. Or mahogany either, if you want to go in for that kind of money."

"Both very suitable," Mr. Cleary said, "in their way. Of course there's nothing quite like enduring bronze." Then he looked over at my grandfather and said, "Well, P.J.? What do you say? Are you going to give me my answer? Or are you going to keep me waiting as long as one of my little patients?"

"So you want an answer!" my grandfather said, talking all of a sudden in his real loud voice. He put all his mixing stuff and bottles down and looked right at Mr. Cleary with his light blue eyes. "You're a great man for answers, aren't you, Cleary? Hah? You want an answer from me. You want an answer from a dead man. And you want an answer from Almighty God Himself! There are you, in your little morgue at midnight, just you and your corpse and your chemistry set, and what do you do but ask idiot questions to something that can't possibly answer you. And why? *Because the soul is gone!* And when you ask your foolish questions, when you ask him to move a finger or to blink a blue eye, you're not asking him for a sign! What you're really doing is asking Almighty God for a miracle! 'Just give me the loaves and the fishes all over again, O Lord, and I'll believe!' Isn't that a great faith, though? Doubting Thomas the Apostle and Arthur B. Cleary the Undertaker! I'd be ashamed of myself if I were you, Cleary, even daring to ask a thing like that! A man with your training and background to be discussing the Faith as if you were a superstitious peasant or a child! Why you're hardly any better than that poor little Canuck out there!"

And my grandfather waved his hand at the peep hole, and I knew that he meant Onesime the soda clerk. My grandfather was never mean to Onesime and I guess he liked him all right, but he always talked about him as if something was wrong with him. I didn't know what this was, unless it was maybe that he was a French Canadian. He was always very nice to me, and I liked him fine, and when I would go out and talk to him while he made me an ice cream soda — every time I came over to my grandfather's drug store I could go out and sit up at the fountain and have a free soda —, putting more ice cream in it than anybody else I ever saw, he would always laugh and joke with me and tell me about when he was a boy up in Quebec, Canada. He was a kind of funny looking man in a way, because even though he wasn't very old he had all white hair and very weak eyes which were even a lighter blue in color than my grandfather's. I remember that when I saw him the first time I went into the back room where my grandfather and his friends were and I asked why Onesime looked like that.

"That's because he's what they call an albumen," Mr. Williams said.

"Come come come, Charlie!" Dr. Brady said. "*Albumen!*"

"Albino!" my grandfather said, suddenly seeming to get mad. "Albino, not albumen! Albumen's the white of an egg! Good God Almighty, Williams, the boy's here to listen to some intelligent adult conversation! And what kind of conversation does he hear? *Albumen!*"

Anyway, I liked to talk to Onesime, even though he talked like Mr. Lacasse, although not so fast. I asked him if he was really an albino, and he said he was, and then I asked him if there were lots of other albinoes in his family, and he said no, he was the only one. And then one day, when there was nobody else in the front part of the drug store, he looked around and reached into his wallet and took out a picture. He handed it to me and said, " 'Ere, Joey: jes' took a look on dis. Jes' see if it's anybodys you reckonize, dere!"

And I looked and saw it was a picture of two little boys, maybe even smaller than me, and the funny thing was that both of them, even though they were so small, had little black cassocks on, just like priests. There was an arrow in blue ink on the picture which pointed to one of the boys, and when I looked again I saw it looked just like Onesime, only when he was a boy.

I said, "Is that you, Onesime? When you were little?"

"You bet you!" he said. "You reckonize me, anh?" He seemed happy that I did, and he took his picture back and looked at it for a minute. Then he laughed. "By gosh darn, Joey, I change some since dose day, anh?"

"What were you dressed up like that for?" I said. "Were you an altar boy?"

He laughed again. "Not jes' an altar boy," he said. "No sir! A real pries'! Dey was gonna make a pries' on me, Joey! In de seminaries dere, up in Saint Jovite! My fadder and mudder, dey sent me dere w'en I was a li'l kid! I bet you never saw a pries' so small as me before!" He held up the picture again and said, " 'Ey, Joey: 'ow you like my rosary bead? Pretty good, anh?"

And I could see when I looked at the picture again that he had this great big rosary with tremendous beads all wrapped around him like a rope and hanging down almost to the ground. What surprised me, though, wasn't the big rosary, but instead it was the picture and everything Onesime was saying, because all of the priests I had ever seen were grown men, as old as my father or my grandfather, even, and when I saw Onesime and his friend in their little cassocks I wondered if it was all different up there, and if they had a lot of boy-priests going around to different churches all over Canada. It gave me a kind of funny feeling, and I was glad when Onesime told me that wasn't the way it was at all, and that he had never gotten to be a real priest but had only studied to be one for a while. He said that up where he lived there were plenty of places just full of little kids whose fathers and mothers had sent them away to be priests some day after they had studied for a long time, maybe years and years and years. Onesime said he hadn't studied too long, and that he had quit after only a couple of years. When I asked him why he just scratched his head and humped up his shoulders and looked as if he didn't remember any more.

At first, when I thought over what he had said, I really didn't believe all of it, but later in the back room when I asked my grandfather he said that it was all true, and not to be surprised because that was the way they did things up there.

"A very primitive people, the Canucks," he said. "They're not at all like us."

"Not too much culture there, would you say, P.J.?" said Mr. O'Donnell, who was the only one in back with him at the time.

"No no, none at all," my grandfather said. "Even their language is a queer jabber that nobody but themselves can understand: part French, part English, and part squirrel for all I know. And their priests are no better than the rest of them. I yield to no man in my respect for the clergy, you all know that, but the Canuck priests are a poor lot. Trouble makers, you know."

"They're apt to go into business for themselves quite a bit, isn't that it?" Mr. O'Donnell said. "*Skismatics*, I believe they call them."

"Oh, yes," my grandfather said. "There's no real faith there. And they're very backward as well. Don't ever go to confession to a Canuck priest if you can help it. You could tell them you murdered your mother that morning, and unless you told them in that broken lingo of theirs they'd give you three Hail Marys and tell you to go home and have wine with your dinner. Oh yes, a very ignorant crowd. I have it on good authority they're a great embarrassment to the Holy See!"

But I liked Onesime anyway, even if the Canucks were like that, and even if he did quit the seminary a long time ago and became just plain Onsime behind my grandfather's soda fountain instead of a priest who could say Mass and everything.

One day when I went to my grandfather's drug store a little bit later than I usually did, I saw a priest I had never seen before come in, all by himself, and sit down at one of the marble tables. He was an old man, who must have been as old as my grandfather or maybe even older, except that he had lots of white hair which was parted right in the middle, and big thick eyebrows which you noticed right away because they didn't match his white hair but instead were very black. He was tall and thin and walked very straight, and when he came into the drug store he didn't look anywhere but straight ahead, and went right to his table in a kind of slow marching way, one foot going right in front of the other. When he sat down he sat very straight, too, not bending or leaning on the table, and even though he didn't call over to Onesime or even look at him, almost as soon as he sat down Onesime was hurrying over to him with an ice cream soda which was so full it was spilling over the sides.

" 'Ere you are, Fadder," he said. "One coffee hice cream soda, hextra special, jes' de way you like it!'"

And the old priest nodded at him, but without any smile at all, and said something to him that I couldn't hear, and then he began to drink his coffee ice cream soda very slowly. And after this there were lots of days when I was there that he came in after me, always all by himself, and always sitting at the same table, and always with Onesime running right over to him with the extra special coffee ice cream soda. Sometimes there were other people standing or sitting at the fountain, waiting for their own sodas, but Onesime always came over to the old priest first, no matter who was there before him. At first I thought that this was because Onesime had started out to be a priest himself, but I didn't know. And then one day, when no one was around and Onesime stayed by the priest's table a little longer than usual, I heard them talking a few words to each other, and I could tell they were talking in French. So then I thought that maybe Onesime had known him up in Canada, and that he was maybe one of the Canuck priests my grandfather talked about. When I asked Onesime, though, he told me that the old priest wasn't a Canuck at all and he hadn't even been up in Canada.

" 'E's Hirish, Joey," he said. "Jes' like you. An' your Grampa. An 'e comes from right aroun' 'ere. 'Ow come you doan' know dat? I'm surprise on you. Dat's Fadder Sheridan!"

From the way he said it I guess I was supposed to know who Father Sheridan was, but I didn't. I hadn't even heard anyone talk about him. So I decided to ask my grandfather about him, but then, just as I was going to do that one day, my grandfather began to talk about him himself. He was looking out through his peep hole and all of a sudden he said, "Back again! His Reverence!"

All the other men seemed to know who he was talking about, even though they didn't look. Mr. McManus said, "A human tragedy, that. I thought he'd be dead by now. How old would he be, would you say, P.J.?"

"No older than me," my grandfather said. "But it's not a question of age, McManus. Not with him."

"Aged in the wood, more likely," Mr. Cleary said. "Still, it's a different kind of beverage for him in here, at any rate. Is there a clerical discount for ice cream sodas, P.J.?"

"He pays," my grandfather said. "I'll say that for him. He pays."

Dr. Brady said, "I haven't seen him in years. Professionally, that is. I suppose he's still on the best of terms with our old friend John Barleycorn?"

"Easy, easy," my grandfather said, and I saw that he was looking at me, sitting there on the steps. "Little pitchers have big ears, gentlemen." Which was what he sometimes said when he suddenly remembered I was here and he didn't want me to hear any more of what they were talking about. When that happened he usually began to talk about something else, but I guess he must have forgotten to do that today, because he looked back through the peep hole again and after a couple of seconds he said, "At one point, some years ago, I tell you what I would have done any time I saw that man: *I would have taken my hat off to him!*"

"A brilliant man," Mr. McManus said, nodding his head and puffing on his cigar. "Our own Cardinal Newman. They say he can read Latin the way you and I would read the baseball scores."

"But today," my grandfather said, going on with what he was saying, and looking at everybody, one after the other, the way he sometimes did whenever he was going to say something important, "today, do you know what I'd do? *I'd keep that hat on!*"

"Oh, there's no doubt about it," Dr. Brady said. "He did wrong, very wrong."

"He did the worst thing a priest could do!" my grandfather said, his voice getting loud again. "By his behavior he gave scandal! And we all know what the Gospel says on that one: 'But who shall offend these little ones, put a millstone round his neck and drown him in the sea!'"

"Which little ones are those, P.J.?" Mr. O'Donnell said.

"Good God Almighty, O'Donnell!" my grandfather said, and you could see he was getting mad. "It's like talking to a child, talking to you! I'm using a figure of speech: little ones means all of us! In general! We're all of us God's children!"

I kept looking at my grandfather, thinking of him and Mr. Cleary and Dr. Brady as little ones, when Mr. Cleary, who was at the peep hole, said, "Hello! I wouldn't be surprised if God's children weren't due for a little visit!"

"What?" my grandfather said, looking at him.

Mr. Cleary pointed to the peep hole. "See for yourself," he said. "His Reverence!"

My grandfather went over to the peep hole as fast as he could, but even before he had a chance to look through, the brown curtain across the doorway was pushed back and there in the doorway, not coming in or going back, but just standing there, not moving, was Father Sheridan! And maybe it was because I never expected to see him there, or because he was there so fast it was almost like magic — I mean, my grandfather just was talking about him and the curtain whooshed back and there he was, tall and thin and not even moving, looking as though he might have been there all the time, listening — that when I saw him I could hardly breathe! He looked like a kind of a ghost, with his black suit and his pale face and his white hair and black eyes that seemed to be way deep in his head, and all I could think of when I looked at him was what my grandfather had said about him: "*He did the worst thing a priest could do!*" I didn't know what this was, but I knew it must be something pretty awful and I wondered if he might not do it now, all over again, or if my grandfather, who was so mad at him he wouldn't even take off his hat to him any more, would suddenly begin to yell at him in his loudest voice and, even though he was a priest, tell him to get out of his drug store and stay out!

But nothing like this happened at all. For a minute nobody did anything, with Father Sheridan just standing where he was, still not moving, and my grandfather and his friends not moving much, either, and not saying anything. Then, suddenly, Father Sheridan took a step forward, right into the room, and looked at all the men and said, "P.J. Gentlemen. The Theology Club is still in session, I see."

He had a very deep voice, the kind of voice I didn't expect him to have at all, partly because it was kind of nice to listen to. My grandfather, instead of getting mad and shouting the way I was sure he would, just said in a polite fast voice, "Good afternoon, Father." And then all the others said good afternoon Father, too, just like my grandfather, not as if they were mad at him at all, but in a funny kind of hurried-up way, as if they didn't want him to be mad at them, either.

After this nobody said anything right away, with Father Sheridan standing now in front of the doorway, not smiling, looking just the same as when he had come in, kind of still and white and spooky. He didn't even seem to see me, and I was glad of that, although by now, even though I was still a little scared, I wasn't scared quite as much, because I could see that my grandfather had decided to be nice to Father Sheridan and that nothing bad would probably happen.

My grandfather coughed a little now and said, "Well, Father. This is a warm day. For this time of year."

"It is warm, P.J.," Father Sheridan said, in his deep voice. "But then, it is July, P.J."

After this nobody said anything at all. After another wait Mr. Cleary all of a sudden gave his big laugh and said, "I'll tell you this much, Father: in my profession we have very few kind words to say for the month of July! July is not exactly known as your undertaker's friend!"

Mr. McManus laughed at this and said, "There's one good thing about that, Art. I'll bet ten cents you get no complaints from your clients!"

"True enough," Mr. Cleary said. "True enough. You might even say that my little clients were in the nature of silent partners!"

Then the other men laughed at this, and I saw that they were all looking over at Father Sheridan, I guess expecting him to laugh, too. But he didn't; he didn't even smile. He just looked back at them, just the way he had since he came into the room. Then suddenly he looked away from them, and for the first time since he came in he looked right at me! I wanted to look away from him, but I couldn't, because his deep black eyes were looking at me in their steady way, and all I could do was look back at him, feeling kind of scared again and wondering what was going to happen next. But what happened was that Father Sheridan turned to my grandfather and said, "I haven't met this young man as yet."

My grandfather kind of jumped at this and said in the hurried-up way, "The grandson, Father. Peg's boy. You remember Peg of course, Father? The daughter? Stand up, boy! Where are your manners!"

And he started to swing his short arms back and forth, as if he was trying to help shove me up on my feet. Usually, of course, I would have stood up as soon as a priest came into the room, but this time, what with being kind of scared and everything, I had just stayed right on the steps, as far back as I could get. But now I stood up, as fast as I could, with my grandfather still swinging his arms as if I wasn't getting up fast enough, and with Father Sheridan just standing there with his hands in back of him, just the way they had been since he came in. Then he took one of his hands and stuck it out in front of him; I saw that it was long and white and just a little shaky. He bent one finger at me, signaling for me to come closer to him. So I went, slowly, and when I got almost to him, my grandfather said, in his loud important voice, "This is Father Sheridan, boy. Speak up now and say hello to Father."

And I would have said hello, just the way he told me to, but Father Sheridan put up his hand and said, "He's a boy, not a parrot. I'll take it for granted he can say hello." Then, looking down at me, he said, "Tell me your first name."

"Joe, Father," I said. Then, I don't know why, I said, "Or Joey."

"Joe. Or Joey," he said, in his deep voice. "I've seen you in here often. You like to come here, do you?"

I just nodded my head, and then he nodded his. "That's understandable," he said. "The conversation of wise men is always attractive."

And then he looked around, slowly, first at my grandfather, then at all the others, almost as though he was waiting for them to say something. But I guess they didn't want to, and they didn't even seem really to be looking much at him, but more at each other instead. So after a few seconds he looked back at me and suddenly he said, "How is your father?"

And I was so surprised I didn't answer him right away, not only because I didn't even know he knew my father, but also because whenever I met anybody at my grandfather's they almost never said anything about my father. They always said, "How is your mother," I suppose because she was born over here and they had known her a long time, while my father was still kind of a stranger to them. So I didn't expect it at all when Father Sheridan asked me his question, but after I got over being surprised I was glad he did, and I said, "He's fine, Father." And then I said, "Do you know my father?"

He nodded his head, just once and only a little way forward. He said, "Oh yes. I know him quite well. He's a fine man. Will you tell him that Father Sheridan was asking for him?"

I said, "Yes, Father."

He gave his short nod again and said, "Good boy." Then he put out his hand to me and said, "Goodbye, Joe."

I said, "Goodbye, Father," and I shook hands with him. I couldn't see whether his hand was still a little shaky or not when he took mine, but it didn't feel shaky: it felt very dry and smooth and strong. Then he backed up so that he was standing in the doorway once more, and I knew that he was going to go. He reached up and grabbed the brown curtain with one hand, but before he pulled it he stopped and said to me, "How old are you, Joe?"

"Nine and a half, Father," I said.

"Nine and a half," he said. "A good age." He looked at my grandfather and his friends again, and then he said, "Just about the ideal age, I would think, for the general conversational level. Goodbye, P.J. Gentlemen." And he stepped back and pulled the curtain in front of him and he was gone. He went so fast that he didn't even have time to shake hands with my grandfather or with any of the other men.

After he was gone everybody seemed to get mad at him all over again. My grandfather ran over to the peep hole, I guess to watch Father Sheridan go out the front door. When he turned around again so that I could see him his face was all red, and the big blue vein was sticking out on his forehead, and even his thin white hairs which were usually combed out just right were now all mussed up and he even looked more like a bald man than anything else. He was so mad that he could hardly talk. I never saw him so mad, and I didn't even know why.

"Only one thing in the world stood between that man and the worst lashing he ever got in his life!" he said, and he was really yelling. "And that is the respect I have for the Roman collar!"

"As well as the presence of the boy, of course," Dr. Brady said. "I think all of us were thinking of that. I know I was. Otherwise . . ."

"And the presence of the boy of course!" my grandfather shouted, agreeing with him. "And don't think Father High-and-Mighty didn't count on that! Don't think for a moment he's above hiding behind a child's knickerbockers!"

"I almost let go on him there once myself," Mr. Cleary said. "And then I said to myself, 'Don't lower yourself, Art. Don't get down to his level.'"

"I thought he got a little sarcastic there," Mr. O'Donnell said. "Near the end."

"Oh shut up!" my grandfather said, getting mad at Mr. O'Donnell now. And then, as if he suddenly remembered something, he turned to me and said, "I don't want you hanging around that man. Do you understand me?"

I didn't know what he was talking about. I said, "Why would I hang around him?"

"Never mind the questions!" my grandfather said, now sounding as if he was getting mad at me. "If I'd wanted to give you reasons, I would have given you reasons! I'm just telling you not to, that's all!"

"I thought he seemed very interested in our young friend," Mr. Cleary said. "I don't suppose there's another little peculiarity there?"

"That's enough of that kind of talk!" my grandfather said. "He's bad enough without being that! Do you think he's a Frenchman? Or an Italian? No, the point is that when you've disgraced yourself so that decent, self-respecting adults will have nothing to do with you, you start talking to anyone that'll talk to you, and that includes children! But not this child!" And he turned again to me and said, "Now: is that clear?"

I told him it was clear, and then he and the other men started to talk about Father Sheridan again, and I couldn't understand any of what they said, so pretty soon I went out of the back room and said goodbye to Onesime and started to walk home the way I had come. I kept on thinking about what terrible thing Father Sheridan could have done that made them all so mad, but I couldn't even guess what it could be. And I was all mixed up, because even though he had scared me at first, and even though I knew he must have done something awful, and even though my grandfather had told me to keep away from him, I kind of liked him in the end, especially after what he said about my father. So I didn't know what to do, and I thought when I got home I would ask my mother about him and see what she said, and also maybe I could find out what he had done that was so bad.

But when I finally got home, later that afternoon, I forgot all about this and all about Father Sheridan too, because I no sooner got in the front door than I smelled the cigarette smell, and I saw the suitcase at the foot of the stairs, and I ran as fast as I could up the stairs and sure enough, there on the second floor, standing in the door of my room and waiting for me, was my father!

"Hi, buddy!" he said, holding out both his arms to me. "Back early from the office?"

And sometimes he did this, coming home by surprise without telling anyone he was coming, so that the first thing we would know about it might be when we heard the door of a car slam outside, and when we looked out it would be Mr. Lacasse's taxi, and coming up the front walk, in his blue suit or his gray one that always looked as if they had just been pressed, would be my father, walking fast now, looking up at the front window, and waving. Whenever he did this I never expected him, I was always surprised, and I think my mother was, too. Sometimes, though, she didn't seem as surprised as I was, but anyway, you could see she was so happy that it didn't really make any difference whether she was surprised or not.

So I ran at him now and he picked me up and spun me around and hugged me and I hugged him and kissed him, and then my mother came out, smiling, because she had been behind him in my room, just waiting for me to see my father. And then we all went downstairs and pretty soon we had supper, and all the time my father talked and told jokes and told us about all the things that had been happening to him since the last time he had been at home with us. And he asked me about what had been happening to me, and about Charlie Ferguson, and about how I was doing at school, and I showed him my report card, which was okay. And everybody felt fine again, with even Alma smiling when she came in to serve the supper and getting so interested in what my father was saying that she stayed in the kitchen that night, listening, instead of going up to Amos 'n' Andy.

The funny thing was that I was so excited about my father coming home that I forgot to say anything to anybody about how I met Father Sheridan. But later that night, when I was in bed and my father was in my room and had just finished telling me the newest story he had made up about Lord Crispin and Sir Chutney, I suddenly remembered, and I began to tell him about what had happened in my grandfather's drug store. When I came to Father Sheridan's name my father looked up as though I had surprised him, and when I finished he said slowly, "Well well!" He looked over at my mother who had come in while I was talking, and she looked back at him but didn't say anything. I said, "He said I should tell you he was asking for you."

"I'm glad of that," my father said. "He's a remarkable man."

"Grampa said he did something terrible," I said. "He said he did the worst thing a priest could do."

"Well," my father said, "your grandfather is a remarkable man, too. In a slightly different way." Then he looked over at my mother again. "What a town," he said. "All heart." My mother still didn't say anything, but she looked kind of worried, and my father said to me, "And did Grampa tell you anything else about Father Sheridan?"

"No," I said, "except that he didn't want me to go near him again."

"I see," my father said. Then he said to my mother, "I guess I must have been out of town when that rule was passed."

My mother said, "What rule?"

"The one called Grampa Takes Over," my father said.

My mother looked worried again and said, "Oh, you know how he is. . . ."

"I do, I do," my father said. I didn't know what they were talking about, but then my father said to me, "You see, Father Sheridan's sort of a special friend of mine. I suppose that's because when your mother and I were married, he was the priest who married us."

Which was another big surprise to me. And then my father told me that they were married here in Saint James Church, which was the parish we lived in, and that Father Sheridan had been the pastor of Saint James in those days.

I said, "Why isn't he the pastor now?"

My mother said now, "Because he went away."

"Where did he go to?" I said.

"To another parish," she said. "A few miles from here."

"Why did he go?" I said. "Was it a better parish than ours?"

"It's a different kind of parish from ours," she said.

It was a funny kind of talk, with my mother talking not the way she usually did but as though she didn't really want to talk at all. And then my father, who was sitting down at the end of my bed, suddenly hunched himself up nearer to me and rubbed me hard on the top of my head, the way he sometimes did. "Look," he said, "let's clear up a few things about Father Sheridan. First of all, he certainly didn't do the worst thing a priest could do — although exactly what that would be I don't know. Maybe arguing with your Grampa."

"That's not fair," my mother said.

"I know it," my father said. "But that's all right, too. In fact," he said to me, "I don't think he even did anything so terrible at all. Unless of course he did it to you this afternoon. Did he pull a gun on you? Come at you with a knife?"

I knew of course he was only kidding, but I said, "No. He didn't do anything. He was even kind of nice."

"I'll tell you why that is," my father said. "It's because he's really kind of a nice man. In fact, a very nice man. Of course even nice men can make a mistake now and then, can't they? Maybe things don't come out the way they think they will, or maybe they get all caught up in situations they never expected to get caught up in at all. Anyway, there they are, and sometimes they don't see how to get out. There are people like that." And he looked at my mother again. "And not only priests," he said.

I didn't know what that meant, but I guess my mother did, because even though she didn't say anything she got her worried look again, and then my father smiled a little and reached up and pulled her down so she was sitting on my bed beside him.

"So then," he said, "sometimes people like this who may not be lucky enough to have families of their own to come back to, or may not even have anybody around to talk to, sometimes they get lonely, they get tired, and sometimes . . . well, sometimes they take things that make them less lonely and tired."

"Like medicine?" I said.

"Like medicine," he said. "In a way. And after that they may say or do things that aren't really bad, you know, but that some other people don't expect them to say or do. And then there's usually trouble, especially if most of the other people are like somebody we know not a million miles from here."

My mother shook her head and said, "Jack . . ."

"Don't stop me now," he said, "just when I'm doing so well. This explanation has everything: clarity, style . . . look," he said to me, "do you understand any of this?"

"Not very much," I said. Because I really didn't except that my father didn't think that Father Sheridan had done anything that was so bad after all. So I understood that much of it and he nodded his head.

"Fair enough," he said, "because that's really what I want you to understand. So that if you meet Father Sheridan again you'll know that you're meeting a nice man and you'll behave nicely towards him. You know, polite and friendly and all that."

I said, "Grampa said —"

"I know what Grampa said," my father said. "Now, Grampa's a fine man and he buys a swell grade of chocolate syrup, but I think he probably just forgot that Father Sheridan is a friend of mine. So we'll just forget what he said to you, and if he mentions it again you can tell him I told you what to do. It may seem strange to him, but he'll get over it."

"Listen," my mother said, putting her hand on top of my father's, "I'm not so sure I'm wild about this. Oh, I don't mean about Pa; I'm talking about the other thing. I think we're taking a chance. . . ."

"What chance?" my father said. "In having him say hello? You know, we're not talking about a life partnership: for one thing they don't really share the same interests. Unless of course the party of the first part has taken to building homemade radios in his basement. Or Joey has secretly become a Biblical scholar." He looked down at me and said, "You haven't been boning up on the Old Testament while I've been away, have you?"

"Huh?" I said.

"There you are," he said to my mother. "No danger. Look: all I'm saying is that I don't want any boy of mine turning his back and running like a scared rabbit from a decent and rather remarkable man who's had a little too much of that already. That's the first thing. The second is that whatever the party of the first part's got, it's not catching. And the third is that even if casual meetings should grow into casual conversations — I don't think they will, but if they should — , then that's all right with me too. Because when the party of the first part is right, he's fine: there's certainly no one around here as able or intelligent. Or as good."

"When he's right," my mother said. "Well . . ."

"Well, there the odds are all in our favor, I'd say. I don't know if the problem still exists in that quarter: it may, or it may not. And if it does, it's hardly a high noon proposition and our young man isn't exactly a night owl. No, I don't see any trouble. Whatever influence — if any — comes from that source will be all to the good. Or at least I think so. And with all due respect to great men, I think it could even offset some of that Old Sod pharmacy small talk. I wouldn't be mad at that."

Then they talked some more, but not for very long, and when they stopped my mother was kind of agreeing with my father, or at least saying "all right," not sounding as though she was really positive. I didn't understand a lot of what they were talking about, except that it was all about me, and that "the party of the first part" was probably Father Sheridan, although I didn't know why my father called him that, and I never did find out what he did. Anyway, after a while my mother had to go downstairs to see Alma and she came up to my pillow and looked at me and then kissed me goodnight. My father said he would be down in a couple of minutes, and then my mother went out and my father said, "Move over." So I did, over nearer the wall, and he lay down on the bed beside me and turned out the light. He said, "Now let's see: we've had the prayers, haven't we?"

I said yes, because I'd said them when I came upstairs with him in the first place, but I guess he didn't remember. Then, after a minute, he said, "Now . . . any unfinished business?"

"No," I said. "I guess not. Only . . ."

"Only?" he said.

"Grampa might be mad at me,' I said. "About Father Sheridan."

"I'll tell you what I'll do," my father said. "I'll have a word with him. I don't think you'll have any trouble. Now go to sleep."

So I closed my eyes and tried to go to sleep, but I couldn't right away. It was kind of a hot night, but getting cooler now, and I could feel a soft breeze coming in the two side windows. The air had a good fresh smell, like grass that had been hot all day cooling off, and outside everything was very quiet. We had two big trees out on the front lawn and most nights you could hear some wind going through them, or you could hear a car going by, but tonight you couldn't hear any noise from outside for a long time. Then I heard a dog bark: a big, deep, coughing bark, and I knew it was Mr. McCullough's dog, being let out to go to the bathroom. He was a terrible looking dog who was huge and dirty white with pale brown spots and who drooled all the time and lay down in the middle of the road. One time I asked old Mr. McCullough what kind of a dog he was, and he said he didn't know, but he thought he was half airedale and half moose. Anyway, I listened to him bark for a while, and then they let him in and it was all quiet again. Pretty soon, away off, I could hear a train whistle, and I knew that this late it would be a freight train going to New York or some place. I listened to it get closer, and I thought about what trains were like, and I said out loud to my father, "Can you sleep good on trains?"

"What?" he said.

So I asked him again and he said, "Sure. Like a top."

Then the train went by, not stopping at the depot, and everything got quiet once more. I listened now as hard as I could, just to see what I could hear, but all I could hear was my own heart, beating away, and the quiet noise of my father, lying beside me, breathing. So I opened my eyes, and of course it was dark, but not too dark. By now the moon was out, and after a couple of seconds I could see everything in the room in a kind of thin blue light, and when I turned my head just a little I could see that my father was lying on his back, with his eyes open too, just looking up at nothing special. And maybe he knew that I was look-ing at him, because now he twisted a little and lay on his side, and his eyes were looking right into mine and maybe an inch away. He stayed there, just looking at me like that, for a little while, and then he took one of his hands and put it up to my cheek, and just let it lie there, nice and light and easy.

"Joey, Joey, Joey," he said. "Dear little Joey!"

And I was so happy he was home and here lying beside me I felt like crying. I pushed myself even closer to him and put my arms around him and put my face against his, hugging him hard just to show him how glad I was he was back. And he put one of his arms across me now, hugging me back, with a couple of big tugs. Then he whispered to me, "Everything okay?"

"Uh huh," I said, and stayed as close to him as I could, and then I guess I fell asleep.

FOUR

B UT that was all in the summer, meeting Father Sheridan like that,
and with my father coming home by surprise on the same day, and
now I was ten and back in school again. Since I was in the fifth grade
this year that meant I had to go to Grover Street School, because Chambers Street School, where I had always gone up to now, only went to the
fourth grade. Grover Street School, which had both the fifth and the
sixth grades, was the school you went to before you went to Junior High,
and it was a big ugly brick building that was about the oldest school in
the city. Inside, right over the water bubbler on the first floor, was a sign
that said that Abraham Lincoln had stood right here to say hello to everybody that came to see him when he was in the city one day a long time
ago.

Chambers Street School was pretty near to my house, but Grover
Street School was about a mile away. I would walk there every morning and come home at noon for lunch, then walk back to school again
and come home when school let out in the afternoon. Sometimes I
walked by myself, but mostly I walked there with Charlie Ferguson and
Dewey Ballou, two friends of mine who lived near me. On really bad
days we took the eight o'clock bus which left from the corner and went
right past the school, but I didn't like this so much. It went through the
main part of the city and made lots of stops and was always crowded,
and the bus driver was always Mr. Devine, a fat man with big purply lips
and not many teeth who always yelled things at us when he let us off.

"There they go!" he would yell. "Eeenie, Meenie, and Minie! That's
all there is, there ain't no Moe!"

Or else he would say, "Hey, boys, if you're so smart, tell me this:
what's the capital of Algebra?"

Or else: "I'd make a couple of jokes for you boys, but I see your
mothers have made three better ones!"

He would say these things just as we were getting down from the bus, and we could look back in through the windows and see that he was turning around with a big wink at the people who sat right in back of him and rode with him every day, and they always laughed at what he said. Dewey and Charlie said they would like to get even with Mr. Devine, and I said I would, too, but we couldn't think of any way to do it. So in the end we didn't do anything, except not to ride on the bus unless the weather outside was so terrible that we had to.

Anyway, it was a lot better to walk because it was fun, and we could take our time and fool around and stop whenever we wanted to. We always went by the back way, which was away from all the streets and was down by the sandpit, and then past the Samascut Cotton Mill, and then down along the railroad tracks as far as the trestle that crossed over the Samascut River. We ran across this trestle every day as fast as we could go. It wasn't a very long trestle, but it was high up above the river, and even though the river wasn't very wide or deep here there were big rocks sticking out of the water, and when you looked down you could see the river going fast and making foam against the rocks. There was a narrow bridge right beside the trestle which had been put there for people to walk on and which had a railing you could hang on to, and for the first couple of weeks we went on this. Then one day Charlie said wouldn't it be great not to go on this bridge, but instead to go right down the middle of the trestle, in between the rails where the trains went, and walking on the railroad ties? We talked about this for a long time, wondering if you slipped and fell were the ties close enough together to keep you from falling through into the river, or what you would do if suddenly a train came along and you were only halfway across? Finally I decided I didn't want to do it, but then Charlie said, "I dare you!" and so after a while I did, and then Dewey did, and then Charlie did last of all. At first I walked very slowly, being careful to go only one tie at a time, remembering not to look down at the river, and listening for any train whistles. But after a few times we all went faster, and pretty soon we were running across without hardly thinking about it at all. Every once in a while, though, I thought I heard the sound of a train, and then I remembered what Alma had told me about her Uncle Dabney who had once got hit by a freight train and got carried along on the front for twelve miles until they came to the next town and stopped.

"That Dabney was stuck to that cow-catcher like gum!" Alma said. "And the cinders they picked out of that man!"

"What happened to him finally?" I said.

"He limped," she said. "Dabney limped somethin' awful for the rest of his days!"

But mostly I didn't think about Dabney or other people that got hit by trains. I just ran across the trestle, going to school and coming back from it, and the only time I didn't was when we all decided to walk along the foot bridge instead. This was so that we could stop in the middle and lean over the railing and maybe spit down and watch the wind blow the spit almost straight out before it hit the water, or maybe just look up and down the river banks on both sides to see if there was anything special or different down there from the last time we looked. Usually all we saw was empty bottles or broken wooden boxes or pieces of paper that had floated in, or else some crows just poking around on the sand, but one morning, right on the flat kind of beach which came out just under the trestle, we saw a man all sprawled out and lying with his face down so that it looked as though he couldn't even breathe! Dewey said he bet it was a tramp, and at first we thought he was asleep, and then we thought he might be dead. Charlie said somebody should go down and see, but it turned out nobody wanted to, so we all got some pebbles and stones and began throwing them down, trying not to hit him, but to get near him to see if he would move. Nothing happened right away, but we kept throwing, and all of a sudden the man kind of wiggled in the sand and then, very slowly, he got up on his hands and knees and started to crawl around, not standing up and walking but just crawling around like a dog. Then he started to cough, big terrible coughs that almost made him fall down, and when he finished coughing he crawled down to the edge of the river and lay down and splashed water on his face.

"Oh boy!" Charlie said. "Look at him! Maybe he's wounded! I bet he's wounded and trapped down there and can't get up and needs somebody to rescue him!" And then he called down, "Hey, mister! Look up here!"

The man looked up right away, and when he saw us he stood up fast and began shaking his fist at us. He looked around quickly and picked up a rock and threw it at us, and then he started to run up the bank and come after us, shouting at us all the time he ran. So we ran too, because by now we were scared and thought that even though we had a head start, he might catch us before we got to school. But he must have stopped somewhere, because by the time we got up to the street that took us to school we looked around and couldn't see him anywhere. So the only thing that happened was that, after that, we didn't go to school by the trestle again for almost a week.

Every morning we got to school just about in time to line up at the front door with all the others in our grade. Then the Victrola would start to play inside, with a different one of us every week to stand by it and wind it up, and we would all march in, two by two, and up the stairs to our room, while the band on the record played different marching songs, like "The Monkey Wrapped His Tail Around the Flagpole." I didn't mind the marching, because it was kind of fun, with the teachers marching beside us, every once in a while yelling, "Stop clowning, Edward!" because Edward Jaworski, who was Polish, would make them mad by marching with his legs high up in the air and with his knees pointed way out and would pretend that he was falling down.

When we got to our room we would go to our desks, which must have been very old desks, because some of them had names and dates carved into the tops of them from a long time ago. My grandfather told me one time that he had gone to Grover Street School when he was a boy, and when he found out that was where I was going to go, he wrote them a letter asking if I could sit at the same desk he had sat at. He didn't get any answer for a long time, and that made him mad, and then finally they wrote him a letter telling him they didn't have any idea where he had sat, and that made him even madder.

Anyway, we all went to our desks and fooled around for a minute until our teacher came in, and said good morning, and we all stood up and said good morning back. Then while we were still standing we all bowed our heads and said the "Our Father," with Charlie and me and all the Catholics finishing with the regular "deliver us from evil, amen" ending, and with all the Protestants going on with the other "for Thine is the power and the glory" one, and with Jerry Fineman and Ethel Morton standing but not saying anything because they were Jewish.

Our teacher in the fifth grade was Mrs. McCambridge, and it was the first time I had ever had anybody that was married as a teacher. All the other teachers I knew, no matter how old they were, didn't have any husbands, but my mother told me that Mrs. McCambridge used to be a teacher a long time ago before she was married, but now her husband couldn't work any more because he had had a lot of heart attacks, and since they needed more people to teach school they took her back again. She was a very tall and strange-looking woman. She was very thin with high sharp shoulders and small blue eyes that never seemed to open all the way. Her nose was long and very thick, and it turned up so much at the end that when she came at you, with her head kind of ducking out in front of the rest of her, sometimes it seemed that she was really looking at you with her huge open nose instead of her little half-closed eyes. But even though she looked funny she was nice to us, and she taught us English and History and Geography and Arithmetic in a way that was kind of interesting. Sometimes when she was tired of teaching she just sat back and told us different things about the city, and how it used to be a long time ago. That wasn't so interesting, but you could see she liked it a lot.

"This is our own history, boys and girls," she would say, leaning back with her eyes even more closed than usual. "And I suppose it means so much to me because, you see, I used to be a Twomley!"

I didn't know why this would be, because I didn't even know what a Twomley was, and nobody else in the fifth grade did, either. But when I asked my mother, she told me that was Mrs. McCambridge's name before she had married Mr. McCambridge, and that because the Twomley family was almost the first family to come to the city when it got started, she was probably very proud of it.

So that was all right, even though it wasn't very interesting, because she was good in other ways, such as explaining things over again, and giving good marks, and answering questions without getting mad. The only time she got at all mad and told us not to ask her any more questions, please, was sometimes late in the afternoon, just before school was over for the day. Then she would start to get kind of nervous, and even though she would keep talking to us it would be in a different way, as though she wasn't paying any attention. She kept looking out the window, and at first I didn't know why, but then after a couple of weeks I knew that she was really looking for Mr. McCambridge who came by to pick her up every day when school was over in his beat-up maroon Dodge. Usually he drove up just a few minutes before the last bell, and by looking out the window she could see him just as he turned around the corner from Hollins Street. We could always tell when she saw him, because then she stopped looking out the window and would lean back in her chair in a slumpy kind of way and smile and blink her little eyes a couple of times and then say that well, boys and girls, she guessed it was time to go home. Then she would get all her things together and put them in her big black pocketbook, and sometimes she would be out of the room almost as soon as we were, hurrying down to the car, looking funny with her head so far out in front of her, with Mr. McCambridge looking at her out of the Dodge window, and flapping one hand at her, and moving slowly out of the driver's seat so that Mrs. McCambridge could do the driving on the way home. I always wondered why he would let her be the one to drive, especially since she had only those little peery eyes, but Dewey told me that he heard two of the other teachers talking, and that it was because of Mr. McCambridge having all his heart attacks, and that he wasn't even supposed to drive a car at all. Which I guess was why Mrs. McCambridge was so nervous at the end of every day.

At Grover Street School Mrs. McCambridge was the only teacher I had, except for Mr. Saint Onge, who came around once a week to teach us Music. Somebody told me one time that Mr. Saint Onge was the only man teacher in the city, and I know he was the only one I ever had. He was a small man, maybe just about as tall as my grandfather, but my grandfather seemed bigger because he was sort of solid looking, while Mr. Saint Onge was little and light and walked with kind of skippy steps. He carried around with him things that were light, too, like his pitch pipe and his baton, and he was always smiling a fast jumpy little smile. He had funny hair that was almost orange in color but was getting all gray in places, and behind his back we all called him "Ongo." This was on account of his forehead. It was high and bulgy, and in the funny papers there was one about a little man from another planet who had no ears but a big forehead just like Mr. Saint Onge, and his name was Ongo. So that was what we called Mr. Saint Onge, and it was pretty good because "Ongo" sounded okay if you put it together with his last name: Ongo Saint Onge.

Anyway, Mr. Saint Onge went around from school to school, running into all the rooms once a week to teach us songs and how to read music, smiling fast and tapping the teacher's desk with his baton and saying, "Now boys, now boys!" when it got too noisy. Sometimes he would split the room up into parts with all the girls being alto or soprano, and most of the boys being baritone with big Teddy Colucci, who had stayed back, being a bass. So Mr. Saint Onge would blow on his pitch pipe and wave his arms and we would all sing all kinds of songs, but you could tell that the ones Mr. Saint Onge liked best were the ones about being a sailor and going off to sea. He had a huge voice, which always surprised you every time you heard it — coming from so little a man, I mean — , and he knew millions of songs about Shipwrecks and Defying the Storm and things like that, but the one he liked to sing more than all the others was the one called "A Capital Ship."

"Oh, a Capital Ship for an Ocean Trip," Mr. Saint Onge sang, waving his arms to lead us, "Was the Walloping Window Blind!"

So we all joined in and sang right along with him, because by now we knew it by heart. For a little while everybody sang together, but then pretty soon, when we came to the part about, "Then Blow Ye Winds, Heigh Ho!" most of us would begin to stop, not because we were tired or didn't want to sing, but because Mr. Saint Onge was beginning to sing loud, and you knew that in a couple of minutes nobody could hear anybody else. And anyway, it was better to just sit there and watch, because by now he was at the place where he started getting all excited and where he stopped waving his arms up and down since he wasn't leading us any more but was singing all by himself. He started to walk fast back and and forth across the front of the room, holding one hand up above his eyes and sticking his head out as though he was looking out into the storm, and then he would spin around and make believe he was walking hard into the wind, and then he would stagger and start to fall and hold on to the music stand which I guess was supposed to be the mast, pretending now that he was the captain of the ship, and all the time singing away, louder and louder, so that now you could hear him all over the building. One time, right while he was singing his loudest in the worst part of the storm and trying to get back to his cabin, he slipped and fell down to his knees, and his coat flipped up and you could see that he had a big place in his pants which was almost worn all the way through and you could see the white of his underwear. But then he got up again and turned around and sang even louder than he ever had about staying at home from now on because his roving days were over, and when he came to this part we knew that it was all over. So then he stood up in front of the room, looking at us, and all panting and sweating, and a couple of the kids clapped their hands, and Mr. Saint Onge made a kind of little bow and wiped his head with his handkerchief and said that well well, he seemed to have forgot himself, and then he blew his pitch pipe again and we all went back to singing something different.

Then after this on other days he did the same thing a few times more, I guess forgetting himself all over again, and I always thought it was kind of good to see, but then sometimes it made me feel funny, too, as though maybe I shouldn't be watching at all, what with Mr. Saint Onge pretending so hard to be a big captain at sea, when all the time he was really so little and skinny with his underwear showing through. When I said this to Charlie one day he said that was what he thought sometimes, too. But we both kept on watching anyway.

So that was what the fifth grade was, and I liked it fine most of the time. Every day when school was over I came home, but since I didn't have to get home until around five o'clock now, usually I stopped and fooled around with Charlie and Dewey and some of the other kids, playing ball in Cooney's Field, down at the far end where the big kids weren't playing, or else going over to Mr. Cannon's orchard and hoping that Mr. Cannon wouldn't be around, so that we could pick some pears or some apples, or else if it was no good outside going to Dewey's house because he had a good Ping-Pong table in his cellar. After we had some milk and cookies we went down and played some Ping-Pong. Dewey usually won most of the games, partly because it was his table and he played all the time, but also because he was good at most games. He said this was because his father had been good too, and that in fact his father had been a very famous athlete. I guess he might have been, because when you went into Dewey's cellar the first thing you saw, hung up on the wall next to the Ping-Pong table, was a picture of Mr. Ballou with

Jack Dempsey, who was Heavyweight Champion of the World. It was a picture from a newspaper, and underneath, it said "Local Fight Fans Meet Champ." There were a lot of people in the picture standing around Jack Dempsey, and you wouldn't be able to pick out Mr. Ballou very easily except that somebody had drawn a big circle in ink around his head and an arrow in ink pointed to him. Dewey said that one time his father was going to become a prize fighter but his friend Jack Dempsey called him up on the long distance telephone and asked him not to.

"Why not?" I said. "Was he afraid your father might beat him?"

"I guess so," Dewey said, but Charlie told me later he didn't believe this, and neither did I. Anyway, I didn't like Dewey's father much. He was a big man who looked strong, all right, and he had a red face and short curly black hair all over his head, and whenever I met him he always got up close and talked in my face and he always smelled as though he had just been eating cinnamon or something. Sometimes when we were coming up from the cellar Mr. Ballou would just be getting in from the lawyer's office which he had, and he would always stop and say hello to us, never calling us by our right names but always something like, "Ace" or "Tiger." Then he would spin around to Dewey and kind of crouch down to Dewey's size and put up his hands like a fighter, and then Dewey would put up *his* hands like a fighter, and Mr. Ballou would laugh and say, "Attaboy! Never let them get the drop on you!"

Then he would turn back to us and ask if we had just come up from the Game Room, which is what he always called his cellar. When we said yes, he would always say, very fast, "Who won?" And then when we told him Dewey did he would smile and shake his head and get all proud and turn to Dewey again crouching down in his fighter's position and saying, "Attaboy!"

Once in a while, if he wasn't too busy he would talk to us for a few minutes, standing there in the hall, asking us if we liked sports, and saying "Attaboy!" when we said we did, and telling us about his friend Jack Dempsey, and sometimes, when he came in a little late, and laughing a lot, he would show us some of the things he used to do when he was a famous athlete. His favorite one was to make believe he had a football tucked under one of his arms and then, all bent over, he would run full speed down the front hall, coming right at us with his other arm straight in front of him, and his hand turned up as if he was going to push us in the face with it, hard. We always got out of the way, fast, and he would go rushing by us, always stopping just before he ran smack into the far wall and the big painting of Pope Pius. Then he would turn around and look at us and say, "The Old Forearm Shiver!"

One time when we were coming up from the cellar Dewey's father must have come in just before we got up, because he was going up the stairs to the second floor and didn't see us. But I saw that he had his arm in a sling, and when I asked Dewey what happened, he said that a couple of nights ago his father and mother and some friends of theirs had been at a party and his father had tried to show them the Old Forearm Shiver while they were out walking along the street, and his foot slipped or something because he had given the Old Forearm Shiver to a Packard car and had broken his hand. So I said I was sorry about this, but actually I was kind of glad, because that meant he wouldn't be able to do it to us for a while.

But one day, about a month or so after school started, instead of going to Dewey's or playing after school, I went down to Hethering's store on Main Street

97492

DATE DUE

813.54 O18S
O'Connor, Edwin
The best and the last of
Edwin O'Connor

Ohio Dominican College Library
1216 Sunbury Road
Columbus, Ohio 43219

DEMCO